D1294576

AGRIBUSINESS COORDINATION

A SYSTEMS APPROACH TO THE WHEAT, SOYBEAN, AND FLORIDA ORANGE ECONOMIES

HD
9049
W5
1428

AGRIBUSINESS COORDINATION

A SYSTEMS APPROACH TO THE WHEAT, SOYBEAN, AND FLORIDA ORANGE ECONOMIES

Ray A. Goldberg

Associate Professor of Business Administration
Harvard University

DIVISION OF RESEARCH

GRADUATE SCHOOL OF BUSINESS ADMINISTRATION

HARVARD UNIVERSITY • BOSTON 1968

WITHDRAW

211025

© Copyright 1968 by the President and Fellows of Harvard College

Library of Congress Catalog Card No. 68–18718

Printed in the United States of America

Foreword

THIS MONTH marks the fifteenth anniversary of the formal inauguration of a Program in Agriculture and Business at the Harvard Business School. In December 1952 the Advisory Committee adopted a statement of objectives for the Program wherein the broad purposes were stated as being to "conduct studies of agricultural and industrial relationships through analyses of technical, economic, and human factors which govern these relationships, particularly the decision-making points, and stimulate sound action in the light of these studies so that industry and agriculture may contribute most efficiently toward meeting their responsibilities in our growing economy."

The first study under the program was undertaken by John H. Davis and Ray A. Goldberg to provide "a description in quantitative terms of the character and extent of the existing interrelationships between agriculture and the industries which supply agriculture and which process and distribute the products of agriculture." A new word was coined to express the closeness of the interdependence and the manifold interrelationships of agriculture and business, and the study was published by the Division of Research in 1957 under the title, *A Concept of Agribusiness.* That volume set forth the overall structure of agribusiness and provided a frame of reference for later studies.

The pattern of succeeding studies under the program has been to focus on particular commodity segments and to analyze the problems involved in those sectors of agribusiness. Three such studies have been published by the Division and a fourth is in process.

This study goes back to the basic concept of agribusiness itself and reflects the conviction of the author that if managers of firms engaged in agribusiness or if government administrators involved as participants in or regulators of agribusiness are to develop effective strategies or policies, they must understand fully the total commodity systems in which they participate and the interaction of their parts. The study itself aims at demonstrating the usefulness of the concept by developing and contrasting the structures, behaviors, and performances of three commodity systems and the special institutional arrangements devised to coordinate the successive stages of such systems. It thus moves from the static picture of the structure of the entire agribusiness system to the dynamics of three commodity systems in agribusiness.

The Whitehall Foundation has been one of the key sources of support for the Program in Agriculture and Business since its inception, and it provided further support by a specific grant to the School for this study. Additional support for the project came via grants from the Bache Foundation and from the Chicago Board of Trade. We are all deeply grateful for this generous support of our research activities in this important problem area.

BERTRAND FOX
Director, Division of Research

Soldiers Field
Boston, Massachusetts
December 1967

Acknowledgments

THIS STUDY would not have been possible without the cooperation of the many individuals, firms, and organizations that contributed data and expertise. To all I am greatly indebted.

From industry I received invaluable assistance. Mr. Hugh W. Schwarz, director of corporate planning for The Coca-Cola Company and formerly president of the Minute Maid Groves, Inc., read various drafts of the manuscript. His incisive comments and enthusiasm for the project will long be remembered and appreciated. Other individuals reviewed material and provided helpful suggestions regarding those sections most directly related to their industry and operations. These industry leaders include Mr. Dean McNeal, executive vice president, Mr. George S. Pillsbury, executive vice president, and Mr. Anthony C. Owens, vice president, all of the Pillsbury Company; Mr. Henry Cragg and Mr. John St. John, formerly chairman and president of the Minute Maid Company and currently vice presidents of the Food Division of The Coca-Cola Company; Mr. Bernard J. Rothwell II, president, and Mr. Norman J. Kautz, vice president, of the Bay State Milling Co.; Mr. Lowell Andreas, executive vice president of the Archer-Daniels-Midland Company; Mr. M. D. McVey, vice president of Cargill, Inc.; Mr. Loren W. Johnson, executive vice president of the Continental Grain Company; Mr. Robert W. Rutledge, executive vice president, Mr. Frank D. Trovillion, executive assistant, and Mr. Robert C. White, economist, of the Florida Citrus Mutual; Mr. Homer Hooks, formerly general manager of the Florida Citrus Commission; Mr. Robert Martin, chairman of the Chicago Board of Trade; Mr. Robert L. Raclin, partner, Paine, Webber, Jackson and Curtis; and Mr. Aaron S. Yohalem, senior vice president, Mr. Robert F. McCleod, vice president, Mr. Amos Flint, Jr., director of commodity tradings and Mr. Nelson Eddy, corporate economist, of Corn Products Company. Participants from other agribusiness organizations were also interviewed and provided much useful information.

Many divisions of the U.S. Department of Agriculture gave unstintingly of their resources. I am especially grateful to the Honorable John M. Schnittker, Undersecretary of Agriculture, whose comments and constructive suggestions added immeasurably to the study. Mr. Kenneth E. Ogren, former director, and Mr. Robert E. Olson, former deputy director of the Marketing Economics Division of the Economic Research Service; Mr. Nathan M. Koffsky, former director of Agricultural Economics; Mr. William R. Askew, Mr. George W. Kromer, and the late Robert H. Masucci all reviewed drafts of this manuscript and provided not only helpful conceptual suggestions but also new statistical information. Mr. Alex C. Caldwell, administrator, and Mr. Ronald C. Callander, director of the Trading Division of the Commodity Exchange Authority, gave me information on the wheat and soybean futures markets and prepared a statistical breakdown to fit the requirements of this study. Mr. Joseph G. Knapp, former administrator of the Farmer Cooperative Service, Mr. Martin A. Abrahamsen, deputy administrator, and Messrs. Daniel H. McVey and Martin A. Blum of the Marketing Division of the Farmer Cooperative Service made available a wealth of new material on the activities and operations of key cooperatives involved in U.S. agribusiness. Mr. Joseph A. Carter and Mr. H. R. Goldstein of the Agricultural Stabilization Service supplied grain storage data.

At the Department of Commerce, Miss Beatrice N. Vaccara, assistant chief, National Economics Division, gathered the input-output data necessary to update the agribusiness flow charts.

To my Faculty colleagues at the Harvard Business School whose wisdom has benefited this study, I wish to express my deep appreciation. Professor Bertrand Fox, Director of the Division of Research, provided sound counsel at every stage of development of this research and patiently reviewed each draft. Professor Henry B. Arthur, George M. Moffett Professor of Agriculture and Business, carefully reviewed the early drafts and was a constant source of intellectual interchange and encouragement. Professor Edmund P. Learned, Charles Edward Wilson Professor of Business Policy, was especially helpful in my efforts to interpret the broader implications of this study to the business manager and the public policymaker. Other colleagues examined various sections of the manuscript and made many valuable suggestions. They include Mr. William Applebaum, Lecturer on Food Distribution, Professors Francis J. Aguilar, Robert W. Austin, and Gordon Donaldson, and Research Associates William L. Day and Rowan C. Vogel.

Faculty members of other institutions also took an interest in the development of this study. Professor Emeritus O. B. Jesness and Professor Willard W. Cochrane of the University of Minnesota and Professor Roger W. Gray of the Stanford Food Research Institute respectively reviewed the sections on cooperatives, governmental relationships, and futures markets.

I wish to thank the following associates for their help: Miss Ruth Norton, Editor and Executive Secretary of the Division of Research, for her expert assistance and extreme patience in editing and guiding this study from manuscript to publication; Miss Audrey Barrett for her meticulous development of the bibliography, index, and help in making last-minute changes in the text; Mrs. Virginia Pond and Miss Roma Dearness for invaluable secretarial assistance on successive drafts; Miss Mary Robinson and Miss Caroline Timmerman of the Data Processing Bureau for their accurate presentation of the various tables contained in the study; and Mrs. Marjorie L. McLaughlin of the Audio-Visual Department for her art work in developing many of the charts.

I also appreciate the imaginative efforts of Mr. Patrick Requa of the Colonial Press to expedite publication of this volume.

I am indeed grateful to Dean George P. Baker and Associate Dean George F. F. Lombard for freeing me from other responsibilities and for providing the necessary funds to complete this study. Their continued encouragement of research effort directed toward improving the managerial techniques of agribusinessmen in order to meet the challenges of the domestic and world food and fiber economy has been most heartwarming.

My father, Mr. Max Goldberg, has my affectionate appreciation. As a statesman in the agribusiness community who has long held a broad view of the world food and fiber system, he has had a direct influence on my developing a systems approach to decision making.

Finally, to my wife Thelma I express special thanks. She not only reviewed and constructively criticized countless drafts and developed and sketched many charts and tables, but also served as a constant source of inspiration and encouragement during the three years it took to complete this project. Our young children, Marc, Jennifer, and Jeffrey, made their contribution by being patient and remaining quiet while I was working at home.

While all these people, and many others, share in making this publication possible, I take full responsibility for the data and opinions contained herein.

RAY A. GOLDBERG

Soldiers Field
Boston, Massachusetts
December 1967

Table of Contents

List of Exhibits

List of Tables

APPENDIX TABLE OF CONTENTS

The Decision-Making Process in U.S. Agribusiness

I

Introduction

BUSINESSMEN, government leaders, and others involved in agribusiness are constantly faced with the tasks of formulating company strategies and public policies to meet the ever-changing needs of the United States and world food economies. The central concept behind this study is that if managers, private and public, are to develop effective strategies and policies, they must be fully aware of the total commodity system in which they participate, and they must understand the interaction of its parts. The purpose of this study is to illustrate and develop this concept, and to present, analyze, and evaluate a commodity system approach to agribusiness industries.

An agribusiness commodity system encompasses all the participants involved in the production, processing, and marketing of a single farm product. Such a system includes farm suppliers, farmers, storage operators, processors, wholesalers, and retailers involved in a commodity flow from initial inputs to the final consumer. It also includes all the institutions which affect and coordinate the successive stages of a commodity flow such as the government, futures markets, and trade associations.

These coordinating institutions and arrangements play an especially important role in agribusiness commodity systems because of the unique agronomic characteristics of these industries. The phenomenon of seasonal production of crops, combined with year-round consumption of the food products, results almost inevitably in serious imbalances between supply and demand. These imbalances are further aggravated by unforeseen weather conditions over which the producer has no control, and the vagaries of the weather often result in actual supplies varying greatly from the levels planned. In addition, improved technology has increased yields per acre and has shortened harvest periods, both of which have aggravated the year-to-year production adjustments. To the extent that price is relied upon as the key mechanism in a market system for bringing supply and demand for agricultural products into balance, the price swings become severe, and these in turn generate operational and organizational problems up and down the vertical chain from farm supplier to ultimate food distributor and cause extreme fluctuations in farm incomes.

Such fluctuations in the U.S. food economy have proved to be economically and socially intolerable, and they have given rise to government programs devised to provide a better balance between supply and demand, to alleviate temporary imbalances, to smooth out price swings, and to stabilize farm incomes. Thus, the government is often an integral part of an agribusiness commodity system, in contrast to its position as an external factor in many other industries. The public administrator becomes an active participant in agribusiness commodity systems. His roles may vary considerably: law enforcer, information center, educator, researcher, as well as an active participant in pricing, marketing, and production decisions.

Initially, the federal government developed programs to deal with the farm problem and focused its efforts at that level. This intervention, however, had repercussions throughout the entire commodity system, and additional programs were devised on a piecemeal basis to alleviate the adverse side effects of previous programs. One government program seemed to beget others. Today the picture has changed and government administrators are beginning to devise programs which take into account an entire agribusiness commodity system. It is a central thesis of this study that the public policy maker will be in a better position to formulate wise policies if he understands their implications for the total commodity system.

In addition, the public administrator's participation in a commodity system leads to interaction with other participants. These interactions, in turn, generate new private as well as public policies. Where the government is involved in pricing and production decisions, the definition of common objectives is important in determining the ways in which the public administrator, the private businessman, and all other participants in the system can work together. These common objectives can be better determined if all participants have a similar understanding of the interdependent components of their commodity system and the present and potential ways in which the system can serve the consumer in an effective manner. And both public and private policy makers are better able to attain effective cooperation and interaction if they have a common understanding of the commodity system of which they are a part. To provide such understanding is a key objective of this study.

The uncertain agricultural production patterns that have resulted in government participation in commodity systems have also led businessmen to devise many types of institutions and arrangements that help to mesh one stage of a commodity flow with an earlier or later stage. The progressive changes in our society from small local food markets supplied by nearby production and processing to large national and international markets require a diverse and complex food system. Seasonal production and the long distances involved in the assembling, transporting, and storing of food, requiring fast communication up and down the producer-consumer chain, have given rise to elaborate and varied coordinating machinery and communication devices to tie together the various parts of a commodity system; all these have added to the complexity of our total food complex.

For any agribusiness firm participating in a commodity system, this complexity makes more difficult a thorough understanding of the commodity system environment in which it operates. And the importance of the external environment in formulating company strategy for all types of firms has been well documented by many authors, and especially so by Professor Edmund P. Learned of the Harvard Business School. Learned, commenting in an as yet unpublished manuscript, states: "Within the external environment are almost countless factors that exert a shaping force over what management can or must do. Adapting the decisions and activities of the firm to factors that impinge from the outside is one of top management's most imperative and challenging tasks. By the term 'adapting' we do not mean to imply making only passive responses; there must be creative adaptations as well." [1]

In this study general management responsibilities

[1] *The Role of General Management.*

are not considered to be limited to the development of short-range and long-range strategy, organizational structures, informational and control devices for the internal management of the company, and negotiations with outside people and external elements on the firm's behalf. Even more important, and often overlooked, is management's responsibility to have an economic and social interest in the viability of the firm's commodity system. In most cases the well being of the individual firm is dependent upon the growth and profitability of its total commodity system. Fertilizer and farm machinery manufacturers cannot sell to an impoverished farming community. Farmers must have customers desirous of the foods made from their crops and livestock products. Processors require quality and plentiful supplies, and distributors must have the varieties and qualities of food necessary to meet the changing food desires and requirements of the ultimate consumer. Each commodity system is competing against other systems to satisfy consumer wants. Business managers must have the ability to place themselves outside of their commodity system and to re-examine the long-run trends that will affect it. From this analysis, managers will be able to develop creative strategies for the system that will insure its effective response to consumers' needs.

A conviction that the businessman can greatly improve the viability of his firm's position and the prospects for its profitable survival by approaching his problems from the broader perspective of his total commodity system was the final reason for this study. The articulation of this systems approach aims not only at the improvement of private policies in agribusiness, but also at a greater contribution by private firms to the development of public policies for agribusiness.

This study is an extension of the original purpose of the Agriculture and Business Program at the Harvard Business School. The original concept of the Program was to analyze the complex interrelationships that exist between the farmer and those that supplied him with inputs and those that processed and marketed items that had their origin on the farm so that the private decision maker could take on more responsibility for the effective performance of U.S. agribusiness and its many segments. *A Concept of Agribusiness*[2] described these interrelationships and developed a conceptual scheme for portraying and analyzing alternative private and public policies for the U.S. agribusiness economy. This study moves from the description of the total agribusiness economy to a schematic analysis of the ever-changing structure and

[2] Davis and Goldberg, *A Concept of Agribusiness.*

performance of a widely divergent group of commodity systems.

In order to analyze the critical features of the structure and behavior of agribusiness commodity systems, the author selected three systems that represented an important cross section of agribusiness in food grains, oilseed crops, and fruits. These commodity systems are the wheat, soybean, and Florida orange industries. Although these commodity systems are an integral part of all of agribusiness and the total economy, it is possible to identify the important interrelationships from farm supply to ultimate food distribution that make up the market structure of these industries.

These three were selected because of the wide range of changes that are occurring in this diverse, but representative, group of industries. Consumption changes alone are illustrative of the diversity of these three systems. During the period from 1945 to 1963, civilian per capita consumption of wheat flour decreased from 161 pounds to 116 pounds, or 28%. Per capita consumption of margarine and salad oils made from soybean oil increased 127% and 100% respectively, while soybean meal utilization increased 164%. In the case of the Florida orange industry, one new product, frozen orange juice concentrate, changed every feature of this commodity system. From 1946 to 1963, per capita consumption of frozen orange juice concentrate increased over 11,000%, while per capita consumption of canned orange juice decreased 39%, and of fresh oranges, 73%.

Each of the three commodity systems has had a distinct pattern of development. Wheat is by far the oldest and most complex commodity system, and is representative of the interrelated dynamic changes that are occurring in domestic and international agribusiness. The crop is produced in 41 out of the 50 states, and it is still the largest cereal crop even though consumption has declined with a change in consumers' diets to higher protein foods and to more fruits and vegetables. At the same time, export markets for wheat have expanded, with over 50% of the U.S. crop being exported in recent years. The wheat system also developed new product forms of processed flour and bread, cake, and pie products that responded to the alterations in U.S. eating habits. And finally, many new forms of coordination have been developed in this increasingly complex wheat system.

The soybean industry is one of the most rapidly expanding in the United States. The increased consumption of animal proteins and vegetable fats in both the United States and other developed countries has expanded both the domestic and international markets for soybean food and feed products. At the same time, the joint products of the soybean (meal and oil) have not had identical growth patterns, and this has resulted in special government programs to offset some of the imbalances in the system. Finally, because the soybean industry is one of the newer agribusiness industry systems, it has been able to utilize some of the institutions and arrangements developed in other agribusiness industries in the formation of its own market structure.

In the case of the Florida orange industry, the development of the frozen orange concentrate product only two decades ago caused drastic changes in this industry system. Because this industry is concentrated in a few counties in one state, however, it has been possible to develop better coordinating and communicating devices than in the wheat and soybean industries. Other special characteristics distinguish this industry; for example, new orange trees do not bear fruit for four years and an orange grove is productive for as long as sixty years. The 40% increase in Florida orange production in the 1966–1967 crop has also presented some major challenges and opportunities to the participants in this system. In addition, the recent development of "synthetic" orange products has added another important feature to this agribusiness commodity system.

Although each of the commodity systems selected for this study has unique structural and performance patterns, the analysis of the three systems, taken together, has general application for managers in all agribusiness commodity systems. The continuing supply and demand imbalances are basic underlying conditions which greatly influence the private and public policies of the participants in other agribusiness industries as well as in the wheat, soybean, and Florida orange industries. In addition, the major trends that will probably be affecting practically every agribusiness manager are clearly evident in a variety of ways in each of the three selected systems.

In the sections of the study that follow, Chapter II examines the changes in the dimensions of agribusiness in the postwar period and the specific factors which have affected each of the three commodity systems.

This introductory section of two chapters is followed by three sections covering the three commodity systems: Section II on wheat, Section III on soybeans, and Section IV on Florida oranges. Each section deals with the structure of the commodity system, including the channels of product flow, the numbers of firms and entities, ownership patterns, marketing systems, and arrangements. The behavior and performance of each commodity system is then examined and analyzed. Among the measures covered are the profitability, price stability, competitive behavior, and adaptability of each system.

In Section V a number of critical trends are identified which will affect agribusiness systems in the future.

The implications of these trends for the participants, not only of the three commodity systems but of agribusiness generally, are set forth in this section.

The final chapter summarizes the total study and discusses the major conclusions in terms of challenges and opportunities for the private and public managers involved in these and other agribusiness commodity systems.

II

The Changing Dimensions of Agribusiness

THE MANY commodity systems that make up agri-business in the United States are constantly changing in response to major economic, political, social, and technological forces. Several economic factors have increased the demand for new types of food and serv-ices. Rising income levels combined with a world population explosion have increased the food and nu-trient requirements of the world at a more rapid rate than the development of local resources in many countries. Also economies of scale have resulted in fewer but larger units in practically every stage in the vertical U.S. agribusiness structure. Politically, the development of regional trading areas has led to trad-ing blocs and new trade agreements that may facili-tate a more effective movement of farm supplies and farm products between nations. Socially, the mobility and faster pace of living have resulted in the develop-ment of new, easily prepared foods available at any place and any time, from airplane hot packs and space ship food tubes to snack time innovations and drink-able breakfasts. The application of technology has improved the inputs into agriculture, such as feed, fertilizer, seed, pesticides, and farm machinery; pro-duction on the farm; and the processing, packaging, transportation, wholesaling, and retailing of food prod-ucts.

Over the past several decades these forces of change have resulted in a major food revolution in the United States. This food revolution can be seen at all stages of the agribusiness complex: vast changes in the quan-tities and quality of farm supplies, increasing pro-duction efficiency on the farm, expanding needs of domestic and foreign consumers, new marketing and processing activities responding to these needs, and the interactions among them. As a result of these changes a whole new style of living has been created. It affects the types of foods eaten, where they are eaten, the method of food preparation, when and how

food is obtained, and the methods of packaging, pro-moting, transporting, processing, storing, and produc-ing the food needed to satisfy the manifold wants of the many segments of the consuming public. The food revolution, in reality, represents the application of science and technology to the food and fiber industry.

These and other interrelated forces of change that resulted in the U.S. food revolution have brought about new dimensions and interrelationships in the many segments that make up the total U.S. agribusi-ness complex. These changing dimensions may be il-lustrated by a comparison of the Agribusiness Flow Charts for 1962 and 1947 in Exhibits II-1 and II-2.[1]

From these exhibits the reader will note that food and fiber purchases by the consumer increased from $72.9 billion in 1947 to almost $118 billion in 1962. This increase of over $45 billion, or 62%, reflects not only population growth of 29%, but also rising in-comes which enabled consumers to upgrade their diets, use more foods, and utilize more services. Even so, food and fiber purchases constituted a smaller pro-portion of total consumer expenditures in 1962 (30%) than in 1947 (44%). This indicates that income levels are increasing to the point where addi-tional satisfactions are being met by non-agribusiness industries and that production, processing, and dis-tribution efficiencies have kept food costs from be-coming burdensome. It also implies increased com-petition for the consumer's dollar from alternative product and service offerings.

A simple summary comparison of the total dollar transactions in 1947 and 1962 of the major segments of agribusiness as depicted in Exhibits II-1 and II-2 is set forth in Table II-1. The "farm sector purchases"

[1] These charts are derived from the 1947 and 1958 input-output data. The tabulation of the data for these years and the extrapolations for 1954 and 1962 are set forth in Appendix Table II-1.

7

and the "food and fiber processor purchases" lines of the table summarize the two banks of boxes in the flow charts representing inputs into and one level of outputs of farms. The "wholesale and retail purchases" line comprises purchases both from the processing industries and directly from the farm. Finally,

chases increased some 63% from 1947 to 1962 whereas farm sales increased only 23% during the same period. Food and fiber processor sales to wholesalers and retailers increased some 50%, and consumers increased their dollar purchases by 62%. These broad changes in the rates of expansion of the

EXHIBIT II-1

AGRIBUSINESS FLOW CHART: 1962

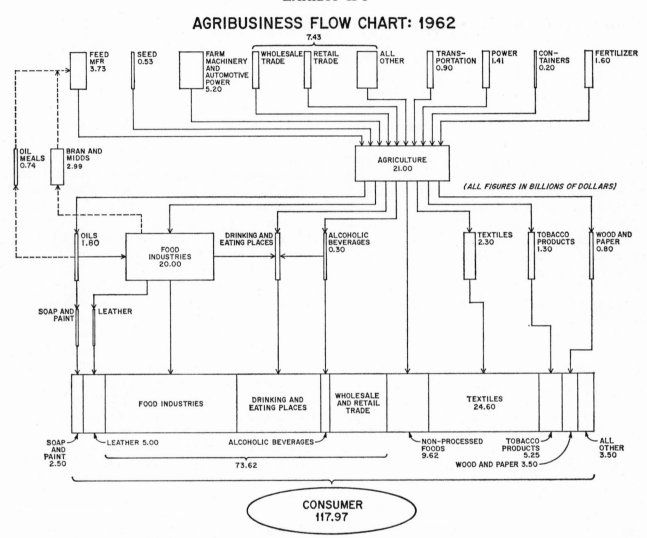

SOURCE: Derived by the author with the cooperation of the U.S. Department of Agriculture by extrapolation from the 1958 U.S. Department of Labor Interindustry Study released in 1964.

the "consumer purchases" line represents sales to final consumers by farmers, processors, and retail establishments. In addition, the differences between the successive pairs of lines represent the value added by various sectors of agribusiness, and these are also set forth in the table.

From Table II-1 it is quite apparent that the off-farm segments of agribusiness are expanding much more rapidly than is the farming segment. Farm pur-

major segments of agribusiness are further evidenced in the value-added figures. The value added by the farm sector actually decreased $1.5 billion or 9% from 1947 to 1962, indicating the efficiency of the increased purchased inputs and the lower price levels of most farm products. The value added by food and fiber processors and wholesalers and retailers increased some 74% and 135% respectively, indicating the introduction of additionally processed foods, new foods, and new means of distribution. The decline in the value added by the farm sector (even when one adjusts for the abnormality of the 1947 base year) suggests that the producer is becoming increasingly more dependent on others for his major farm supplies and more dependent on a rapidly changing domestic and

crease, and feed purchases with a 54% increase all suggest that the farmer no longer provides his own seed, feed, fertilizer, and power to the extent that he did in earlier years. The utilization of such purchased inputs have lowered per unit production costs of most farm items considerably. These manufactured inputs

EXHIBIT II-2

AGRIBUSINESS FLOW CHART: 1947

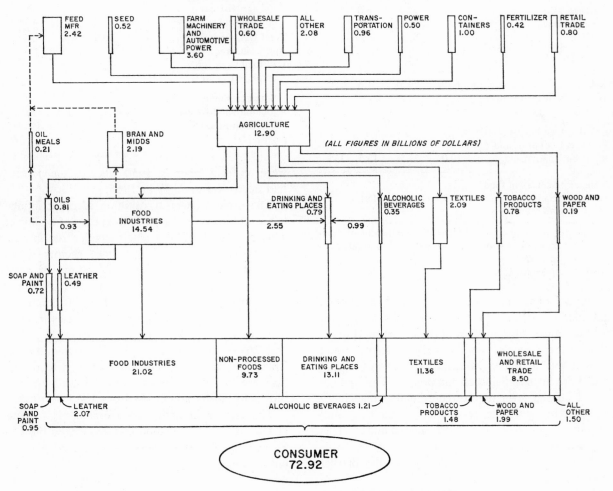

SOURCE: U.S. Bureau of Labor Statistics, Division of Interindustry Economics, October 1952.

world food and fiber market. This does not mean that the producer's role is becoming less important, but rather that he cannot afford the luxury of ignoring the importance of his interdependence and interrelationships with those who supply his inputs and those who purchase the industrial and consumer products that originate on the farm.

The growing dependence of agriculture on manufactured inputs is clearly apparent in the exhibits and Table II-1. Individually, such items as fertilizer with a 281% increase, farm machinery with a 44% in-

also help farmers to produce more uniform qualities of crops and livestock.

The commercialization of agriculture has also come about through changes in the processing and distribution systems of agribusiness. The development of mass distribution systems and the increased consumer orientation of distributors and food and fiber processors in these systems have led to a wider variety of new products and increased emphasis on uniform quality of agricultural inputs. The emphasis on uniform quality has led in turn to pressure for larger farming pro-

TABLE II-1. Dollar Volume of Transactions of Major Agribusiness Segments: 1947–1962

	Dollar sales (in billions)		Increase from 1947 to 1962	
	1947	1962	Dollars	Percent
Farm sector purchases (Farm supply sales)	$12.9	$21.0	$ 8.1	63%
Farm sector value added	16.4	14.9	−1.5	−9
Food and fiber processor purchases from farm sector (Farm sales)	29.3	35.9	6.6	23
Food and fiber processor value added	33.6	58.6	25.0	74
Wholesale and retail purchases (Food and fiber processor sales)	62.9	94.5[a]	31.6	50
Value added by wholesale and retail firms and from imports, etc.	10.0	23.5[a]	13.5	135
Consumer purchases of food and fiber products (Retail sales)	72.9	118.0	45.1	62

[a] Estimates made for this study by U.S. Department of Agriculture and Bureau of Labor Statistics personnel to attain comparability with 1947 data.
SOURCE: Appendix Table II-1.

TABLE II-2. Changes in the U.S. Agribusiness Work Force: 1947 and 1966

	1947	1966	Percentage increase from 1947 to 1966
	(millions of people)		
Farm supply industries employment	5	5.7	14%
Farm workers	10	5.6	−44
Food and fiber processing and distribution employment	9.5	12.0	26
Total agribusiness employment	24.5	23.3	−5%
Total U.S. work force	60	76.6	28%
Agribusiness as a percent of total work force employed	41%	30.4%	

SOURCE: Author's estimates based on U.S. Department of Agriculture and Bureau of the Census data using the same basis as set forth in Davis and Goldberg, *A Concept of Agribusiness*, pp. 10–11.

duction units and in some cases to vertical integration. And market orientation and new technology have brought about major changes in the agricultural product mix; for example, the sharp rise in soybean and citrus output, and changes in the production methods of such products as livestock and poultry. The changes on and off the farm require coordinating machinery that help to mesh the production, processing, and distribution processes in an effective manner. This coordination task has led to the use of more sophisticated arrangements which in turn affect the market structure of the agribusiness complex.

These changes are also reflected in the allocation of human and financial resources. Table II-2 presents changes in employment in various agribusiness segments from 1947 to 1966 as well as a comparison of agribusiness employment with total U.S. employment. The most striking change shown in Table II-2 is the sharp decline in employment on the farm, a decrease of 44% from 1947 to 1966. The decline in farm labor is so much greater than the modest decrease of 9% in "value added" in the farm sector that it emphasizes the extent to which purchased inputs have been substituted for farm labor. This change is confirmed by other data which indicate that 40% of farm inputs

were on-farm labor in 1950 whereas the percentage had decreased to 21% in 1965.

The same type of substitution of other inputs for labor took place in the off-farm sectors of agribusiness. This is clear from the much smaller percentage increases in employment for those sectors than the corresponding figures of dollar volume of sales or value added which appear in Table II-1. At the same time, however, the growth in activity in these off-farm sectors was such that significant increases in employment took place, 14% in the farm supply industries and 26% in the processing and distribution sector. These increases were not great enough to offset the decrease in farm labor so that total agribusiness employment fell by about 5% from 1947 to 1966.

The decline in agribusiness employment occurred at the same time that total employment in the United States was growing by about 28%. Consequently, agribusiness employment as a percentage of total domestic employment fell sharply, from 41% in 1947 to just over 30% in 1966. It is important to note that the food and fiber needs of the economy are being met by a smaller proportion of our work force, yet even at 30% agribusiness is still a very large part of our economy.

The composition of agribusiness employment in 1966 was such that three persons were employed off the farm for each one on the farm. This is startling evidence of how much broader are the ramifications of agribusiness problems than just at the farm level.

The replacement of labor in agribusiness with capital resources is evident in a summary of the estimated financial assets utilized by the major segments of agribusiness for 1947 and 1964 as presented in Table II-3.

A comparison of total assets for 1947 and 1964 for each of the three segments of agribusiness reveals a sharp increase in assets for each segment and a

TABLE II-3. Changes in Assets of Major Segments of Agribusiness: December 31, 1947, and December 31, 1964

(In billions of dollars)

Assets	Farm supply 1947	Farm supply 1964	Farming 1947	Farming 1964	Processing and distribution 1947	Processing and distribution 1964
Inventories	$2.1	$6.2	$9.0	$8.9	$11.1	$26.4
Other current assets	2.6	7.1	20.5	39.6	9.7	27.0
Total current assets	(4.7)	(13.3)	(29.5)	(48.5)	(20.8)	(53.4)
Fixed assets	2.7	11.2	102.5	189.1	7.3	28.6
Other non-current assets	0.6	2.5	—	—	1.7	5.0
Total assets	$8.0	$27.0	$132.0	$237.6	$29.8	$87.0

SOURCE: These data are derived from the USDA Balance Sheet of Agriculture and the reports of the Federal Trade Commission and Securities and Exchange Commission on United States Manufacturing, Retail and Wholesale Corporations, according to methods set forth in *A Concept of Agribusiness*, p. 10.

much greater percentage increase for the off-farm segments than the farm segment. This pattern is consistent with the widespread substitution of capital for labor in agribusiness and the relative rates of growth of the various segments.

The increase in total assets employed on the farm reflects both the types of additional capital inputs described previously and also the fact that land has become a more intensively used resource and has increased in value. Part of the increase in value is also due to the capitalization of anticipated income flows, partially encouraged or supported by government price support programs. Many economists, including Dr. Willard W. Cochrane,[2] have maintained that appreciation of land values has been one of the most important equity benefits to the producer who continues to hold his land.

It is also interesting to note that whereas inventories increased sharply in line with other assets in the off-farm sectors, they remained essentially stable in the farm sector. This seeming anomaly is explained by the fact that a major proportion of agricultural product inventories are owned by the U.S. Government and not by the farmers themselves.

The forces of change that influence the structure

[2] *The City Man's Guide to the Farm Problem*, p. 66.

and performance of agribusiness are both national and international in scope. The international factors are becoming increasingly important in helping to form the new dimensions of agribusiness. In 1966 more than one out of every four harvested acres in the U.S. were utilized in supplying commodities for the export market. These exports are expected to increase from $6.6 billion in 1966 to $8 billion by 1970 and to $10 billion by 1980. Not only are the dollar and quantity volumes increasing but the product mix is changing to meet rising income and expanding population needs. For example, Table II-4 compares ex-

TABLE II-4. Wheat, Corn, and Soybean Exports: 1956 and 1966

(In millions of bushels)

Crop	1956	1966	% Increase 1956 to 1966
Wheat	545	860	58%
Corn	117	734	527
Soybeans	85	246	189

SOURCE: USDA, ERS, *Foreign Agricultural Trade of the U.S.*, March 1962 and March 1967.

ports of three major crops in 1956 and 1966. These changes in the export product mix are indicative of the types of demand involved. The exceptionally large increases in corn and soybean exports reflect the increasing demand for feed grains and soybean products to meet the growth of livestock and poultry consumption which in turn stems from improved income levels. The much smaller increase in wheat exports is more closely related to the basic food demands and population growth of developing countries. Not only is the United States the most important exporter of agricultural products in the world; it is also the only nation with sizable "reserve" stocks which many now consider to be "international reserve" stocks.

The United States agribusinessman is not only shipping commodities overseas in response to the needs of developed and developing countries but technology and marketing system know-how as well. A recent report by the President's Science Advisory Committee[3] estimates that the United States must not only double its exports in the next 20 years, but together with other nations it must increase the use of fertilizer in the developing free world from 6 million tons per year in 1966 to 67 million tons per year by 1985. Other farm inputs will be needed such as pesticides, machinery, and seed. All this expansion will involve the development of more complex and efficient farm supply and food transportation, storage, and

[3] *The World Food Problem*, The White House, May 1967, Vol. II, p. 375.

EXHIBIT II-3

FUNCTIONAL ORGANIZATION OF U. S. FOOD AGRIBUSINESS, 1967 (EST.)

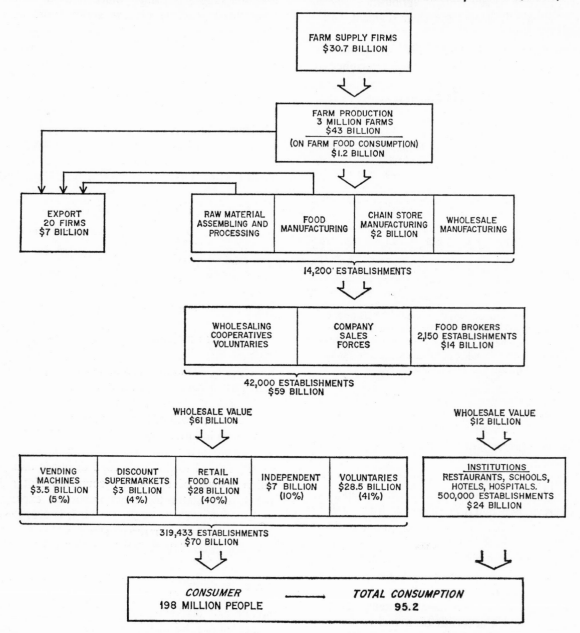

distribution systems throughout the world. The foreign market for food and farm supplies will almost certainly expand more rapidly than the domestic market.

Changes are also taking place in the infrastructure of domestic and international agribusiness. As an example, the new transportation devices of unit train loads of grain and "big John" cars domestically and the development of large export vessels make all markets much more interdependent and competitive. The exporter in the United States can now ship corn to move across the Atlantic for a mere 3 cents a bushel.

All the forces of change that have brought forth new dimensions for agribusiness and its many commodity systems have resulted in the current functional organization of the U.S. food complex as presented in Exhibit II-3. (The reader will note that this diagram excludes fiber processing and distribution.) This chart gives some indication of the importance of new distribution channels: for instance, discount supermarkets, vending machines, new types of markets (institutional), and the increasing dollar importance of manufactured farm supplies and the processing and distribution segments of agribusiness. As styles of living vary, and as major technological, social, economic, and political developments take place, the functions of this food complex, its products, and its human and physical resources, as well as its coordinating devices, will change drastically. Such dramatic alterations will affect the formulation and implementation of meaningful policies by the private and public managers in each of the agribusiness commodity systems that will be analyzed in the sections of the study which follow.

Wheat

SINCE BIBLICAL times wheat and its flour and bread products have been considered the staff of life. In the United States, in spite of a major shift in consumption habits and a decline in the consumption of food products made from wheat and wheat flour, this commodity still ranks as the number one food grain. The rate of decline in U.S. wheat consumption per capita has slackened in recent years, and with a continued increase in population, the flour and baking industry should gradually expand in product volume to meet domestic consumption requirements.

The most dramatic changes in volume in the U.S. wheat economy have occurred in the exports of U.S. wheat and flour. A world population explosion, coupled with crop disasters in India, China, and Russia and widely fluctuating wheat production in Western Europe, has placed tremendous demands on the United States as the major "surplus" producer of wheat. Our wheat production, reserve stocks, and reserve acre policies are as important to the world's agribusiness activities as they are to the U.S. agribusiness complex. Not only are these supplies important as normal supplies and buffer stocks in the world wheat economy, they are fast becoming a possible major ingredient in meeting the protein nutritional requirements of undernourished populations. If new "lysine" wheat varieties or enriched wheat and wheat products become more readily and economically available, they may serve as the major and cheapest food in fighting world protein malnutrition.

As a "basic" food, and the most important world food grain, wheat has had to meet the dramatic changes of domestic and world wheat food requirements. Much of the coordinating machinery that was created by or for the U.S. wheat system was of a patchwork nature. During and immediately following World War II, domestic surpluses soon changed to

shortages. Once the war torn countries of the world were able to return to normal production patterns, the maintenance of U.S. wartime price incentives or supports resulted in U.S. wheat surpluses. In spite of acreage controls, new technological inputs created larger crops faster than acres planted to wheat could be reduced. The high support prices and resultant wheat surpluses in turn prompted "emergency" storage programs, which have changed the entire nature of the U.S. grain industry. The difficulty in maintaining high domestic wheat price support programs in the face of mounting domestic wheat surpluses and high storage costs and the increased competition for world wheat markets led to lower cash supports. These cash supports at $1.25 a bushel were supplemented by a payment of a certificate[1] with cash value to the producer. These former wheat surpluses also led to "surplus disposal" and "world economic development" programs. Such attempts to balance domestic wheat production against domestic and foreign consumption needs have taken place in an environment that consists of many political, economic, and social forces. The price of wheat to one million U.S. wheat producers, the price of bread to the consumer, and the food requirements of developing nations will remain important political as well as economic questions.

The domestic government price support and storage programs and the P.L. 480 disposal programs as well as the U.S. participation in the International Wheat Agreement, are important elements of the wheat system, but they represent only a few of the many insti-

[1] This certificate is issued to a wheat producer who plants in compliance with government programs, and is based on the proportion of the U.S. wheat crop used for domestic consumption (35% in 1967). The payment is financed by a 75-cent flour milling certificate and the balance is paid out of the U.S. Treasury. In 1966 it was worth $1.32 a bushel (see page 51).

tutions and arrangements that make up and have helped to shape the U.S. wheat industry. Other elements include: (1) farm, bakery, wholesale, and retail cooperatives; (2) national and state associations of wheat producers, grain elevator operators, exporters, millers, bakers, wholesalers, and retailers; (3) futures markets; (4) national farm organizations (Farm Bureau, Farmers Union, National Farmers Organization, Grange); (5) various forms of contract integration; (6) transportation networks and different wheat and wheat product rates; (7) all the grade, standard, inspection, education, research, and health activities of the U.S. Department of Agriculture; (8) unique credit facilities of the Farm Credit Administration; (9) The activities of the Commodity Credit Corporation — payment-in-kind program, storage rates, sales price policies; (10) the help and guidance of the Farmer Cooperative Service of the U.S. Department of Agriculture; (11) unique labor contracts for "drop delivery" of bread; (12) the development of private label bread production and marketing programs; and (13) various international commodity arrangements.

These institutions and arrangements have been developed during a time when many technological changes were occurring in the wheat industry: (1) new varieties of wheat; (2) new methods of protein separation; (3) the development of new products and the use of frozen dough and other changes in ingredient forms; (4) new transportation methods and (5) new forms of corporate and cooperative business organization.

The instruments of coordination listed above helped the participants of the wheat system adjust the system and its parts to the changing needs of foreign and domestic consumers. Throughout this study "coordination" refers to the bringing together of the many parts of a system for common action in carrying out the many functions that have to be performed in satisfying the ultimate consumer of wheat food products.

The coordinating patterns in the wheat economy evolved over time. In the early stages of the system, various participants in railroad operations provided incentives for developing markets for new wheat production and, similarly, new procurement opportunities for flour mills. In many commodity systems the catalytic and coordinating activities of supporting infrastructure industries are necessary for a smooth functioning of product flow from producer to consumer. In the current U.S. wheat economy the coordinating leadership is located in many segments of the system such as major exporters, retail chain bakers, flour mills, and vertically and/or cooperatively integrated firms.

In the pages that follow, the structure of the wheat industry system will be described and analyzed in the light of market, technological, and political developments that have changed the consumption, processing, and production patterns of this industry. One note of caution: The wheat industry exists as a separately defined entity only in a conceptual sense. In actual practice practically all participants in the system are engaged in other operations, crops, or related products. Nevertheless, the following analysis of the central core of the wheat economy provides decision makers with an overall description of the structure and major workings of the major segments of the wheat system and an opportunity to relate their specific firm's or entity's operations to the total industry system of which they are a part.

Chapter III describes the major forces of change that help to shape the current wheat economy. Chapter IV sets forth the structure of the wheat economy resulting from the forces of change. Chapter V analyzes the behavioral and performance patterns of the wheat system.

III

The Dynamics of the Wheat Economy

As THE MOST important domestic and international food grain crop in terms of dollar value of production, wheat has received more attention in public policy than has any other commodity. Depending upon the domestic and international consumption requirements of the food and feed products of this crop, public policies have alternatively encouraged or discouraged wheat production and/or consumption through various price support, acreage control and export programs.

Prior to World War II, wheat surpluses were accumulating rapidly in the United States. The increase in domestic and international consumption of wheat products brought about during the war and the immediate postwar period reduced inventories and wheat shortages occurred. The government policy at that time was to have high price supports to encourage production. After the postwar adjustments were made in the world's agricultural production, the United States once again became a "surplus" producer. Price supports on wheat were maintained but acreage controls were instituted, and the number of acres that could be planted to wheat were reduced. Improved varieties and expanded use of fertilizer, chemicals, and farm machinery, however, increased wheat yields per

acre at a rate that exceeded the effect of acreage reduction, as Table III-1 indicates.

On May 5, 1966, the U.S. wheat acreage allotment for 1967 was increased by the Secretary of Agriculture by 15%, or 7.7 million additional acres. Again on August 8, 1966 the Secretary increased the allotment by an additional 8.9 million acres in order to encourage increased production to meet changing world demands. This makes the national wheat acreage allotment 68.2 million acres.

A slackening in the decline and possible leveling off of per capita consumption of wheat products, the volatility of international wheat markets, the U.S. role as world wheat price stabilizer, and the significance of wheat prices to the farm income of a major segment of American agribusiness have led to a variety of government policies and administrative decisions. These new policies have had to be taken into account by the participants of the wheat system as they adjust their firms' operations and industry structure to meet domestic and international environmental forces of change.

CHANGES IN DOMESTIC CONSUMPTION

Consumers spend over $8 billion each year for food products made from wheat. The form in which these products have been consumed has changed over the past several decades. Much less home baking occurs. New improved products from wide assortments of flours and shapes of fresh and "brown and serve" bread, to exotic combinations of pastries, rolls, biscuits, cakes, cookies, cereals, and unique snack items are now available to all segments of the market. A few of these product changes are indicated in Table III-2.

Table III-2 shows that the demand for specialty bakery and cereal products is increasing whereas the

TABLE III-1. U.S. Wheat Production, Acreage, and Yields: Selected Years, 1949–1966

Year	Production (1,000 bushels)	Acreage harvested (1,000 acres)	Yield per harvested acre (bushels)
1949	1,098,415	75,910	14.5
1954	983,900	54,356	18.1
1959	1,117,735	51,716	21.6
1964	1,283,371	49,762	25.8
1965	1,315,613	49,560	26.5
1966	1,310,642	49,843	26.3

SOURCE: *Wheat Situation*, February 1967, p 22.

production of white bread products has increased only slightly. The increase in bran and midds and other wheat by-products used in the poultry and livestock industry indicate that there has been a more rapid

TABLE III-2. Index of U.S. Production of Wheat Food Products Shipped by Producers: 1954, 1958, and 1963 (1954 = 100)

Product	1954	1958	1963
White flour except flour mixes	100	108	122
Grain mill products (bran, midds, etc.)	100	109	178
Bread and related products	100	109	114
Biscuits, crackers, and cookies	100	114	132
Cereal products	100	114	148
Spaghetti and macaroni	100	110	126
U.S. population (in millions)	161.8	171.5	186.6
U.S. civilian per capita consumption of wheat flour (in pounds)	126.0	121.0	116.0

SOURCE: *Census of Manufactures*, 1963, and USDA, ERS.

increase in demand for wheat flour by-products than for wheat flour. From this it can be inferred that there has been an increase in wheat flour milling for overseas markets and that the by-products of such milling remain in the United States and are sold to an expanding domestic feed industry.

The broad changes in domestic consumption of wheat products represent not only product changes but also changes in the attributes surrounding the product, including quality, freshness, services, packaging, display, and promotion, that differentiate the product in the mind of the consumer.

Changes in wheat end-product consumption indicate the great desire of marketing and processing firms to differentiate their products through more "convenience" preparation and packaging, and to take advantage of the consumers' growing affluence and leisure time by promoting "snack" wheat food products. On the other hand, the advent of large retail trading areas and mass distribution centers encourages mass promotion and uniform grades and standards. This mass market requires large-scale processing to meet the retailers' volume requirements for a staple item such as white bread. These changing domestic consumption patterns affect the size, shape, location, and operations of the decision-making centers of the wheat market structure.

Consumer demand for wheat products in the United States as translated into wheat requirements is shown in Table III-3. A great many varieties of wheat are necessary to produce the many bread, cereal, sweet goods, cake, and flour products demanded by the public. As new products are developed, flour millers,

bakers, and the like are attempting to tailor-make flours for specific end uses by either using new air classification techniques[1] or blending several types of wheat.

TABLE III-3. U.S. Domestic Food Use of Wheat, by Type of Product: 1959–1960 (In millions of bushels)

Product	Hard	Soft	Durum	Total
Bread	200.15	—	—	200.15
Rolls	10.27	—	—	10.27
Biscuits and muffins	—	2.87	—	2.87
Crackers	3.40	18.53	—	21.93
Cakes	—	6.11	—	6.11
Pies	—	2.52	—	2.52
Other sweet goods	11.38	8.10	—	19.48
Alimentary paste products	8.20	—	22.00	30.20
Flour:				
All purpose	85.57	72.33	—	157.90
Whole wheat	2.38	—	—	2.38
Cake	—	12.21	—	12.21
Prepared mixes	—	22.34	—	22.34
Wheat cereals	9.65	1.99	—	11.64
Total	331.00	147.00	22.00	500.00

SOURCE: USDA, ERS, "Utilization of Wheat for Food."

Although the physical characteristics of the wheat crop have not limited the end-product use solely to bread and rolls, these products are still the most important food items produced from wheat and wheat flour (see Table III-3). The decline in per capita consumption of wheat flour products would undoubtedly have been greater, however, if new products and forms of products had not been created. In the last few years average annual per capita consumption of flour products has tended to level off although the decline continues at a decreasing rate (see Table III-4). The industry is hopeful that this leveling off in per capita wheat and flour consumption means that the wheat economy will grow with population increases. In the past, the change in eating habits resulting in a decline in wheat products consumed per capita was just about offset by population increases.

Because bread dominates the end-product use of wheat flour, many private and public policy makers have used the price of a loaf of bread as compared to the price of wheat as a means of measuring the changing cost and function structure of assembling, storing, and processing wheat into bread and distributing that bread to the ultimate consumer. As labor, transportation, processing, and new product innovation costs

[1] Air classification techniques are processes developed by the flour milling industry to separate types of protein (high and low) from the same grade of wheat, thereby creating tailor-made protein flour.

TABLE III-4. U.S. Per Capita Consumption of Wheat, Whole Wheat, and Semolina Flour and Total Bushels Consumed: Selected Years, 1949–1965

Year	Per capita consumption (pounds)	Total consumption (1,000 cwt.)
1949	136	202,096
1954	127	205,482
1959	121	213,835
1963	116	219,798
1964	116	223,651
1965	115	224,421
1966	114	224,380

SOURCE: *Wheat Situation*, February 1967, p. 23.

change, the spread between wheat prices and bread gradually grows larger. The spread between wheat and bread prices has led policy makers to develop programs that can shift part of the price support financing from the U.S. Treasury to the consumers. The assumption, which is essentially correct, is that the cost of the wheat in a loaf of bread is so small that a 50-cent a bushel change in the price of wheat to the farmer would result in less than a 1-cent change in the price of a one-pound loaf of bread. There is a further assumption that there is an inelastic demand for wheat products by consumers (many economic studies have so indicated).

TABLE III-5. Dollar Weekly Expenditures for White Bread by U.S. Families Subdivided by Income Categories: 1960

Family income	Weekly food expenditures	Weekly white bread expenditures	White bread expenditures as % of total food expenditures	% of total dollar food expenditures	White bread expenditures (52 weeks) as % of total income
All families	$21.17	$0.69	3.3%	—	—
Under $3,000	11.35	0.43	3.8	21.2%	0.745%
$3,000–$5,000	18.23	0.66	3.6	20.4	0.858
$5,000–$7,500	23.13	0.79	3.4	26.8	0.657
$7,500–$10,000	26.41	0.81	3.1	16.7	0.481
$10,000–$15,000	29.35	0.79	2.7	11.2	0.329
$15,000 and over	31.43	0.66	2.1	3.7	0.229

SOURCE: Linden (ed.), *Expenditure Patterns of the American Family.*

A 1960 Bureau of Labor Statistics food consumption study, analyzed and released by the National Industrial Conference Board,[2] tended to indicate that all families spent, on the average, less than 1% of their annual income on bread (see Table III-5). Families

[2] Linden (ed.), *Expenditure Patterns of the American Family.*

that earned $7,500 a year or less (this represents small families as well as lower income groups) spent a greater percentage of their total income for white bread than did families that were larger and/or had higher incomes. The significance of these statistics is that all income groups spent a relatively small percentage of their food dollar and of their total income for bread. The statistical averages support the contention that the "milling certificate" that is used as a means of financing wheat price supports is slightly regressive in that in 1960 families that earned $7,500 or less paid a larger percentage of their income for bread and also accounted for 68.4% of total dollar food purchases. But these figures also indicate how small bread purchases were compared with income patterns in 1960.

With a decline in the market price support level of wheat in 1964 and the development of higher yielding and (in some cases) poorer milling quality wheat, coupled with a growing livestock and poultry feed market, feed wheat and wheat by-products of flour milling were becoming more important factors in the ultimate consumption of wheat products. Table III-6

TABLE III-6. Wheat and Wheat By-Products Used as Feed in the United States: 1958–1963 Average and 1963, 1964, and 1965
(In millions of bushels)

Crop year[a]	Wheat for feed
1958–63 average	38.0
1963	10.9
1964	58.6
1965	143.9

[a] The crop year begins July 1.
SOURCE: Obtained from USDA, ERS, May 1967.

indicates the rapid increase in feed wheat and by-products used in feed manufacture in the last two years of compensatory payments to wheat producers (1964 and 1965). As the "cash" price support for wheat was lowered, some wheat varieties declined in price value and became competitive with feed grains. This has provided a broader market for wheat which in turn helps to support wheat at least at a level comparable with some feed grains.

The major decline in wheat consumption in the United States has occurred because of the change in dietary habits from less cereal to more vegetable and animal proteins and to fruits and vegetables as a result of a change in work habits and an increase in income levels. The per capita decline in consumption of wheat products seems to have decreased during the past four years. New products and processes have been developed for wheat products that meet the diverse needs of the many segments of the U.S. food market. These products appeal to the new life style of the consumer: more dining out and an increase in the consumption of casual snack-time foods.

The wheat industry also appears to be entering a new era of additional feed consumption of wheat as government price policies change permitting wheat to be competitive with feed grains in the livestock and poultry feed markets. The improvement in the quality of bran and midds (the by-products of flour milling) may also be a factor in the increased use of these products in the expanding mixed feed industry and may also be important in the future development of low cost high protein foods for the international market.

CHANGES IN EXPORT CONSUMPTION

The export consumption changes for U.S. wheat and wheat products have been more dramatic than have domestic consumption trends. In the decade 1955–1965 wheat and flour exports more than doubled from 346 million bushels in 1955 to 867 million bushels in the crop year 1965–1966. This growth in U.S. wheat exports occurred as the total world wheat trade expanded greatly (see Exhibit III-1), with the United States increasing its percentage of the world wheat market from 32.5% in 1955 to 38.7% in 1965.

EXHIBIT III-1

WHEAT AND FLOUR: WORLD EXPORTS BY COUNTRY

The world export market not only has changed in terms of value, but also in terms of customer composition. The shortages of wheat in India, China, and Russia have been significant factors in the world wheat market in the past several years. Red China (excluded from trade in the United States) in 1965–

1966 purchased approximately 240 million bushels of wheat (primarily from Canada). Russia entered the world market in 1963–1964 and bought 350 million bushels, reduced its purchase to 70 million bushels in 1964–1965, and upped it to 300 million bushels in 1965–1966. The United States has participated in sales to Russia but to a much smaller degree than has Canada. In addition, in June 1966 Russia and Canada announced a three-year wheat sales agreement which makes U.S.-Russian wheat sales activity seem less likely during this period.

The principal growth in the U.S. wheat trade has been through concessional sales under the P.L. 480 program[3] which averaged over two-thirds of total U.S. wheat exports during the seven years 1959–1965 (see Table III-7). The largest P.L. 480 customer has been

TABLE III-7. Exports of Wheat for Dollars and Concessional Sales Under the P.L. 480 Program: 1959–1963 Average and 1963, 1964, and 1965

(In millions of bushels)

Crop year	Dollar payment wheat exports	Concessional wheat exports	Total exports
1958–63 average	215.0	463.1	678.1
1963	352.7	503.4	856.1
1964	157.7	567.3	725.0
1965	298.0	569.2	867.2

SOURCE: *Wheat Situation*, October 1966, p. 26.

India, whose imports accounted for 269 million bushels in 1965–1966. Other large wheat P.L. 480 recipients include Brazil, Korea, Pakistan, Egypt, and Yugoslavia. The major dollar sales customers in 1965–1966 were Japan, 73 million bushels; Netherlands, 53 million bushels;[4] United Kingdom, 21 million bushels; Philippines, 16 million bushels; Venezuela 15 million

[3] The Agricultural Trade Development and Assistance Act of 1954 has become known as Public Law 480 or the Food for Peace Program. There are four major titles under this act. Title I of the act provides for the sale of U.S. farm commodities for the currency of the recipient country. Title I sales are made to countries which lack the necessary foreign exchange to obtain their food requirements through regular commercial channels. Sales made under these conditions and those sales made under the other title of the act are sometimes referred to as "concessional" sales. Title II of the act provides for grants of food for disaster relief and other assistance. Title III of the act provides for domestic and foreign donations of food for distribution by nonprofit voluntary relief agencies of the United States and international organizations, and barter of surplus food and fiber in exchange for strategic materials for stockpiling and for services needed by U.S. Government agencies. Title IV of the act provides for long-term dollar credit sales of surplus agricultural commodities to friendly countries. [For more details of the P.L. 480 program see USDA, Foreign Agricultural Economic Report No. 17, Financial Procedures Under Public Law 480.]

[4] Much of this was shipped to other European destinations.

bushels; France, 11 million bushels; and Belgium, 10 million bushels.

The increased world trade of wheat up to the summer of 1966 had little effect on world wheat prices because of the relatively large U.S. wheat stocks (see Table III-8). In essence the United States was pro-

TABLE III-8. Average Monthly Prices per Bushel of Canadian Wheat, No. 1 Northern, at Winnipeg:[a]
1961–1965
(In U.S. dollars)

	1961	1962	1963	1964	1965	1966
January		1.82	1.82	1.90	1.88	1.85
February		1.82	1.82	1.93	1.78	1.87
March		1.82	1.82	1.92	1.78	1.88
April		1.82	1.82	1.91	1.78	1.88
May		1.82	1.81	1.90	1.78	1.89
June		1.82	1.81	1.90	1.78	1.92[b]
July	1.73	1.82	1.80	1.90	1.79	
August	1.78	1.83	1.78	1.90	1.79	
September	1.79	1.85	1.78	1.90	1.80	
October	1.78	1.84	1.86	1.90	1.81	
November	1.79	1.83	1.89	1.90	1.81	
December	1.80	1.81	1.89	1.90	1.82	

[a] Used as world wheat price basis; basis Fort William and Port Arthur; average of prices fixed daily by Canadian Wheat Board converted to U.S. currency.
[b] Preliminary.
SOURCE: *Wheat Situation*, July 1966, p. 30.

viding a price umbrella for its competitors. Competition for dollar sales became especially severe in 1964–1965, and the United States changed its position from being the price stabilizer to one of a price competitor in the market; the price of world wheat in competitive export markets dropped 10 cents a bushel in one month (January–February 1965, see Table III-8). Since February 1965 the United States has been gaining back some of the dollar markets it lost (see Table III-7).

With U.S. wheat reserves reduced to lower levels and U.S. commitments (domestically and internationally) greater than U.S. production in 1966, restrictions on some P.L. 480 wheat shipments may occur from time to time until the increased acreage allotments for 1967 production have the effect of meeting the expanding consumption requirements or until other programs are developed. In addition the "world price" for wheat will probably continue to remain strong.

Because there are over 60 domestic wheat price support programs around the world, world wheat prices represent subsidized adjustments to meet alternative offers from export countries. In this sense most U.S. wheat for export (both commercial and P.L. 480) is subsidized in order to permit U.S. exporters to be competitive in world wheat markets.

In summary, the U.S. wheat export market is expanding rapidly, primarily to fill the needs of developing countries whose agriculture production has not kept pace with the increases in their population. The United States is also becoming more aggressive in the commercial markets, as rising income levels and the development of new eating habits, together with the growing world population, increase the demand for wheat and wheat flour products. Because protein malnutrition is such an important problem in many countries, many nutritionists have advocated the adding of lysine and other amino-acids to wheat to make the protein content of this cereal grain more comparable with animal and vegetable proteins. Also additional research on wheat by-products will be continued to help feed the developing nations. These products will not only include "bulgur," a wheat "rice substitute," but other products more compatible with the diets of the various countries receiving protein food products. The world wheat export market will continue to be a major factor in the development of the U.S. wheat system. In the years 1959–1965 U.S. wheat exports were larger than domestic consumption. This trend is expected to continue even though total domestic consumption is increasing (see Table III-9). The com-

TABLE III-9. U.S. Wheat Consumption Domestically and Internationally: 1959–1963 Average and 1963, 1964, and 1965
(In millions of bushels)

Crop year	Domestic disappearance	Exports	Total consumption
1959–63 average	595.4	678.1	1,273.5
1963	588.5	856.1	1,444.6
1964	643.6	725.0	1,368.6
1965	731.4	867.2	1,598.6

SOURCE: *Wheat Situation*, February 1967, p. 2.

mitments to the developing countries and the growing demand of the dollar markets will mean that more of the unused wheat production reserves of the United States will be needed to meet world wheat requirements.

CHANGES IN PRODUCTION

Wheat, although grown in practically every state of the union, is not of a uniform class or quality. Each of the five main classes of wheat (hard winter, hard spring, soft white, soft red, and durum) has unique properties that generally make it more suitable for one wheat product than another. In the *theoretical* market structure of the wheat economy, the consumer reaches back toward the producer through various marketing channels and markets to indicate, by price, his preference for various quantities of the several classes of wheat. *In practice,* wheat is harvested once a year (in the spring for winter wheat and in the fall for spring wheat) and is consumed throughout the crop year. Year-to-year changes in quality and quantity of each major class of wheat are more dependent on weather than on consumer preferences.

Inventory management of the wheat crop from year to year is a major occupation of each segment of the wheat economy from producer to retailer. Balancing the initial raw product production and quality variations against changing domestic and export consumption patterns requires not only viable and flexible marketing and processing decision makers, but also institutions and arrangements that are able to coordinate these many functional activities in an efficient manner.

The technological revolution on the farm in recent years has added to the difficulties of inventory management. With the aid of better-than-normal weather and improved fertilizer, seed, chemical, and mechanical inputs, the wheat producer's yield per acre in the seven years 1960–1966 has averaged 150% of 1950 (see Exhibit III-2). The development of mechanical harvest combines of increasing size and power has cut harvest time periods from as much as ten weeks to two weeks. The rapid harvesting of the crop has meant increased pressure for on-farm and off-farm storage and assembling facilities and has put a strain on transportation facilities.

EXHIBIT III-2

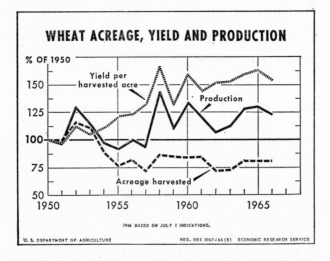

WHEAT ACREAGE, YIELD AND PRODUCTION

1966 BASED ON JULY 1 INDICATIONS.

U. S. DEPARTMENT OF AGRICULTURE   NEG. ERS 3967-66 (8)   ECONOMIC RESEARCH SERVICE

Although many wheat farms cannot be classified as large farms (some 82% of total production coming from farms with less than $40,000 total sales),[5] the

[5] USDA, ERS, August 1963.

average size of wheat farms in specialized wheat regions is increasing as indicated by Table III-10. There are two primary reasons for this growth in size: one is economy of scale, and the other is that the wheat

TABLE III-10. Average Size of All Farms in Selected Areas of Specialized Wheat Regions: Specified Years, 1910–1959

Specialized wheat producing regions	*Acreage per farm*						
	1910	*1920*	*1940*	*1945*	*1950*	*1955*	*1959*
Spring wheat (upper midwest, typified by North Dakota)	371	437	500	581	633	700	788
Hard Winter wheat (central midwest typified by Kansas)	453	509	529	614	629	712	777
White wheat (Pacific Northwest, typified by Washington and Oregon)	682	727	1,134	1,279	1,318	1,865	2,107
U.S. average	138	148	174	195	215	242	302

SOURCE: U.S. Census of Agriculture.

farmer wants (even without "economies of scale") his enterprise to be of sufficient size to yield enough income to provide a reasonable standard of living for his family, and he has in one way or another managed to avail himself of additional land for this purpose.[6]

The government acreage control program in conjunction with the price support program has reduced the number of acres seeded to wheat (as shown in Exhibit III-2) but there has been relatively little shift in the location of the major wheat production areas. Table III-11 indicates that what few shifts in production areas have occurred have been an increase in the Great Plains States from 68% of total U.S. wheat seeded acres and 48% of total production in 1935–1939 to 74% of seeded acres and 62% of production in 1966, and a decrease in the Corn Belt and Lake States seeded acreage from 17% and production from 26% in 1935–1939 to 12% of seeded acres and 19% of production in 1966. This shift represents more favorable crop alternatives in the Corn Belt States (e.g., soybeans and corn) than exist in other sections. Also the rapid increase in production in the Great Plains area is indicative of greater use of fertilizer and farm chemicals by producers than had oc-

[6] Or, as another possibility, those with smaller land areas have retired from the industry.

curred in the past and also the use of summer fallow during acreage restriction periods.

Given the increased demand for wheat, the increased acreage allowances to producers of wheat complying with government programs, and the lim-

TABLE III-11. Acres Seeded and Production of Wheat, Total United States and by Regions: Averages 1935–1955, Annual 1956–1966

Period	United States	Great Plains	North-west	Corn Belt and Lake States	South	All other states
			Millions of acres seeded			
Average:						
1935–39	73.2	49.8	4.7	12.7	2.8	3.2
1941–45	61.4	43.8	4.2	8.3	2.5	2.6
1946–50	76.7	56.3	5.5	9.8	2.1	3.0
1951–55	71.4	52.0	5.4	9.4	1.9	2.7
1956	60.7	43.5	4.8	8.4	1.9	2.1
1957	49.8	33.4	4.0	8.4	2.1	1.9
1958	56.0	39.7	4.2	8.4	1.7	2.0
1959	56.8	40.1	4.2	8.8	1.8	1.9
1960	54.9	39.4	4.0	8.1	1.6	1.8
1961	55.7	39.7	4.1	8.5	1.7	1.7
1962	49.1	35.6	3.7	7.1	1.1	1.6
1963	53.0	37.9	3.9	8.1	1.4	1.7
1964	55.1	38.8	4.1	8.5	1.9	1.8
1965[a]	56.9	41.4	4.6	7.7	1.6	1.6
1966[b]	53.8	39.9	4.1	6.7	1.6	1.5
			Millions of bushels produced			
Average:						
1935–39	759	371	93	200	32	63
1941–45	985	645	108	148	33	51
1946–50	1,185	760	132	203	30	60
1951–55	1,078	619	146	222	33	58
1956	1,005	550	125	239	39	52
1957	956	544	144	189	34	45
1958	1,457	980	140	254	31	52
1959	1,121	683	148	207	35	48
1960	1,357	910	129	238	35	45
1961	1,235	774	112	262	42	45
1962	1,094	690	130	208	23	43
1963	1,142	643	139	284	31	45
1964	1,291	762	156	277	48	48
1965[a]	1,327	852	171	219	39	46
1966[b]	1,240	767	148	238	42	45

[a] Preliminary.
[b] July 1 estimate.
SOURCE: *Wheat Situation*, July 1966, p. 34.

ited crop alternatives in most of the producing regions, one would expect these trends in the location of production areas to continue. The major change that may be on the horizon is the unusually high yields of Pacific North Western wheat which may increase that section's importance to the wheat economy.

CHANGES IN PROCESSING AND TRANSPORTATION

The physical properties of wheat are such that when wheat is processed, only three-fourths by weight becomes wheat flour. The remaining fourth of the product, consisting of the outside hull etc. becomes offal in the form of bran and middlings. The flour milling industry in the past became concentrated in the major wheat producing areas of the United States (see Exhibits III-3 and III-4). Bran and middlings, although

EXHIBIT III-3

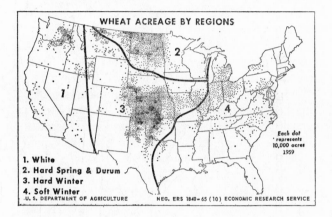

utilized as a feed ingredient in many parts of the United States and in overseas markets, may have some transportation advantage in being processed in areas adjacent to flour mills because of their close proximity to many large feed mill operations, some of which are owned by flour mills. Originally this transportation advantage was an incentive to locate most flour milling activities in the major wheat producing areas. Buffalo was the exception because of cheap water transportation and the dairy feed market in the East. In the last few years innovations in barge, truck, and rail transportation have reduced freight rates on wheat (an easily storable item). The rates on flour have not been reduced because flour is much more perishable than wheat and cannot utilize some of the same types of transportation facilities, such as barges. This change in rate relationships between wheat and flour has encouraged the construction of flour mills closer to population centers. As one follows the vertical commodity flows from wheat-to-flour-to-bread the perishability of the product increases and production takes place closer to the product's market areas. In essence then, the physical properties of wheat and its products do influence patterns of domestic production, processing, and distribution location. The adaptability of wheat in its raw form permits wheat handlers to take advantage of transportation innovations (barge and truck).

EXHIBIT III-4

Location of Mills: 1963, and Consumption of Flour: 1958

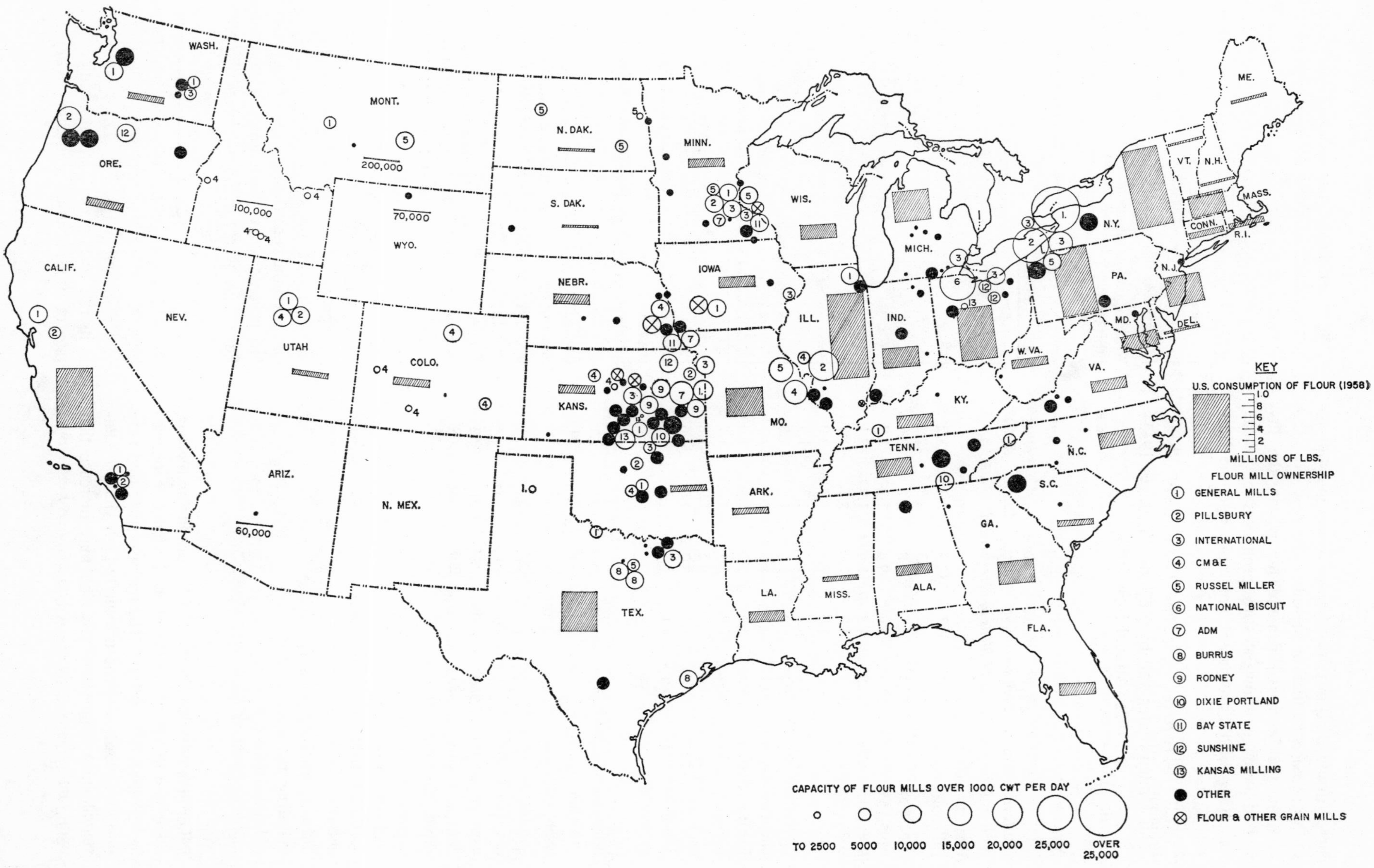

New forms of transportation are more difficult to utilize by the handlers of the perishable end products of wheat such as flour and bakery goods.

The change in milling-in-transit rates to permit more rail competition with truck and barge shipments of wheat has placed the milling-in-transit "captured" customers of the railroad at a distinct disadvantage. Previously, the milling-in-transit customer had the same rate as any competitors located in production or consumption centers because he was given a through milling-in-transit rate. Once truck and water carriers provided cheaper forms of transportation at assembling or distribution points, however, several railroads reduced rates at these competitive points but not for their milling-in-transit customers who had only rail as their principal form of transportation. In essence the railroads considered them to be "captured customers." Many flour mills have been closed in the Kansas City area because of these changes in freight rates and new ones are being built in large population centers in such states as Pennsylvania and Florida.

Changes in transportation rates also affect other operations of the wheat economy. For example, it is cheaper to ship wheat from the Atlantic coast to Europe than it is to move it from a subterminal market such as Fargo, North Dakota, to a terminal market such as Minneapolis, Minnesota, some 250 miles away. These low overseas rates make U.S. wheat competitive in world markets, but they also make overseas flour milling operations extremely competitive with U.S. flour manufacturers.

Other transportation changes, such as complete train rates on wheat and annual contracts on wheat shipments by both elevator operators and flour millers, place the large automated firm at a distinct advantage in the wheat economy. Such transportation contracts and changes are expected to increase at a rapid rate and affect the size and location of every segment of the wheat economy.

Transportation costs of the end product of wheats — bread and related products — have also brought about changes. The rapid increases in labor costs and intracity trucking costs have led to private label manufacturing and integrated production, shipping, and retail operations for bread and bread products to reduce high distribution costs. They have also led retailers who have compact distribution points to integrate backward into the manufacture and distribution of their own private label bread products.

Not only have there been dramatic changes in domestic transportation, but new, large export shipping vessels have been developed capable of transporting over one million bushels of wheat in one shipment.

These new shipping vessels will lead to huge storage and distribution centers in Europe, just as in the United States, with feeder systems fanning out to all the major consuming areas. This will improve the efficient flow of agricultural exports from this country, as well as

TABLE III-12. Wheat Support Prices Around the World: 1961

Country	Local units	Dollar per bushel equivalents[a]
Algeria	New francs per metric ton	2.67
Argentina	Peso per 100 kg.	1.16
Australia	s. and d. per bushel	1.76
Austria	Schillings per 100 kg.	2.65
Belgium	Belgian francs per 100 kg.	2.57
Brazil	Cruzeiros per 60 kg.	2.22
Canada	Canadian dollars per bushel	1.29[b]
Chile	Pesos per 100 kg.	1.40
Colombia	Pesos per carga[c]	2.81
Denmark	Kroners per 100 kg.	1.94
Ecuador	Sucres per Spanish quintal	2.52
Egypt	Egyptian pounds per ardeb	1.63
Finland	Finmarks per kg.	4.44
France	New francs per 100 kg.	2.26
Germany (West)	Marks per metric ton	2.97
Greece	Drachmas per kg.	2.45
Iran	Rials per kg.	2.17
Ireland	s. and d. per barrel[d]	2.12
Italy	Lire per 100 kg.	2.83
Japan	Yen per 60 kg.	3.01
Kenya	Shillings per 200 lbs.	1.97
Mexico	Pesos per metric ton	1.99
Morocco	Dirhams per 100 kg.	2.10
Netherlands	Guilder per 100 kg.	2.31
New Zealand	s. and d. per bushel	1.95
Norway	Kroners per metric ton	3.82
Pakistan	Rupees per maund	2.07
Portugal	Escudos per kg.	2.86
South Africa, Rep. of	Rands per 200 pounds	2.35
Spain	Pesetas per kg.	2.47
Sweden	Kroners per 100 kg.	2.38
Switzerland	Swiss francs per 100 kg.	4.11
Syria	Syrian pounds per metric ton	4.15
Tunisia	Dinars per 100 kg.	2.72
Turkey	Kurus per kg.	1.90
United Kingdom	s. and d. per cwt. (112 lbs.)	2.03
United States	U.S. dollars per bushel	1.79
Yugoslavia	Dinars per kg.	1.38

[a] Individual or average, fixed or target, base, floor, or final prices for standard types and grades. The f.o.b. points vary. Some prices are subject to one or more deductions. Some are gradually increased by specified amounts during a designated period after harvest to offset farm storage costs.

[b] On March 1, 1962, the Canadian government increased the price of Canadian $1.50 per bu. (U.S. $1.39 per bu.), which was made retroactive to the beginning of the current marketing season, August 1, 1961.

[c] One carga wheat = 140 kg. (5.1 bu.).

[d] One barrel wheat = 280 lbs. (4.67 bu.).

SOURCE: Food and Agricultural Organization of the United Nations.

developing a parallel food and fiber market system for Europe and other developed and developing nations.

GOVERNMENT PROGRAMS

Another important dynamic force of change in the wheat economy is the United States Government. By this time the reader must be fully aware of the complete interdependence of the governmental and private decision makers in the wheat economy. The behavioral patterns of the wheat economy have therefore been dependent on the interactions of the participants of the wheat economy and public policy makers.

Much of the wheat economy has acquired many of the attributes of a public utility. The government, with the help and advice of the participants of the wheat economy, regulates the location of major wheat inventories, time of shipment, percentage of wheat to be transported by American ships, international wheat subsidies, domestic subsidies on alternative wheat products (food versus industrial and certain feed products), mergers or lack of mergers, storage rates, income supports and type of support, etc. The government through the Commodity Exchange Authority and other agencies is informed of each firm's position in the futures markets (if the amount is over 200,000 and a maximum of 2,000,000 bushels for speculation purposes) and is kept informed of all export shipments, storage levels, and quality of government stocks. The government has, from time to time, changed wheat standards to meet the changing requirements of several segments of the wheat economy. By changing these standards, one segment or area may benefit at the expense of another. The government has also developed a host of international programs that restrict and shape the world trade patterns of the U.S. wheat economy.

The wheat market structure is not only shaped by domestic and export wheat programs of the United States Government, but its behavioral patterns are shaped by the domestic and international government programs of other nations. Table III-12 lists the domestic support price for wheat in 43 countries of the world as of 1961. This table gives but one indication of the complex network of domestic and international wheat programs that affect the manner in which the wheat economy performs.

NEW TECHNOLOGICAL DEVELOPMENTS

The rapid development of new technology in the wheat industry now permits dough freezing, bread freezing, continuous flour mill and bakery operations, and separation of protein levels within various grades of wheat. All of these technological improvements affect the operations of the individual decision maker in his tasks of procuring, assembling, processing and distributing wheat and wheat products. The frozen dough techniques make possible the development of new products, such as brown and serve rolls and bake-your-own-bread packages. The protein separation methods broaden the variety of classes of wheat that can be used for different end products — bread, cakes, crackers, biscuits. New freezing and chemical developments reduce shrinkage and loss from stale bread items because most products have longer shelf lives. As a result of these processes that maintain "freshness" for longer periods, the shipping area is enlarged and larger and more efficient bakery and retail units can be used. Other frozen food technologies have been developed that permit the expansion of product lines to include frozen doughnuts, frozen pies, and frozen dessert cakes. All these products cater to the taste, desires, and convenience requirements of the consumer.

In essence, then, this general description of the dynamics of the wheat economy suggests that the participants in the wheat system have participated in and reacted to many forces of change. The remaining chapters of the wheat analysis will describe the structure and performance of the wheat system as it adjusts to its changing environment.

IV

The Wheat Complex

THE RAPID changes in production and processing and marketing summarized in Chapter III have had an impact on the total wheat economy in terms of (1) marketing channels utilized, (2) number and size of units, (3) ownership patterns, (4) the development of coordinating institutions, and (5) the increase in all forms of integration. The current wheat economy is portrayed in this multidimensional manner in Exhibits IV-1, IV-2, and IV-3. These exhibits will serve as a broad framework for describing and analyzing the performance of the wheat complex as a whole and for assessing the performance and opportunities of the individual participants that comprise the wheat system.

THE MARKET STRUCTURE

THE CHANNELS OF DISTRIBUTION

The movement of 1,103 million bushels of wheat from producer to consumer in the 1963–1964 crop year is shown in Exhibit IV-1. As explained in the notes accompanying this exhibit, some 97% of total farm wheat production moves from the farm into various marketing channels. One note of caution; the wheat industry exists as a separately defined entity only in a conceptual sense. In actual practice a wheat producer raises many other crops and engages in other farm practices in addition to wheat production. Similarly country and terminal elevator operators handle all grains grown in their product and market territories. In addition many wheat millers are integrated into many related activities such as mixed feed businesses, grain merchandising, consumer foods, and restaurant chains. Food wholesalers and retailers obviously distribute thousands of food products in addition to those made from wheat products. In spite of the diversity of operations that exists at every stage of the vertical structure of the wheat industry, an examination of the central core of the wheat complex produces a picture of the wheat market structure at a given moment of time. This system makes use of established and recently adapted coordinating institutions to help facilitate the movement of wheat and wheat products from producer to consumer and to organize the various functions in the system in an effective and efficient manner.

Exhibit IV-1 indicates that the primary markets for farmers in 1963–1964 were country elevators (910 million bushels) and country subterminal elevators (124 million bushels). On the whole, the country elevator was still the first market for the producer's wheat, but the number of such elevators was decreasing and the size was increasing to serve the larger, more mechanized wheat farms. In addition, the shortened harvest season, improved highway system, increased production on larger farms, and specification buying of wheat has hastened the growth of *country subterminals*[1] to handle the harvest volume bulge and provide more services for the farmer, the terminal elevator, the ultimate processor and export customers as well as government storage services.

The terminal elevator, on the other hand, was being by-passed as country subterminals have increased in importance in the wheat marketing system. The ability of the country subterminal to duplicate the sorting, cleaning, blending, and storage functions of the terminal elevator and utilize the offal or "screenings" in the local farm feed wheat market has placed many terminal elevators at a logistic disadvantage. Furthermore, many wheat processors have tended in recent years to build flour mills closer to population centers. The direct

---

[1] Country subterminals are classified as country elevators that purchase a majority of their grain from other country elevators. Subterminals provide some of the services of both country and terminal elevators. These subterminals are located in country positions and have considerably larger storage and handling capacity than do country elevators.

EXHIBIT IV-1

Marketing Channels for U.S. Wheat: 1963–1964

(In millions of bushels)

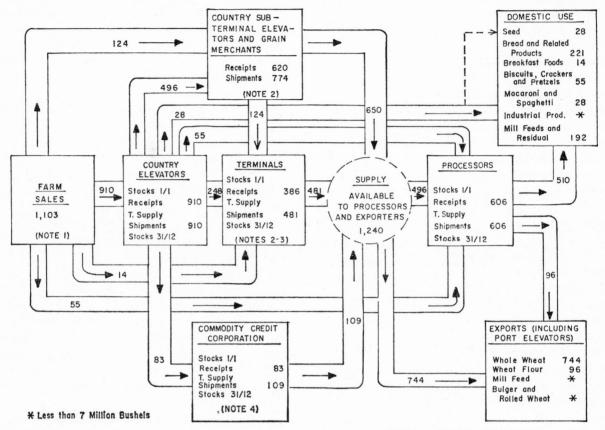

✷ **Less than 7 Million Bushels**

NOTES TO EXHIBIT IV-1

1. Total supply during the 1963–1964 marketing year was 1,378 million bushels. Off-farm sales (97% of total production in 1963–1964) totaled 1,103 million bushels, or 80% of the total supply. Reduction of off-farm carryover in commercial storage totaled 249 million bushels, or 18% of the total supply, and entered the marketing channels from the terminal and subterminal elevators. Reduction of carryover in CCC-owned bin sites totaled 26 million bushels, or 2% of the total supply, and entered the marketing channels from CCC storage sites.

2. Difference between shipments and receipts is accounted for by the 249 million bushels of carryover in commercial storage mentioned in Note 1. It was assumed that 154

million bushels of this carryover (62%) entered the market through subterminal elevators, while 95 million bushels (38%) entered through terminal elevators. These proportions reflect the percentage of supply originating in off-farm sales which was ultimately handled through each of these two market outlets.

3. Terminal receipts are based on the volume of inspected receipts. Fourteen terminal markets include Chicago, Duluth, Hutchinson, Indianapolis, Kansas City, Milwaukee, Minneapolis, Omaha, Peoria, Sioux City, St. Joseph, St. Louis, Toledo, and Wichita.

4. Difference between shipments and receipts is accounted for by the 26 million bushels of carryover in CCC-owned bin sites mentioned in Note 1.

movement from country subterminal elevators to processing facilities is enhanced by such a processing strategy.

There are offsetting factors, however, that have maintained the terminal elevator as an important marketing channel in the wheat economy. First and foremost, the expanding volume of wheat exports (as noted previously) promoted the development of terminal elevator port facilities and terminal elevators on interior waterway systems, including major rivers and the Great Lakes. Second, the government storage pro-

gram, as a result of the large wheat surpluses in the 1950s and early 1960s, encouraged the construction of terminal elevators primarily for a storage operation. Third, the current transportation emphasis on "wheat trains," "big John cars," and other devices requires the utilization of terminal elevator facilities that have railroad track capacities and unloading and loading equipment of great magnitude capable of handling huge volumes with utmost speed to minimize transportation costs and freight car demurrage charges.

Exhibit IV-1 understates the importance of terminal elevators because the "volume handled" figures do not include major *export* terminal facilities. In spite of this understatement, terminal markets, in which most terminal elevators are located, handled only 248 million bushels of wheat from country elevators, 124 million bushels of wheat from country subterminals, 14 million bushels of wheat from farmers, and an estimated 95 million bushels of terminal "stored wheat" [2] for a total of 481 million bushels. On the other hand, country *subterminals* handled 496 million bushels of wheat from country elevators, and an estimated 124 million bushels from the farm for a grand total of 620 million bushels of wheat purchased from farmers that did not pass through the terminal elevator channel.

The box entitled "Supply" in Exhibit IV-1 is used to indicate the convergence of wheat supplies from terminals, country subterminals, and Commodity Credit Corporation storage sources (obtained from bin sites, and all off-farm storage facilities including country elevators, country subterminals, and terminal elevators). The wheat movement from these three marketing channels was split into two major flows — one stream of 496 million bushels shipped to wheat processors and the other of 744 million bushels transferred to wheat exporters.

Wheat processors, in addition to obtaining 496 million bushels of wheat from the supply sources noted above, also acquired 55 million bushels directly from farmers and another 55 million bushels from country elevators.

Exporters obtained 744 million bushels of wheat from country subterminals, terminal elevators, and a wide variety of government storage warehouses as noted in the supply and exporter boxes in Exhibit IV-1. This 744 million bushels of wheat was then put through port terminal elevators and from there into ships. Another 96 million bushels of wheat was obtained in the form of flour from wheat processors and exported. Exhibit IV-1 demonstrates that, in terms of millions of bushels of wheat handled, the export channel dominated the total wheat economy, accounting for over 840 million bushels compared with the domestic use of 538 million bushels in the 1963–1964 crop period.

A brief overall view of the marketing channels for wheat would not be complete without noting the general categories of domestic consumption. Of the 538 million bushels of wheat transformed into domestic wheat products, 28 million bushels originated from country elevators and were sold back to the farmer in the form of seed wheat; the remaining 510 million bushels were obtained from wheat processors. Al-

[2] See Note 3 of Exhibit IV-1.

though bread products have declined as a percent of total wheat products consumed in the United States, as noted earlier in this chapter, they still dominate the domestic wheat industry accounting for 221 million bushels of wheat in 1963–1964. Breakfast foods accounted for 14 million bushels, and macaroni and spaghetti for 28 million bushels of wheat utilized for wheat food products. The remaining 192 million bushels of wheat products consisted of the offal of the flour milling process (bran, middlings, and Red dog) especially suitable as an important ingredient in the mixed feed industry and other residual items. Because bran and middling products are such a significant residual in the flour milling process, many flour millers are also in the mixed feed industry. To simplify the marketing channel chart for wheat, the mixed feed industry was not included as a separate category.

Over the years the major impacts on the utilization of marketing channels for wheat described in Exhibit IV-1 have been: (1) the technological revolution on the farm encouraging the development of subterminal markets that were virtually nonexistent in the immediate postwar period (1947–1949); (2) the impact of government wheat surpluses and the resultant on-farm and off-farm storage build-up; (3) the transportation revolution and the change in transportation rates between wheat and flour products and between milling-in-transit and nontransit rates; and (4) the dominance and expansion of U.S. wheat and wheat products in world trade which resulted in expanding the importance of export facilities, especially those located on combination water, truck, and rail locations.

FIRMS AND ENTITIES

The technological and transportation revolutions in the wheat industry not only affected the physical volume flow through expanded and new channels; they also resulted in a change in the number, size, and type of enterprises that make up the wheat system. The wheat economy in 1963, as described in Exhibit IV-2, consisted of over 1 million wheat producers,[3] over 10,000 country and terminal elevators (concentrated in a few hundred cooperative or other business-type enterprises), 200 commission and/or brokerage firms, almost 300 flour mills and companies, 5,000 wholesale bakers (concentrated in 20 national firms, 3 cooperative associations, and 45 grocery chain bakers), 260,000 retail firms (including 30,000 mass retailers and 19,000 retail bake shops), and 20 export firms

[3] The Department of Agriculture includes over 1,500,000 farmers who have or once produced wheat as part of its acreage control and price support program.

EXHIBIT IV-2

Firms and Entities in the U.S. Wheat Economy: 1963

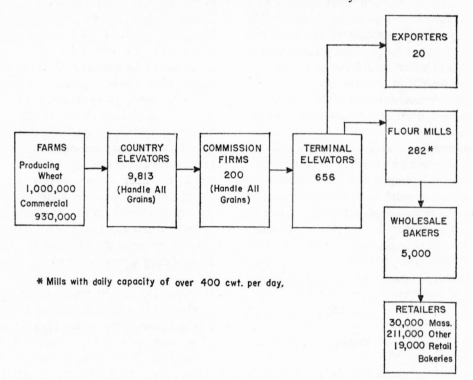

* Mills with daily capacity of over 400 cwt. per day.

(with most of the volume handled by four major companies).

In many decision-making centers in Exhibit IV-2 the number of firms is decreasing and the remaining firms are handling larger volumes of wheat, flour, and other wheat foods and by-products. This trend is substantiated by Table IV-1 which is an overall summary of the changes in the number of firms between the census years 1947 and 1958 for the major sectors of the wheat economy. Table IV-1 also shows that the population increased from 146 million to 173 million during this period, together with an increase in the total amount of wheat consumed domestically and exported.

As Table IV-1 shows, there were decreases in the number of firms in all segments of the wheat economy except terminal elevators. In addition the physical volume of wheat and wheat products was expanding even though per capita domestic consumption had been declining until the four years 1962–1966.

TABLE IV-1. Number of Firms in Major Sectors of the Wheat System Compared with Wheat Consumption and Production: 1947 and 1958

Firms	1947	1958
Farms reporting wheat harvested[a]	1,147,000	931,000
Country elevators[b]	8,408	7,000
Terminal elevators[b]	391	690
Flour and meal mills[c]	1,243	814
Bakers (wholesale)[c]	7,796	5,180
Retail bakers[d]	20,161	19,235
Grocery stores[d]	378,320[e]	259,796
U.S. population (millions)[e]	146	173
Total wheat consumed domestically[f] (millions of bu.)	466	484
Total wheat exported[f] (millions of bu.)	340	443
Total U.S. wheat production[f] (millions of bu.)	1,359	1,457

[a] Census of Agriculture.
[b] Bureau of Census, *Census of Business Wholesale Trade.*
[c] Bureau of Census, *Census of Manufactures.*
[d] Bureau of Census, *Census of Business, Retail Trade.*
[e] Includes meat stores in 1947.
[f] USDA, ERS.

COORDINATING PATTERNS

From the early days of U.S. history to the present time, various entrepreneurs have devised means of coordinating the many functions that have to be performed in the wheat economy. From Revolutionary days to the turn of the twentieth century, the local flour grinder and the local baker shop worked closely with the wheat producer and assembler. As production shifted from the eastern seaboard (New York State was once the largest "wheat" state in the United States) to the midwestern wheat belt, it was the railroad agricultural agents, the bonanza wheat farms, the commission agents, and eventually the farmers own cooperatives that helped to coordinate the wheat economy from production to ultimate consumption.

As the technological revolution occurred in all phases of wheat operations and economies of scale and specialization took place together with changes in domestic and foreign consumption, a need was created for greater coordination among the various participants of the wheat economy. One of the most important coordinating developments has been the increase in vertical integration (common ownership) of the many segments of the wheat complex.

COMMON OWNERSHIP IN THE WHEAT ECONOMY

Exhibit IV-3 summarizes the ownership patterns in the wheat economy as measured by quantity flows at each stage in the vertical movement from farm to end user.

FARM COOPERATIVES

One of the most important forms of forward integration in the wheat economy is that of farmer cooperatives. Some 40% of all wheat is purchased by country elevator operators from their farmer members, a major portion of which is in turn sold by cooperative commission agents. Cooperative terminal elevators handle 20% of all terminal wheat shipments and some 10% of direct export sales. Cooperatives handle only 1% of wheat flour processing (a specialized durum flour mill that makes semolina flour).

The cooperative type of organization (but not "farmer" cooperative) has also been used extensively in other segments of the wheat economy (see Exhibit IV-3). Wholesale bakers unite cooperatively to compete with large national concerns and handle 30% of the wholesale bakery volume. Cooperative retail food chain organizations are also a significant factor in the wheat economy, accounting for 10% of private label bread operations.

The importance of farmer cooperative and general cooperative organizations in the wheat economy came about for a variety of historical reasons. In the case

EXHIBIT IV-3

Ownership Patterns in the U.S. Wheat Economy as Measured by Quantity Flows: 1963

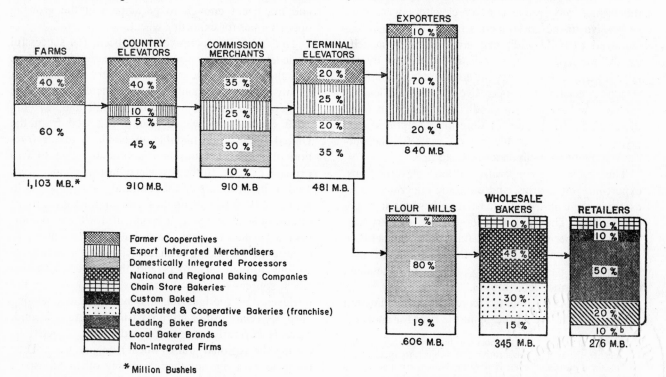

ª See text.
ᵇ The independent retailers also include approximately 19,000 retail bakeries that account for 20% of all bakery dollar volume.

of country elevators, many farmers felt that in the early days of grain merchandising (including wheat merchandising) they were at a competitive disadvantage in dealing with their local market as represented by the country elevator system. They therefore built or purchased their own country elevators to clean, sort, and assemble their wheat shipments for various terminal markets. Many such farmer cooperative elevator operations were financially successful; others failed because of improper management.

During World War II and in the immediate postwar period, once ceiling prices were lifted, grain prices moved up rather sharply. Many cooperative country elevator firms held grain inventories during the price rise and made rather substantial inventory profits on their wheat and other grain holdings. These inventory "windfalls" put the farmer cooperative country elevator operators in an excellent position to respond to their farmer-owners' needs for additional grain storage when bumper crops occurred. The harvest period became exceedingly short, as noted previously, and the movement of a billion bushels of wheat in a relatively short period of time required additional storage space to handle the harvest bulge.

As wheat went from a shortage to a surplus position, the government stepped in and became an important "market" for wheat. The surplus wheat supplies owned by the government had to be stored, and the farmer cooperative country elevators were most responsive to the government's needs. They were encouraged to build additional grain elevator capacity by the rapid depreciation schedules allowed by the government, as noted later in this chapter. In addition various special farm cooperative government lending agencies under the Farm Credit Administration (e.g., the Bank for Cooperatives) were most helpful in supplying funds at reasonable interest rates for the purpose of building additional grain storage.

The presence of cooperative country elevator firms, export-integrated firms, and domestic-integrated processors in the country elevator system has meant severe competition. Thus far, the cooperative country elevators have been most successful in this competition. Many competitors claim that the cooperatives' success is due in part to the tax-exempt status of retained earnings of farmer cooperatives.[4]

The growth of affiliated cooperative commission activity has a historical setting in the fight for coopera-

tive representation in the organized grain exchanges. In recent years the severe competition of the country grain elevator operators has meant that commission fees may be an offset to dwindling profits from grain handling charges in their country grain operations. Furthermore, cooperative commission merchant activities are considered to be extensions of the farmer's control over his marketing channels once his product has left his farm. However, some farmer cooperative country elevator operators are fearful that they may be treated as a "captive grain supply" by their affiliated commission terminal merchants and therefore sell their wheat through noncooperative commission agents. In spite of some noncooperative commission dealings, approximately 35% of all wheat commission transactions are estimated to be handled by cooperative commission agent representatives (Exhibit IV-3).

Two major elements stand out as important in the increase of cooperative terminal operations: (1) the government storage program which permitted guaranteed occupancy contracts for terminal locations as well as rapid amortization of the facilities for tax purposes, and (2) the export programs which encouraged large shipments of wheat requiring terminal facilities in exportable positions. It is to the credit of the cooperative movement that their leadership was farsighted enough to take advantage of government storage programs in expanding their terminal operations and intelligent enough to participate in the growing opportunities for exporting wheat.

The farmer cooperatives have been less successful in developing their own export operations. It is true that their export enterprise (Producers Export, Inc.) is only ten years old and has had an increase in volume of shipments in every year, but it still handles only 10% of the total wheat volume exported from the United States. The inability to obtain a major fraction of the export business is probably due to two primary reasons. In the first place, farmer cooperatives tend to be producer-oriented and are most anxious to get rid of their wheat supplies with a minimum amount of customer orientation. It is difficult for them to compete with international firms that have a century of experience in dealing with the changing demands of various foreign customers and that have alternative wheat sources throughout the world. Furthermore, the intricacies of foreign freight contracts and changing currency relationships are not easily mastered. Second, there is currently no great coordination of activities among the regional grain (wheat) cooperatives. They compete with one another to supply other exporters. In spite of these limitations, a farmer-owned cooperative export firm or firms may become more important

---

[4] In recent years, tax authorities have maintained that farmer members of a cooperative are subject to income tax on "retained earnings" even if they are not distributed in the form of cash payments. Current regulations insist that 20% of earnings must be paid in cash to the farmer to permit him to pay his taxes.

in the future as farmer cooperatives make use of their overwhelming position as major suppliers of U.S. wheat.

Some officials in the cooperative movement claim that they have no interest in flour milling activities as long as they remain so limited in profit potential. One prominent cooperative leader stated: "If they ever decide to 'really' enter the flour milling business, it would have to involve a merger with a significant factor in the market [e.g., General Mills, Pillsbury, International Milling] to provide an outlet for their producers' wheat." Such reasoning again emphasizes producer orientation — how to move the wheat from the farm to the most advantageous market. Some major flour mills in the United States were offered to farm cooperatives in 1965–1966, but as of this writing such offers have not been acceptable to the cooperatives involved.

Exhibit IV-4 summarizes the vertically integrated functions performed by *farmer* cooperatives (the co-

products. The technology of flour and bread product manufacturing and the marketing channels and direct consumer advertising needed for bread products are a great deal different from the assembling, sorting and marketing activities of wheat and wheat by-products. That is not to say that producer-cooperatives in the wheat economy are not interested in additional processing and marketing activities, they are as evidenced by the Farmers Union Grain Terminal Association's purchase of the Froedtert Malt Corporation in 1965. (See Appendix Exhibit IV-1.) But usually these barley, soybean, and durum wheat processing activities stop short of the manufacture and distribution of consumer end products, such as bread and rolls.

Basically, the farmer cooperatives are anxious to control the marketing and processing channels as far up the vertical chain to the consumer as possible, as long as the product is marketed on a commodity basis. Once product differentiation takes place they do not feel adequately prepared for the consumer marketing

EXHIBIT IV-4

Integrated Functions Performed by Farmer Cooperatives in the U.S. Wheat Economy as Measured by Quantity Flows: 1963

(Each bar equals 100%)

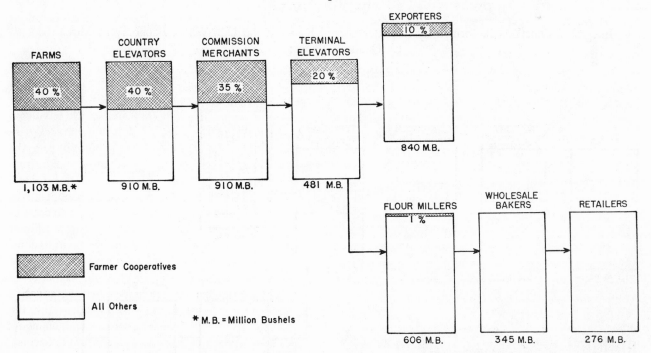

operative organizational firm is extremely important in wholesale bakery manufacturing and in food retailing as noted previously). The reader will note that the forward integration by the producer-cooperative stops short of the manufacture of most flour and bread

processes they face. Such an attitude of course is changing especially since recent cooperative mergers have attracted the necessary managerial skills to enable their cooperative firms to be market oriented. There is also the added danger that in trying to satisfy their farmer-stockholders in the short run, cooperative management may minimize the changing and important supply requirements of their processor and ultimate domestic and export consumption markets to the long-run detriment of their farmer-owners.

EXPORT FIRM OWNERSHIP PATTERNS

Exhibit IV-5 summarizes the vertically integrated functions performed by export firms in the wheat economy, approximately 70% of wheat exports move through export-integrated firms. The leading export integrated firm in the wheat economy, is Cargill, Incorporated. It has country, terminal, and port elevator facilities as well as its own commission firm.

A major factor in Cargill's present vertically integrated position is the historical growth of the firm from a country and terminal elevator firm in the United States to the development of overseas markets as the United States became a major factor in world grain trade. Archer-Daniels-Midland Co., the only other major U.S. based export firm that had its original beginnings in the United States, has flour milling activities as well as country, terminal, and port elevator facilities. Peavey, a smaller American grain export firm, also has flour milling operations but is not con-

sidered one of the export giants. The other major export firms — Bunge Corp., Continental Grain Co., and L. A. Dreyfus Co. — all had their origins outside the United States: Continental and Dreyfus in France and Bunge in Argentina. These firms built U.S. grain facilities and developed into major U.S. grain exporters once the United States became an important source of world food and feed grain. The six firms named above handled approximately 90% of all U.S. wheat export trade during the 1960–1967 period.

The factors that led to the forward integration of some U.S. firms into exporting and the backward integration of the original overseas based firms in the United States can be summarized under one heading — flexibility. By being integrated, the exporter has a ready and direct source of wheat that may have quality, storage, and/or transportation advantages for his firm's operation. The integrated exporter also has alternative markets for the wheat, wheat flour, and wheat by-products he handles. He can satisfy the varying domestic and export requirements by separating out and tailor-making "round lots" of wheat to various buyers' specifications.

Other factors also encouraged integration by exporters into country and terminal grain elevator loca-

EXHIBIT IV-5

Integrated Functions Performed by Exporter-Owned Firms in the U.S. Wheat Economy as Measured by Quantity Flows: 1963

(Each bar equals 100%)

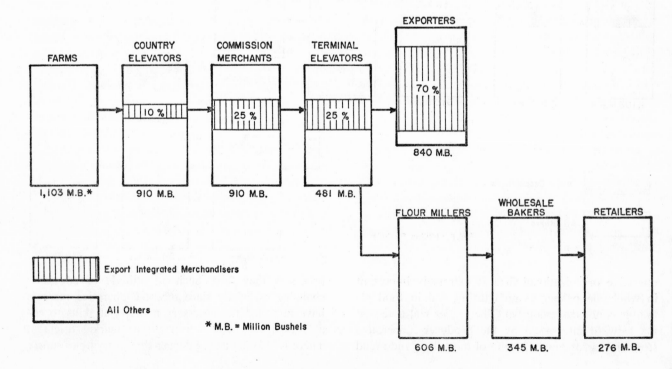

tions. The economic incentives to take part in government storage programs were extremely strong and the changing patterns of alternative types of transportation stimulated exporters to build transportation, assembling, sorting, and processing facility networks. In addition, by owning and operating country and terminal elevators, an exporter who has made a "domestic profit" on his wheat volume may be in a stronger competitive position price-wise in offering wheat overseas. Also, many wheat exporters have their own commission operations which not only handle their wheat procurements from their own country and subterminal elevator facilities, but also act as procurement agents for other wheat supplying firms that are selling to the export market.

The decline of government wheat stocks in 1965 and 1966 also provided another integrative incentive for wheat exporters. In the past, much of this wheat was obtained in huge quantities from the government, which had stored wheat in many of the exporters' own facilities. With a decline in government stocks, the exporter has to rely more on the "normal" trade facilities and there is a strong impetus to integrate backward toward the source of wheat, the farmer. However, the cost of supplying even *one* exporter's wheat requirements through integrated ownership of country or subterminal facilities would be almost $700 million, which is an extremely large investment when compared with the net worth of a typical exporter, which is approximately $45 million. Although there will undoubtedly be more actual ownership of country and subterminal elevator facilities by exporters in the future, the large investment needed to supply all wheat and other grain requirements will mean that further integration will be highly selective and will have some practical limitations.

In summary, all the major exporters are becoming more integrated. Exporters, on the whole, have developed an excellent network of port, terminal, and country subterminal grain elevators. The tendency is for all major exporting firms to increase their terminal and subterminal elevator operations as export volumes increase. Some grain export concerns have developed lease-back arrangements with port authorities or railroads that may build terminal grain elevators as part of the port authorities' or railroads' operations. The leasing of such facilities by exporters limits their investment in fixed assets. Other grain exporters have projects or build grain facilities using their own resources. All the major integrated exporters have thus far ignored wheat processing as another potential part of their operation (with the exception of Archer-Daniels-Midland and Peavey which were involved in flour milling before they entered the export grain market). The past excess capacity in flour milling and the low average profits are strong deterrents to any potential expansion in this direction by the exporters.

DOMESTICALLY INTEGRATED PROCESSORS

Exhibit IV-6 summarizes the vertically integrated functions performed by domestic wheat processors. Part of this integration, as noted previously, was due to the historical growth of individual firms such as Archer-Daniels-Midland and Peavey. In more recent times, these integrated processor firms have reached back in the channels of the wheat market economy in order to (1) have access to specific quantities and qualities of wheat, (2) take advantage of government storage programs, (3) have unique transportation arrangements, (4) provide a captive market outlet for wheat procurement facilities and (5) reduce the procurement cost of wheat.

Many of the largest wheat processors have reached back for their wheat supplies by owning and operating terminal and country elevators, as noted in Exhibit IV-6. In some cases this backward integration has taken place to assure a specific flour miller accessibility to a particular quantity, quality, or geographical location of a supply of wheat. Such accessibility may be important in satisfying the procurement specifications of a certain flour end product, or it may be of significant value in maintaining a favorable transportation rate for both the raw wheat and finished flour.

In several cases, backward integration by the flour miller has been influenced greatly by the government wheat storage program. The government price support programs, which attempted to maintain farmers' wheat prices by offering to buy wheat at a minimum price support level, were leading to the piling up of government "owned" wheat surpluses in the 1950s. The Department of Agriculture desperately needed storage facilities in the face of the mounting wheat surpluses purchased from the farmer. The government responded to this storage emergency by granting farmers and firms building such storage facilities a rapid depreciation schedule (five years), and in some cases guaranteed grain storage occupancy (80% for a five-year period). With such guarantees the flour miller had the government wheat stocks as a potential supply for wheat processing. He could store these government stocks in his own terminal elevators and be paid well for doing so. Furthermore, the flour miller could purchase cash wheat of the same grade, but not necessarily the same baking quality, and substitute this wheat for the government wheat and thus improve his own inventory position (after allowing for the cost of

EXHIBIT IV-6

Integrated Functions Performed by Wheat Processors in the U.S. Wheat Economy as Measured by Quantity Flows: 1963

(Each bar equals 100%)

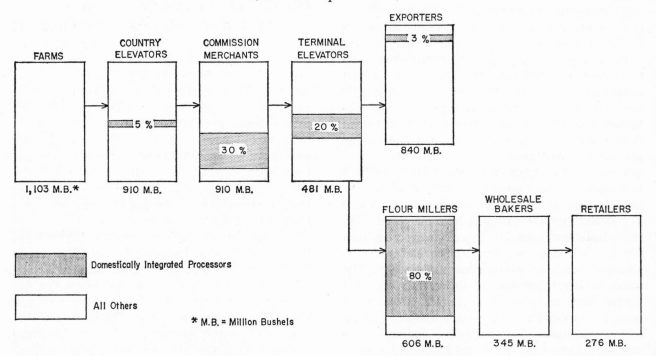

moving the government wheat to processing facilities and for the cost of purchasing wheat and elevating it into the elevator to replace the government wheat).

The wheat processor may own various types of wheat marketing channels not only to protect his inventory position and take advantage of government programs but for the profit (or loss) opportunity of being a wheat merchandiser. Some wheat processors believe that by having a "captive market" to supplement their wheat merchandising activities, they are in an excellent position to move large volumes of wheat through their country and terminal facilities. In addition, by having a market for their wheat, they may not have to sell it at abnormally low prices during a "market glut" [5] or "technical market glut." [6]

Other wheat flour millers believe that "wheat merchandising" is so highly competitive in country and terminal elevator operations and in wheat commission activities that this "channel ownership advantage" would be of doubtful or negative value were it not for government storage and/or quality and freight advantages. Also the development of new flour milling tech-

niques noted earlier may mean that *wheat* specifications can be tailored so that quality variations of wheat may become less important in the future. Consequently owning access to a source of supply may be of limited value in the future especially if government storage operations become less attractive because of low occupancy levels and/or declining storage payment rates.

The importance of flour miller integration in the wheat system is most dramatically indicated in Exhibit IV-6 which shows that integrated flour millers processed 80% of all the wheat utilized by all flour millers. Some flour millers with a keen sense of market orientation have been most effective in communicating their baker-customers' requirements back to their integrated terminal and country elevator operations and to the ultimate wheat producers. A few flour mill firms have developed grade specifications to the point where wheat suppliers now trade as readily for these few firms on the flour miller's wheat grade as on the government's wheat grade. This effective transference of user requirements back to the farmer, together with improved government wheat price support premiums and discounts, has upgraded quality and provided improved price differentials throughout the vertical wheat market system.

[5] A market glut may be the presence of above-normal supplies of wheat in a particular terminal market.
[6] A technical market glut may be the presence of normal supplies during a mechanical market problem, such as a railroad strike or a box car shortage.

On the other hand, some integrated flour milling firms have been unable to coordinate the activities of their various divisions to achieve above average profits for their firms and to improve the operation of the wheat economy as a whole. Therefore it would seem that ownership integration does not automatically produce the potential benefits of procurement and market coordination.

In summary, integrated flour milling firms have many potential advantages over their nonintegrated competitors. They have been able to utilize government storage incentives to build or buy country and terminal elevators. The processor-integrated elevators, in turn, have earned government storage income, have provided the flour mills with first access to various qualities and quantities of wheat, and have allowed flour milling firms to upgrade their wheat inventories.

Many flour millers have integrated forward as well as backward in the wheat economy by producing specialty flour mixes and cake mix consumer products. Those flour milling firms that have been able to diversify their flour product lines and produce consumer packaged goods have developed better profit margins than the remaining integrated flour firms. In many such cases they have reduced flour milling activities and expanded the consumer packaged goods operations.

Finally, the integrated flour miller that services the large wholesale and chain bakers requiring sizable volumes of uniform flour is selling transportation as well as flour. Therefore, as milling-in-transit rates change along with complex barge, truck and rail rate combinations, the integrated flour miller has to reappraise the relationships between his elevator and mill locations and the relationship of flour milling to his consumer flour mixes and bakery products. Such recent reappraisals by some flour milling firms have resulted in the selling or closing down of significant flour milling capacity; for example, the closing of 9 of the 17 flour mills owned and operated by General Mills, Inc., in 1965.

BAKERY AND RETAIL FOOD CHAIN INTEGRATION

With the exception of such firms as the National Biscuit Company and the Sunshine Baking Company, most national and regional wholesale bakers are not integrated with any other major decision-making center of the wheat economy. Exhibit IV-3 indicates that 45% of all wholesale baking products are processed by major national and regional wholesale bakers. This 45% is manufactured and distributed by 20 of the 5,000 wholesale bakers shown in Exhibit IV-2. This concentration of bakery production enables these firms

to have strong bargaining power as they apportion their flour requirements among competing flour millers. Similarly, these large wholesale bakers are in an excellent position to take maximum advantage of their nationally advertised bread and bakery product brands. They have also diversified their product lines to include frozen pies, doughnuts, and specialty bakery products.

To meet the competition of the large wholesale bakers that maintain nationally advertised brands and national wheat procurement organizations, many smaller independent wholesale bakers banded together to form three wholesale bakery cooperatives (Quality Bakers of America Cooperative, Inc., American Bakers Cooperative, Inc., and Independent Bakers). These cooperatives offer their participants national procurement organizations, the use of nationally franchised brands, and centralized management services. These cooperative firms, together with other voluntary chain bakery associations, manufacture and distribute approximately 30% of the total wheat bakery products.

The high distribution costs in the bakery industry encouraged the food chain retailing organizations to manufacture and distribute their own private label bread. Food chains have been successful in cutting distribution costs sufficiently so that they can put a lower retail selling price on their private label bread in spite of equal or slightly higher bread production costs. The consumer has benefited greatly by the competition of the retail chain bakery operations. Although retail chain bakery operations are expanding faster than any other segment involved in bakery operations in the wheat economy, they still account for only 10% of all wheat bakery product sales volume because food chains must have enough retail food outlets in a compact geographical area in order to utilize effectively a bakery manufacturing operation.

By examining the last block in Exhibit IV-3, the reader will note the end product domestic distribution pattern of the wheat industry. Ninety per cent of all retail food sales are made through mass retailers (chain, voluntary and cooperative supermarket organizations). Bakery product sales, however, are not made in the same proportion as all retail food sales.

Approximately 80% of all bakery product sales are distributed through mass retailer outlets. Of this 80% of total bakery product sales, approximately 10% is *manufactured* and *distributed* by retail chains under their own private labels. Another 10% is *sold* as private label bread by mass retailers, but manufactured for them by wholesale bakers. Approximately 50% of the bakery products distributed through mass retailers originate as national or regional brand products or cooperative brand products (such as Wonder Bread and Sunbeam Bread). Twenty per cent of the mass retail bakery products are local branded items.

The mass retail outlets through volume handling, private label purchases, and private label manufacturing and distribution have cut distribution and promotional costs and are in the best position to provide low cost bakery items.

The remaining 20% of all bakery products that are distributed through independent retail outlets and retail bakery stores include many of the regional and national branded items listed above as well as a host of products unique to each individual retail bakery shop. These small independents fill a need for shopping convenience and individual taste preferences. The high distribution costs involved in servicing these units will continue to be a major cost problem for their wholesale bakery suppliers. As a result of these disadvantages, private label bread manufacturing and distribution by retail food chains will probably continue to increase in the future.

NONINTEGRATED FIRMS IN THE WHEAT SYSTEM

Exhibit IV-7 represents a composite picture of the residual firms in the wheat economy that do not have joint ownership with firms in other segments of the wheat system. Farms producing three-fifths of the wheat in the United States are owned and operated by farmers who prefer to rely on the competition among country elevator operators to provide their best market opportunity for wheat rather than form their own cooperative grain elevator markets. Integration (common ownership) becomes a more important coordinating operation as the wheat crop moves into terminal, processing, and export markets. The strong interrelationships that exist between wheat assembling, sorting, storing, milling, and exporting have led to all types of vertical integration — both cooperative and corporate.

The independent, on the other hand, although a declining factor in volume handled in each functional area (with the exception of the closing of General Mills' nine flour mills in 1965), has many major strengths and alternative forms of coordination within the vertical market structure of the wheat system.

In the case of the farmer, during the past several decades he has had the government price support and storage program as an alternate market for his crop without cooperative or corporate help. With the increase in acreage allotments and stronger domestic and international demand for wheat plus a cash certificate

EXHIBIT IV-7

Nonintegrated Functions Performed by Firms in the U.S. Wheat Economy as Measured by Quantity Flows: 1963

(Each bar equals 100%)

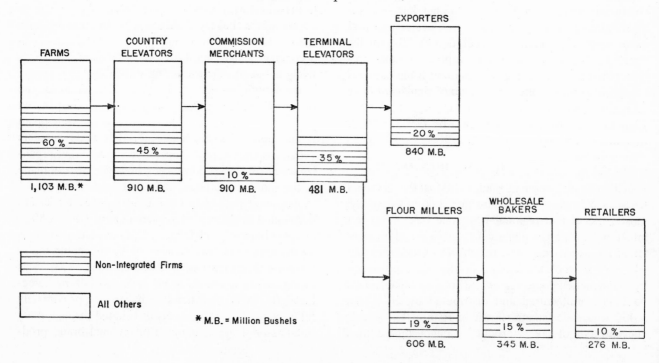

wheat program, he is less concerned with controlling the marketing channels of his wheat crop.

The independent country elevator operator still assembles some 45% of the wheat crop. He is in an excellent flexible position to respond to changes in transportation and merchandising activities. The growth of the country subterminal elevator and the introduction of one-stop country terminal shopping and marketing centers for producers are two examples of the strength of the independent. On the other hand, the forward integration by the farmer cooperative elevator operator and the backward integration by the exporter and processor, together with the loss of government storage revenue as wheat surpluses dwindle, place this segment of the wheat economy in a highly competitive environment.

The most rapid decline of a nonintegrated segment of the wheat economy is that of the independent grain commission merchant (see Exhibit IV-7). Many commission merchants could not adjust to the changing characteristics of the grain trade: government grain handling that by-passed the commission agent; cooperative, processor, and export integration that by-passed the commission agent; and the change in the size and sophistication of the remaining country elevator and country subterminal elevator operations requiring new services from commission agents. The remaining independent commission agents are no longer mere sales representatives of the country elevator shipper. They are primarily merchandisers. As merchandisers they may purchase grain for their own account and rent space from a terminal elevator. They may put together "round lots" at the request of an individual processing or export firm in anticipation of the needs of such firms. These new commission-merchandisers are experts in obtaining unique transportation arrangements or in making profitable futures hedging arrangements for their shippers. They are also kept informed of all new government rules and regulations that may have specific advantages or disadvantages for their country shipper. The independent commission merchant handles only approximately 10% of the wheat moving through all forms of commission agents, but nevertheless he has created a need for his new type of services and should continue to be an integral part of the wheat market system.

The independent terminal elevator operator assembles approximately 35% of all terminal market wheat in the United States (Exhibit IV-7). He has remained an important part of the wheat economy primarily because of government storage operations. Without the incentives of rapid amortization and guaranteed occupancies, mentioned previously, many terminals would not have been built. It is true that many port authorities, railroads, and other groups have built terminal grain elevators to encourage the use of a particular form of transportation or the utilization of a specific geographical trading center. However, these public or transportation terminal facilities represent a small percentage of total terminal grain elevator volume. The independent terminal elevator operators, on the whole, have not participated in the transportation revolution. They have not taken advantage of locating facilities accessible to the networks of rail, truck, barge, and ocean-going transportation. Nor have they been in the forefront of developing storage facilities for new flour milling locations closer to consumption centers. All in all, they have been content to be primarily government grain custodians. Storage rates were lowered in the 1960s and occupancy levels dropped sharply. This adverse storage situation is now forcing some of the independents to become active participants in grain merchandising. In the meantime the pressure of excess storage capacity in certain locations sometimes permits those processors and/or exporters without storage and handling facilities to get lower rates (arrangements on a variable cost basis). The independent terminal elevator operators must become merchandisers as well as storage warehousemen to remain an integral part of the wheat economy. (If not, their future looks rather dim.)

The nonintegrated export firms' volume of 20% of all export shipments represents *the wheat assembled* for those export firms that have made it a policy not to invest in U.S. grain (wheat) storage and handling facilities (see Exhibit IV-7). These firms in the past may not have reached their full profit potential in that they did not take advantage of government storage program incentives to develop facilities to support their export shipments. By not having the potential opportunity of making a profit on the domestic portion of their export operations, these firms may be at a disadvantage in establishing a competitive price for their export customers. In the last few years most of the nonintegrated export firms have become more aware of these competitive handicaps and have changed their policies. Nevertheless, one would assume that the volume of wheat handled by nonintegrated export firms will continue to decline.

The nonintegrated flour millers represent the overwhelming *number* of flour mill companies in the United States, but only handle a relatively small percentage of the wheat volume processed by flour millers, namely, 19% (see Exhibit IV-7). The nonintegrated flour millers in recent years have been faced with several disadvantages. In the first place, by not participating in the government storage programs, they have not had the additional revenue opportunities of storing government wheat. Secondly, these flour millers do not have the advantage of inventory upgrading that may occur when government grain is stored. Third, they may not have access to certain qualities of wheat and the opportunity of taking advantage of unique transportation situations.

In spite of these disadvantages, many independent flour millers currently are among the most profitable flour milling firms in the country, primarily because they have either built new facilities to take advantage of changing transportation rates and new technologies or purchased old facilities at values far below book and depreciated replacement values. As of the summer of 1966 many storage facilities owned and operated by flour millers were not being fully utilized. With excess storage facilities now available to the nonintegrated flour millers at below full-cost rates, these disadvantages of the nonintegrated flour millers would seem to be less important.

Although a great majority of the 5,000 wholesale bakers in the United States are nonintegrated firms, they account for "only" about 15% of the volume of wheat products sold by all wholesale bakers (Exhibit IV-7). The declining importance in the volume of wheat flour utilized by these independent wholesale bakeries is due to several causes. Even though their manufacturing costs are comparable with those of the larger firms, these small independent wholesale bakers have higher distribution costs. Second, these independent wholesalers do not have a national procurement organization or a nationally advertised brand program. Third, the development of private label brands of bread by the chains has proved to result in severe competition for the local independent baker wholesalers. Many independent bakery wholesalers have gone out of business. Others have joined cooperative and other associations to obtain procurement and advertising advantages comparable with those of the major wholesale bakers.

The independent wholesale baker will probably continue to decline as an important volume manufacturer in the bakery business. Unless the nonintegrated baker is able to differentiate his products, obtain union approval for drop deliveries of bread products at the store door, become affiliated with one of the many bakery associations, or become an important private label source of supply for chain store sales, it may be assumed that he will find it difficult to maintain any type of volume position in the wholesale bakery business.

The nonintegrated retailers, like the nonintegrated wholesale bakers and flour millers, have nine times as many retail outlets as do the mass retailers but only account for 10% of the total retail food business (see Exhibits IV-3 and IV-7). Within the independent retail classification, however, there are approximately 19,000 retail bakery stores which account for approximately 20% of all bakery products sold at retail. These retail bake shops have their own individual brands, cater to their customers' unique taste preferences and provide fresh-from-the-oven products. The other independent retail outlets handle a variety of bakery products including major national and regional brands and purchased private label brands.

The nonintegrated retail bakery outlets are faced with many problems. They do not have the economic bargaining power of the major retail chains, they do not purchase quantities in large volume, and they therefore probably pay more for their bakery products than do their larger and stronger competitors. On the other hand, by providing the convenience of a corner store, in terms of location and 7-day, 12-hour service, these small nonintegrated stores will probably continue to be a factor in the retail distribution of bakery products. However, the great distribution costs involved in servicing these units will continue to be a major cost problem for their wholesale bakery suppliers.

SUMMARY

In summary, nonintegrated firms are most important if they are evaluated by the number of such firms in each functional category of the wheat economy[7] (see Exhibit IV-2). However, nonintegrated firms are of declining significance *in each segment of the wheat economy* when measured by the volume of wheat or wheat products handled by these individual firms (see Exhibits IV-2 and IV-3). With the exception of the nonaffiliated wheat producer, it would seem that nonintegrated wheat firms are at a competitive disadvantage in terms of their procurement of quantities and qualities of raw materials at the lowest possible prices. They also have a competitive disadvantage in the promotion and distribution of their finished products. Government storage programs for wheat have been beneficial to both the nonintegrated and the integrated wheat firms. However, the value of inventory substitutions, the timing of major inventory procurements, and the logistical advantages of linked procurement and marketing functions are additional benefits

[7] This is not true for commission grain (wheat) merchants. The number of nonintegrated commission merchants is decidedly less than the integrated commission merchants.

of the government storage programs that cannot be utilized by the nonintegrated firms.

Even though there are many opportunities that may not be available to the nonintegrated entities of the wheat economy, these firms do have one major alternative source of strength. This favorable factor is the flexibility of a one function operation that can enable the firm to change direction rapidly: the development of country subterminals, one-stop farm service centers, specialized flour and bakery operations, new merchandise-commission firms — these are but a few of the examples of this adaptability to a changing wheat system.

COORDINATING INSTITUTIONS AND ARRANGEMENTS

As mentioned earlier in this chapter, the wheat system, during its long historical development in the United States, has required various types of coordinating activities in order to provide an efficient movement of wheat from the producer to the domestic and foreign consumer of wheat and wheat flour based products. In addition to vertical integration, participants in the wheat system have found many ways to improve their operations by a better coordination of their procurement and marketing functions. Some of the earlier coordinating devices consisted of barter relationships between a wheat farmer and the local flour miller and financial relationships between commission merchants and cooperative grain elevator operators, and they usually dealt with only one link in the vertical wheat structure — the producer and his market outlet. The more recent coordinating devices tend to be broadly applied to the *total* wheat system.

THE FUTURES MARKETS

Wheat is second only to soybeans in terms of volume and dollars as the most important commodity traded in U.S. futures markets. In the fiscal year ended June 30, 1966, out of a total estimated value of commodity futures of $71.8 billion, wheat futures accounted for $10.0 billion. The quantity of futures contracts involved represented slightly more than 6 billion bushels of wheat which was the largest wheat futures trade in 26 years. This was in contrast to 2.8 billion bushels in 1964–1965, a former recent high of 5.4 billion bushels in 1963–1964 (the year of the Russian wheat sales and when no effective domestic wheat program was enacted until April 1964) and the low of the last decade of 2.5 billion bushels in 1960–1961. These fluctuations in wheat futures trading reflect changing supply and demand positions and changes in government wheat price supports and government owned inventories. In essence, when the government has been a major outlet for wheat production it has provided a "futures price" of a kind that in many cases took the place of a futures market as a hedging device against a price risk for wheat and wheat flour products.

The major uses of wheat futures markets are hedging (offsetting a long or short position) and pricing inventory or processed products on a spread between the cash and futures price of the commodity ("the basis"). In most commercial uses of the futures market by off-farm participants in the wheat system, it is the latter function, establishing the best arbitrage between the futures and cash price, which is the most important use of the futures market. On the whole, operators (excluding the important speculative element) are less interested in vertical price movements than they are in the relationships between cash and futures markets. The basis is a summary of the competitive and logistical advantages of a cash price for a particular quantity and quality of a commodity at a specified location in relation to a terminal "futures market quotation." In a sense it acts as a coordinating device which forces the businessman to assess the variety of economic factors that are and will affect his ultimate procurement and marketing program.

The existence of three major wheat futures markets broadens the basis concept and permits all the participants of the wheat system to analyze not only the cash and futures price relationship, but also the spreads between the major wheat varieties that are deliverable at the three markets: hard winter wheats at the Kansas City Futures Market, hard spring wheat at the Minneapolis Market, and soft wheat at the Chicago Market (with premiums and discounts for other grades and types of wheat).

Futures trading originally emerged over 100 years ago in the United States out of trading in "forward contracts" that already existed. These contracts were for specific volumes of a commodity, at a specified price and delivery period (similar to the purchase of a new car today). The forward contract became a "futures contract" when the contract changed hands. The ability to transfer the contract is dependent upon uniform standards and grades, the presence of substitute buyers and sellers, and the liquidity or salability of these contracts. The liquidity or salability of contracts led to the establishment of a clearing house responsible for taking the "other side" of every contract to buy or sell. To summarize, in order to work, a futures market must have a homogeneous product (such as wheat), a large number of buyers and sellers, an agreed upon deliverable grade, and a clearing house to facilitate the transference or salability of all contracts. In addition, the futures market was a normal outgrowth of commercial activity in the wheat market system. Hence, there must have been an economic need for a futures market, such as reducing inventory risk, obtaining capital for financing inventories, forward pricing or some combination of these factors.

The futures contract is also consistent with the normal commercial movement of wheat. There are wheat storage facilities at various major terminals in close proximity to the wheat futures market. Participants are thereby assured of available deliverable supplies against futures contracts. Furthermore, the wheat futures market has been able to attract speculation to offset sales of futures contracts by those who are "long product inventories," such as country and terminal grain elevator operators, flour millers, and bakery manufacturers. Finally, the wheat contract has been an equitable one, favoring neither the buyer nor the seller.

Futures trading in grains developed in the United States during the period 1848 to 1870. By 1922 the Grain Futures Act was passed and the Grain Futures Administration was established as a division of the U.S. Department of Agriculture. The Grain Futures Act was amended in 1936 and became known as the Commodity Exchange Act, which developed the administrative body of the Commodity Exchange Authority.

The major functions of the Commodity Exchange Authority are:

1. Licensing of futures exchanges
2. Licensing of brokers
3. Regulating the total number of positions that may be held by any one individual
4. Regulating the volume of trading permitted by one individual in one day
5. Publicizing market surveys
6. Conducting audits, etc.

Through these activities the CEA helps to prevent market corners, fraud, manipulation, and other illegal activities.

All futures markets are regulated by a commodity exchange, and almost all fall under the jurisdiction of the CEA. The exchange is an association of people whose businesses are related to the marketing of commodities. Each exchange develops its own rules, trading codes, and regulating bodies.

Each participant, given his unique position in the wheat system, uses the futures market in different ways, but basically all participants have the same common desire to minimize price risk and widen commercial opportunities by using the basis trading feature of the wheat futures markets. The basis (spread between cash and futures price) should reflect such factors as the cost of storing, handling, insuring, and transporting wheat from a given moment of time to the wheat futures market contract time period and to the terminal market location of the commodity exchange involved. But these factors are constantly changing, therefore, one cannot hedge against a basis change. Actually a good procurement executive or a wheat producer should make a profit on the basis (assuming he assesses the variables involved accurately). For example:

A country elevator operator buys his wheat at $1.50 a bushel [March 1965] from the farmer. At the time of the purchase by the country elevator operator, the futures contract price at the nearest terminal market is $1.70 for July 1965 wheat Kansas City futures. The cash wheat is selling at 20 cents *under* the July futures contract price. The country elevator operator believes this discount should narrow to about 10 cents under the futures contract when more terminal elevator storage space is available and export demand picks up. Therefore, he sells the July futures contract to establish the 20 cent basis.

In April the operator is proved to be correct; the cash wheat has gone down to $1.45 a bushel and the futures has declined to $1.55 a bushel. At this point, the country elevator operator sells his cash wheat at $1.45 (losing 5 cents a bushel on his cash wheat). The country elevator operator simultaneously buys back his July futures at $1.55 a bushel (making a profit of 15 cents a bushel on his futures contract). The combined transaction netted the country elevator operator 10 cents a bushel on his wheat (less futures contracts commission charges).

The farmer uses the wheat futures markets in four ways:

(1) to fix the price of a growing or not yet planted crop;
(2) to fix the price of grain in storage for deferred delivery;
(3) to fix the cost of feed wheat or other grain without taking immediate delivery; and
(4) to speculate in the price of a crop that has been grown but for which storage is not available.

The first two involve being short futures and the second two being long futures.[8]

Table IV-2 and Exhibit IV-8 give the results of comparing three marketing strategies for the wheat

[8] Hieronymus, *Uses of Grain Futures Markets in the Farm Business,* p. 53.

TABLE IV-2. Wheat Marketing Choices: 1959–1963

Crop year	Cash price received by farmers in dollars per bushel		March futures prices in dollars per bushel		Total net revenue stored		
	July 15	Dec. 15	July 15	Dec. 15	Futures	Wheat	Harvest
1959	1.68	1.80	1.95-¾	2.03	$8,871	$8,694	$8,541
1960	1.64	1.75	1.97-½	2.02	8,530	8,444	8,337
1961	1.70	1.84	2.04-⅜	2.06-⅛	8,698	8,894	8,843
1962	1.96	2.02	2.24-⅞	2.16-⅞	9,532	9,794	9,964
1963	1.77	1.95	1.96-¼	2.14-⅝	9,886	9,444	8,998
5-year ave.	1.75	1.87	2.03-¾	2.08-½	9,102	9,044	8,897

SOURCE: *Doane's Agricultural Report*, June 8, 1964, p. 13.

producer: (1) selling his wheat at harvest, (2) storing it until December 15 and paying for commercial storage, or (3) selling his wheat at harvest and speculating in the price of the crop for which storage is

EXHIBIT IV-8

Net Returns from Marketing Wheat Utilizing
Three Alternative Methods: 1959–1963

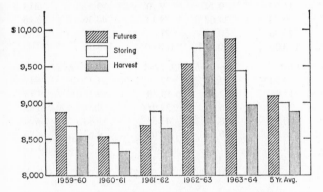

SOURCE: *Doane's Agricultural Report*, June 8, 1964, p. 13.

not available (see Item 4 above). Table IV-2 shows the cash price on July 15 and December 15. The farmer could sell at harvest time (July 15) or store it and sell his crop on December 15. The other alternative would be to use the futures market. Table IV-2 gives the March futures contract price on July 15 and December 15. Based on these different cash and futures prices, a value is placed on each alternative open to the farmer. In most cases the futures market does reflect storage carrying charges and on *the average* provides slightly higher returns for the producer. In any event, this market provides another tool for the producer's use in determining his market strategy in his changing market structure.

Prior to 1964 the price support program for wheat in the market was set at a fairly high price level. The program was announced ahead of planting time, with specific wheat price levels designated for each farmer's specific locality. This wheat price support program was a constant "future price" offer (less approximately one cent each month for storage charges). Therefore, many producers believed that there was no great need for a futures market for farmers, because they looked upon the government price support as a superior substitute. The new price support law for wheat offers a *low* cash market price support and a *cash subsidy* in the form of a certificate payment. This new program, together with a strong domestic and international demand for wheat means that the government price for wheat has been below the market price and that the producer may therefore have stronger incentives to use the futures market.

In order to analyze the other uses of the wheat futures market by other participants in the wheat system, the author, with the excellent support of the Millers National Federation and the Commodity Exchange Authority of the Department of Agriculture, was given access to summarized data of volumes of trading entered into by large traders in the Chicago soft wheat futures markets for 1960–1963, and the Minneapolis spring wheat and the Kansas City hard winter wheat futures markets for the same period (see Tables IV-3, IV-4, and IV-5). In addition, the Millers National Federation provided stock information outlining the industry's wheat and flour stocks as well as the industry's position in the wheat futures market (see Table IV-6).

Several interesting observations and conjectures can be made from these data. The "large trader" data were obtained from traders who have to register a holding of 200,000 bushels in any one future on one contract market. These traders are classified as speculators, domestic merchants, export merchants, or processors. Those traders holding less than 200,000 bushels in any one future on one contract market are classified as "small traders" and their figures are arrived at by subtracting the large traders' open contracts from the grand total of open contracts.

The important relationships that seem evident in the data are as follows:

(1) In the Millers' National Federation material (Table IV-6) the increase in the "short" (selling of) futures position from the March 31, 1964 figure of 783,000 bushels of wheat to the June 30, 1964 figure of 9,036,000 bushels of wheat is indicative of the industry's concern about the changing value of wheat due to the drastic decline in the government's market price support program for wheat. Even with the use of futures to hedge reduced inventories, the inven-

TABLE IV-3. Long and Short Wheat Futures Contracts by Class of Trader as a Percent of Each Trading Month at Chicago Board of Trade: March 31, 1960–December 31, 1963

Class of trader	March 31, 1960 Long	March 31, 1960 Short	June 30, 1960 Long	June 30, 1960 Short	September 30, 1960 Long	September 30, 1960 Short	December 31, 1960 Long	December 31, 1960 Short
Speculators	22.31%	21.05%	16.46%	24.11%	20.67%	14.73%	32.77%	26.48%
Merchants—domestic	5.20	5.43	5.56	7.39	3.00	17.27	1.13	10.43
Merchants—exporters	10.27	6.99	7.67	27.18	1.99	42.79	4.04	17.55
Total merchants	15.47	12.42	13.23	34.57	4.99	60.06	5.17	27.98
Processors	3.70	8.03	11.84	9.13	16.46	9.49	11.76	8.21
Total large traders	41.48	41.50	41.53	67.81	42.12	84.28	49.70	62.67
Total small traders	58.52	58.50	58.47	32.19	57.88	15.72	50.30	37.33
Grand total open contracts	100.00%	100.00%	100.00%	100.00%	100.00%	100.00%	100.00%	100.00%

Class of trader	March 31, 1961 Long	March 31, 1961 Short	June 30, 1961 Long	June 30, 1961 Short	September 30, 1961 Long	September 30, 1961 Short	December 31, 1961 Long	December 31, 1961 Short
Speculators	31.62%	32.46%	25.09%	19.95%	28.92%	21.92%	29.92%	31.80%
Merchants—domestic	1.58	5.82	6.60	9.03	1.16	15.97	2.15	11.81
Merchants—exporters	12.48	17.86	10.34	24.71	0.87	34.29	1.87	26.17
Total merchants	14.06	23.68	16.94	33.74	2.03	50.26	4.02	37.98
Processors	7.19	6.55	5.75	12.95	13.33	5.07	12.21	5.07
Total large traders	52.87	62.69	47.78	66.64	44.28	77.25	46.15	74.85
Total small traders	47.13	37.31	52.22	33.36	55.72	22.75	53.85	25.15
Grand total open contracts	100.00%	100.00%	100.00%	100.00%	100.00%	100.00%	100.00%	100.00%

Class of trader	March 31, 1962 Long	March 31, 1962 Short	June 30, 1962 Long	June 30, 1962 Short	September 30, 1962 Long	September 30, 1962 Short	December 31, 1962 Long	December 31, 1962 Short
Speculators	28.98%	28.17%	29.58%	17.46%	25.37%	20.80%	36.03%	31.09%
Merchants—domestic	3.06	11.84	1.62	18.30	2.22	17.35	2.01	12.68
Merchants—exporters	1.15	15.05	1.10	20.89	1.69	32.33	3.05	20.56
Total merchants	4.21	26.89	2.72	39.19	3.91	49.68	5.06	33.24
Processors	6.43	9.54	1.08	16.99	9.79	7.70	3.27	6.13
Total large traders	39.62	64.60	33.38	73.64	39.07	78.18	44.36	70.46
Total small traders	60.38	35.40	66.62	26.36	60.93	21.82	55.64	29.54
Grand total open contracts	100.00%	100.00%	100.00%	100.00%	100.00%	100.00%	100.00%	100.00%

Class of trader	March 31, 1963 Long	March 31, 1963 Short	June 30, 1963 Long	June 30, 1963 Short	September 30, 1963 Long	September 30, 1963 Short	December 31, 1963 Long	December 31, 1963 Short
Speculators	25.42%	19.79%	24.00%	17.24%	32.28%	22.27%	39.42%	28.12%
Merchants—domestic	3.01	5.93	5.37	11.96	2.22	13.40	3.31	9.83
Merchants—exporters	5.90	19.58	11.84	27.02	6.07	29.97	8.57	20.85
Total merchants	8.91	25.51	17.21	38.98	8.29	43.37	11.88	30.68
Processors	2.67	6.94	3.96	8.18	6.64	10.03	4.62	6.96
Total large traders	37.00	52.24	45.17	64.40	47.21	75.67	55.92	65.76
Total small traders	63.00	47.76	54.83	35.60	52.79	24.33	44.08	34.24
Grand total open contracts	100.00%	100.00%	100.00%	100.00%	100.00%	100.00%	100.00%	100.00%

SOURCE: USDA, Commodity Exchange Authority (unpublished).

tories were not fully hedged and the industry ended up with a *net* long position of 18,962,548 bushels out of a total cash long position of 27,998,548 bushels (the difference of 9,036,000 bushels being hedged by a sale in the futures market).

(2) The data in Table IV-6 also indicate the kinds of inventory management utilized by the flour millers — primarily large *cash* sales for future delivery (e.g., 21,536,437 bushels of wheat sold into flour as of March 31, 1964), and relatively significant but lesser volumes of futures contract sales such as 9,036,000 bushels of wheat futures sales as of March 31, 1964.

(3) From the long and short futures data in Table IV-4 the relatively insignificant percentage volume of futures operations that are conducted by merchant exporters in the Chicago wheat futures market can be noted. There is one exception to the relatively minor activity of the exporters and that is their short position in the September contract for 1960–1963. This may be due to anticipation of flour sales and hedging pressure of flour mills or to a position of going long the basis. More important is the fact that exporters that handled over 50% of all domestic wheat production did not use the futures market in anywhere near the same proportion as smaller domestic firms in the wheat economy. Part of the explanation has been the U.S. Government's policy of offsetting any change in world wheat prices on the down side by an increase in export subsidies to keep the American exporter competitive with his overseas rivals. Another reason for the lack of use of the futures market by the wheat exporters is the better competitive position some of

TABLE IV-4. Long and Short Wheat Futures Contracts by Class of Trader as a Percent of Each Trading Month at Minneapolis Grain Exchange: March 31, 1960–December 31, 1963

Class of trader	March 31, 1960 Long	Short	June 30, 1960 Long	Short	September 30, 1960 Long	Short	December 31, 1960 Long	Short
Speculators	—	0.10%	2.41%	0.75%	—	—	—	—
Merchants—domestic	—	12.74	—	—	5.02%	2.53%	—	7.23%
Merchants—exporters	4.33%	12.46	16.10	4.24	0.29	29.41	—	49.85
Total merchants	4.33	25.20	16.10	4.24	5.31	31.94	—	57.08
Processors	52.32	43.85	16.91	57.10	67.57	58.55	71.72%	41.29
Total large traders	56.65	69.15	35.42	62.09	72.88	90.49	71.72	98.37
Total small traders	43.35	30.85	64.58	37.91	27.12	9.51	28.28	1.63
Grand total open contracts	100.00%	100.00%	100.00%	100.00%	100.00%	100.00%	100.00%	100.00%

Class of trader	March 31, 1961 Long	Short	June 30, 1961 Long	Short	September 30, 1961 Long	Short	December 31, 1961 Long	Short
Speculators	—	—	—	2.90%	3.18%	1.19%	2.97%	2.83%
Merchants—domestic	—	9.12%	—	29.70	—	35.23	8.32	20.59
Merchants—exporters	14.07%	28.91	17.36%	4.85	8.72	15.24	9.56	20.73
Total merchants	14.07	38.03	17.36	34.55	8.72	50.47	17.88	41.32
Processors	30.00	39.22	50.37	47.18	59.23	38.48	39.32	41.59
Total large traders	44.07	77.25	67.73	84.63	71.13	90.14	60.17	85.74
Total small traders	55.93	22.75	32.27	15.37	28.87	9.86	39.83	14.26
Grand total open contracts	100.00%	100.00%	100.00%	100.00%	100.00%	100.00%	100.00%	100.00%

Class of trader	March 31, 1962 Long	Short	June 30, 1962 Long	Short	September 30, 1962 Long	Short	December 31, 1962 Long	Short
Speculators	—	1.94%	2.30%	0.79%	8.10%	2.04%	0.50%	0.50%
Merchants—domestic	—	30.20	11.07	10.93	—	26.39	3.14	5.17
Merchants—exporters	10.11%	3.13	10.86	24.49	12.13	12.53	8.39	32.77
Total merchants	10.11	33.33	21.93	35.42	12.13	38.92	11.53	37.94
Processors	49.55	37.60	49.69	49.48	48.87	33.74	68.32	29.27
Total large traders	59.66	72.87	73.92	85.69	69.10	74.70	80.35	67.71
Total small traders	40.34	27.13	26.08	14.31	30.90	25.30	19.65	32.29
Grand total open contracts	100.00%	100.00%	100.00%	100.00%	100.00%	100.00%	100.00%	100.00%

Class of trader	March 31, 1963 Long	Short	June 30, 1963 Long	Short	September 30, 1963 Long	Short	December 31, 1963 Long	Short
Speculators	—	0.58%	—	—	2.65%	2.65%	1.77%	1.77%
Merchants—domestic	—	29.44	10.96%	4.71%	3.99	22.37	1.54	7.71
Merchants—exporters	36.17%	0.67	29.08	13.77	16.39	13.39	11.81	9.23
Total merchants	36.17	30.11	40.04	18.48	20.38	35.76	13.35	16.94
Processors	31.25	20.96	51.60	48.13	57.16	43.12	68.83	57.26
Total large traders	67.42	51.65	91.64	66.61	80.19	81.53	83.95	75.97
Total small traders	32.58	48.35	8.36	33.39	19.81	18.47	16.05	24.03
Grand total open contracts	100.00%	100.00%	100.00%	100.00%	100.00%	100.00%	100.00%	100.00%

SOURCE: USDA, Commodity Exchange Authority (unpublished).

them have *vis à vis* storage locations and the terminal futures market. One prominent export executive stated that "the futures market tends to favor those exporters with the greatest amount of and most flexible storage capacity adjacent to futures market terminals — e.g., Cargill and Continental." On the other hand, the mere existence of storage activities by these two firms should provide an incentive for them to use the futures market in such a way as to enhance their carrying ("storage") charges. Competitors who manage grain inventories would benefit from this type of strategy as they could "follow Cargill's lead." On the other hand, as one executive put it, "I never know when Cargill is going to change its mind."

(4) The data in Tables IV-3 through IV-6 indicate that in most trading months speculators and small traders (most of whom are assumed to be speculators) take a long position in the wheat and wheat futures, thus permitting processors, merchants, and exporters to go "short the futures" and protect their usual long cash inventory. On the other hand, there is enough speculative "short position taking" to permit these same business entities to go "short the basis," that is, "buy futures and sell to-arrive cash commitments" when there are inverse carrying charges.

Although many other participants of the wheat system in the past have used the wheat futures markets in a limited manner — e.g., large wholesale retail bakery managers or integrated food chain bakery operators — they did so because of the presence of a government price support program that limited overall price fluctuations. The change in the price support

TABLE IV-5. Long and Short Wheat Futures Contracts by Class of Trader as a Percent of Each Trading Month at Kansas City Board of Trade: March 31, 1960–December 31, 1963

Class of trader	March 31, 1960 Long	March 31, 1960 Short	June 30, 1960 Long	June 30, 1960 Short	September 30, 1960 Long	September 30, 1960 Short	December 31, 1960 Long	December 31, 1960 Short
Speculators	0.76%	9.96%	7.80%	2.05%	7.61%	0.54%	4.36%	11.09%
Merchants—domestic	0.01	15.25	9.23	18.77	0.51	16.73	8.91	10.10
Merchants—exporters	11.68	15.05	18.41	24.70	1.49	56.10	0.16	41.16
Total merchants	11.69	30.30	27.70	43.47	2.00	72.83	9.07	51.26
Processors	54.35	28.54	29.61	26.38	53.25	13.84	55.24	24.48
Total large traders	66.80	68.80	65.11	71.90	62.86	87.21	68.67	86.83
Total small traders	33.20	31.20	34.89	28.10	37.14	12.79	31.33	13.17
Grand total open contracts	100.00%	100.00%	100.00%	100.00%	100.00%	100.00%	100.00%	100.00%

Class of trader	March 31, 1961 Long	March 31, 1961 Short	June 30, 1961 Long	June 30, 1961 Short	September 30, 1961 Long	September 30, 1961 Short	December 31, 1961 Long	December 31, 1961 Short
Speculators	6.98%	11.70%	3.98%	8.04%	7.67%	3.10%	8.35%	7.36%
Merchants—domestic	7.81	10.59	10.33	29.67	4.11	28.67	5.39	25.09
Merchants—exporters	2.22	36.48	11.70	29.46	2.03	37.07	—	48.73
Total merchants	10.03	47.07	22.03	59.13	6.14	65.74	5.39	73.82
Processors	50.95	16.50	40.57	12.61	49.65	20.35	52.85	10.50
Total large traders	67.96	75.27	66.58	79.78	63.46	89.19	66.59	91.68
Total small traders	32.04	24.73	33.42	20.22	36.54	10.81	33.41	8.32
Grand total open contracts	100.00%	100.00%	100.00%	100.00%	100.00%	100.00%	100.00%	100.00%

Class of trader	March 31, 1962 Long	March 31, 1962 Short	June 30, 1962 Long	June 30, 1962 Short	September 30, 1962 Long	September 30, 1962 Short	December 31, 1962 Long	December 31, 1962 Short
Speculators	6.58%	6.96%	12.32%	3.82%	13.40%	14.02%	12.98%	21.57%
Merchants—domestic	15.23	30.85	14.32	26.85	6.53	20.45	5.96	25.04
Merchants—exporters	—	37.62	6.65	29.97	0.14	38.82	15.51	17.34
Total merchants	15.23	68.47	20.97	56.82	6.67	59.27	21.47	42.38
Processors	43.23	17.76	18.25	34.59	40.50	16.82	32.85	24.29
Total large traders	65.04	93.19	51.54	95.23	60.57	90.11	67.30	88.24
Total small traders	34.96	6.81	48.46	4.77	39.43	9.89	32.70	11.76
Grand total open contracts	100.00%	100.00%	100.00%	100.00%	100.00%	100.00%	100.00%	100.00%

Class of trader	March 31, 1963 Long	March 31, 1963 Short	June 30, 1963 Long	June 30, 1963 Short	September 30, 1963 Long	September 30, 1963 Short	December 31, 1963 Long	December 31, 1963 Short
Speculators	19.12%	26.84%	22.02%	6.47%	13.43%	13.44%	10.94%	23.70%
Merchants—domestic	4.79	15.53	17.63	33.92	8.52	31.12	6.94	38.63
Merchants—exporters	14.53	16.49	13.81	5.14	2.91	29.60	12.09	10.85
Total merchants	19.32	32.02	31.44	39.06	11.43	60.72	19.03	49.48
Processors	13.98	13.77	17.56	36.73	46.10	16.07	31.97	15.45
Total large traders	52.42	72.63	71.02	82.26	70.96	90.23	61.94	88.63
Total small traders	47.58	27.37	28.98	17.74	29.04	9.77	38.06	11.37
Grand total open contracts	100.00%	100.00%	100.00%	100.00%	100.00%	100.00%	100.00%	100.00%

SOURCE: USDA, Commodity Exchange Authority (unpublished).

program has also increased the use of the wheat futures markets by these managers just as they have increased their use of futures markets for other more volatile price commodities, such as sugar.

In essence the futures market provides a pricing, procurement, and financing procedure over time that is an invaluable aid in coordinating functions in all segments of the wheat system.

TRADE ASSOCIATIONS

Although the wheat commodity system has existed in various forms since the early history of the American colonies, it was only in 1965 that an overall *National Wheat Council* was formed to help coordinate the activities of the many segments of the wheat system. The principal activities of this council are concerned with promotional and educational programs aimed at stepping up domestic and foreign consumer sales of wheat utilizing total industry and government cooperation.

Most of the other trade associations in the wheat economy are primarily concerned with the more explicit and narrow objectives of a particular segment of the wheat economy.

The *National Association of Wheat Growers* is a nonprofit organization devoted to the interests of the wheat growers. It was organized in 1950 and its purposes have been (1) to improve the quality and yield of the varieties of wheat grown, (2) to provide a united group action with respect to legislative matters, and (3) to work with other wheat industry associations in market promotion.

TABLE IV-6. Inventory Policies of Selected Flour Millers by Quarters: 1960–1964
(In bushels and as % of total wheat and flour stocks owned)

Long and short data	*Industry data for quarter ended March 31*				
	1964	*1963*	*1962*	*1961*	*1960*
			(bushels)		
Total wheat stocks and flour stocks owned	79,849,165	87,955,596	109,511,960	85,601,752	75,556,082
Sold into flour	75,728,094	82,992,636	106,531,217	89,664,084	75,405,155
Net futures	783,500ᵃ	2,843,000ᵃ	7,260,000	3,583,000	1,696,000
Net long position	3,337,571	2,119,960	10,240,743	524,332ᵃ	1,846,927
			(percent)		
Total wheat stocks and flour stocks owned	100.0%	100.0%	100.0%	100.0%	100.0%
Sold into flour	94.8	94.4	97.3	104.7	99.8
Net futures	1.0ᵃ	3.2ᵃ	6.6	4.1	2.2
Net long position	4.2	2.4	9.3	0.6ᵃ	2.4
	Industry data for quarter ended June 30				
			(bushels)		
Total wheat stocks and flour stocks owned	49,534,985	71,027,744	104,270,018	68,723,974	54,185,271
Sold into flour	21,536,437	48,711,548	60,871,884	72,198,523	36,493,193
Net futures	9,036,000ᵃ	5,112,100ᵃ	16,363,000ᵃ	2,760,000ᵃ	5,142,000ᵃ
Net long position	18,962,548	17,204,096	27,035,134	6,234,549ᵃ	12,550,078
			(percent)		
Total wheat stocks and flour stocks owned	100.0%	100.0%	100.0%	100.0%	100.0%
Sold into flour	43.5	68.6	58.4	105.1	67.3
Net futures	18.2ᵃ	7.2ᵃ	15.7ᵃ	4.0ᵃ	9.5ᵃ
Net long position	38.3	24.2	25.9	9.1ᵃ	23.2
	Industry data for quarter ended September 30				
			(bushels)		
Total wheat stocks and flour stocks owned	110,878,707	133,815,682	153,961,003	138,622,081	113,007,401
Sold into flour	112,437,765	141,190,354	154,378,355	159,861,711	127,214,196
Net futures	3,186,000	15,338,600	17,598,000	28,279,000	12,643,000
Net long position	1,626,942	7,963,928	17,180,648	7,039,370	1,563,795ᵃ
			(percent)		
Total wheat stocks and flour stocks owned	100.0%	100.0%	100.0%	100.0%	100.0%
Sold into flour	101.4	105.5	100.3	115.3	112.6
Net futures	2.9	11.5	11.4	20.4	11.2
Net long position	1.5	6.0	11.1	5.1	1.4ᵃ
	Industry data for quarter ended December 31				
			(bushels)		
Total wheat stocks and flour stocks owned	88,716,266	119,256,428	118,284,585	127,012,499	98,646,585
Sold into flour	79,092,006	116,778,202	112,920,765	141,668,821	103,045,895
Net futures	5,569,000ᵃ	3,806,000	2,977,000	19,639,600	10,342,000
Net long position	4,055,260	6,284,226	8,340,820	4,983,278	5,942,690
			(percent)		
Total wheat stocks and flour stocks owned	100.0%	100.0%	100.0%	100.0%	100.0%
Sold into flour	89.1	97.9	95.5	111.5	104.5
Net futures	6.3ᵃ	3.2	2.5	15.4	10.5
Net long position	4.6	5.3	7.0	3.9	6.0

ᵃ Denotes "short" position.
SOURCE: Millers' National Federation.

In addition to the National Association of Wheat Growers, there are many *state wheat associations* and *state wheat commissions*. The state wheat associations are active in suggesting legislative programs helpful to the wheat growers in their respective states. The state wheat commissions are nonpolitical and are part of each wheat state's administrative machinery. The commissions are supported by a fee automatically charged against each bushel of wheat sold in the state (the country elevator operator usually acts as a collection agency for the association). With the exception of public policy matters, the state associations and commissions work together in common matters such as market promotion and research activities. These state commissions and associations have developed regional organizations to promote markets for their regional classes of wheat: e.g. *Western Wheat Associates* and the *Great Plains Wheat Association*. The regional organizations, in turn, cooperate with the *National Association of Wheat Growers* in research and promotional activities.

All these associations receive financial aid (up to 30% of their budgets) from federal funds established under Public Law 480 to help them in their wheat export market development programs. In the late 1950s and early 1960s increased P.L. 480 exports created large foreign currency balances held by the United States in the recipient countries. The P.L. 480 Act provided that up to 5% of the foreign currency balances in the recipient country could be utilized for market development purposes for American agricultural commodities. The state, regional, and national wheat associations receive matched funds from P.L. 480 sources to encourage their overseas market development programs.

Just as wheat producers have state, regional, and national trade associations, so do country grain elevator operators. For example, a specific geographical country grain elevator farming area is represented by the *Northwest Country Elevator Association* and in turn is also part of a national organization such as the *Grain and Feed Dealers National Association*. These specific and general trade associations are primarily concerned with the effect of various alternative government policies. These include: (1) the level of grain storage payments, (2) the amount of grain (wheat) that may be handled because of an increase or a decrease in acreage allotments, (3) the priority the government gives to the storage and handling of wheat stored in government facilities (bin sites) versus private grain (wheat) storage, (4) the timing of government grain shipments from a certain agricultural territory, (5) what the occupancy levels of grain storage

are in one territory versus another, (6) who has the first opportunity of purchasing government wheat from specific storage facilities, and (7) interpretations of USDA and private trade regulations. In addition, these country grain elevator associations are used to formulate industry positions on changing transportation rates and modes of transportation, changes in wheat grade standards by the government, changes in the grades used to determine futures contracts on Boards of Trade, and so forth.

Trade associations for commission merchants are of minor importance in today's wheat economy because of the decline of the independent commission merchant. However, most commission merchants belong to the larger national trade associations such as the Grain and Feed Dealers National Association.

Terminal grain elevator operators have their own trade association similar to those of country elevator operators to represent them in matters of legislative and transportation policies as well as standardization of practices, services, and the like. The *Terminal Grain Elevator Association* works closely with country elevator associations and national associations such as the Grain and Feed Dealers National Association.

The wheat exporter, in addition to belonging to the various domestic grain associations, has a *Grain Exporters Association* that represents the exporters' views with respect to the national and world policies that affect the procurement, storage, and transportation of wheat in the international market.

Although there are many flour milling associations that represent flour millers operating within a major wheat-type area (hard winter, soft winter, etc.), the major flour milling association in the United States is the *Millers' National Federation*. The Millers' National Federation has maintained industry cost and sales information, acted as principal spokesman on alternative government policies, and provided funds for research activities. In the past, the Federal Trade Commission has been leery of some of the services provided by the association especially those relating to sales and cost information. The FTC has warned the federation to stop certain of these services that may tend to present uniform price strategy which could be construed as a form of price collusion. In spite of the danger of anti-trust problems, the Millers' National Federation has been an invaluable aid by providing individual flour milling decision-makers with up-to-date information about the pricing and cost structure of the total flour milling industry.

The principal trade association of another major segment of the wheat economy is the *American Bakers Association*. The ABA has an outstanding record as a trade association promoting product and technological research and proving to be an effective spokesman for the entire wholesale bakery industry. Because of the common interests of flour millers and wholesale bakers, the ABA and the Millers' National Federation meet informally twice a year as a joint organization to discuss mutual problems such as baking qualities of flour, product requirements for continuous bakery operations, and general public policies.

In summary, the wheat economy has formed a variety of associations to represent the many participants at different functional levels of the wheat system, but the wide geographical dispersion of wheat production, the segmentation of interests because of the qualities of wheat produced, and the wide variations in opinions and practices as to the utilization of various government wheat price and storage programs have tended to develop trade associations that on the whole have limited their activities to the participants of one segment of the wheat economy. The development of the National Wheat Council in 1965 may be the first step in enabling the various trade associations in the wheat economy to stress the mutuality of interests that exist in the wheat system and to play a more positive role in the coordination of the wheat system.

BARGAINING ASSOCIATIONS

Wheat producers, on the whole, have not been too active in developing bargaining associations (with the exception of their participation in various cooperatives). One such organization, the *National Farmers Organization,* which attempts to raise producers' income by withholding supplies of various commodities from the market at specific times, has various farmer members who may produce wheat. However, because of the effectiveness of the government price support program for wheat, the NFO has not found it necessary to try such withholding tactics on wheat. On the other hand, the change in the price support program to one of "low" price supports offset by cash subsidies may encourage more attempts at withholding by wheat farmers in the future. In addition the NFO has attempted to use "bargaining power" by having country elevators sign "exclusive" storage agreements with the NFO. The purpose of such contracts is to assure the cooperating elevator first chance at earning storage income on the producer's wheat and in return provide better prices for the ultimate purchase of the farmer's wheat. Most country elevators have resisted such tactics because they believe they conflict with the public warehousemen's storage contracts which call for uniform storage rates and no discrimination among customers.

POOL ARRANGEMENTS

A pool arrangement has as its purpose the providing of a season's average price to an individual producer. In most cases a cooperative procurement and marketing organization is involved that gives each farmer selling his grain (wheat) to the cooperative the average market price *for the season* based on grade and quality. The advantage to the producer is that he will not receive the lowest price and may take advantage of a seasonal price increase once the harvest has passed. Once again the presence of a high price support for wheat in the past has made a pool coordinating device unnecessary. However, the change in the price support program has increased the interest of wheat producers and wheat farmer cooperative groups in pool arrangements. Such groups have become especially interested in broadening the use of "Form G" of the price support regulations which permits government price support protection on pooled inventories of commodities. This allows cooperatives to have the protection of government price supports for centralized inventories. Thus far Form G has been primarily limited in use to cotton and soybean products. A task force created by the Under Secretary of Agriculture in 1966 recommended that further extension of Form G to wheat and other commodities did not seem necessary at the present time.

GOVERNMENT ACTIVITIES

Government activities in the wheat economy affect all segments of the system. A food grain as basic as wheat, so widely grown, and having major international trade considerations has had a variety of domestic and international government programs to help correct major imbalances between production and consumption and to improve the economic viability of the producers. Because of such uncontrollable factors as weather and disease, and the fact that a crop is produced only once a year, it is very difficult for producers to have much control over total crop production or to adjust rapidly to a major change in consumption requirements. The circular swings from surpluses to shortages and back to surpluses and the resultant patchwork of government programs (many of them not flexible enough to help the wheat system adjust to major changes) have drastically altered the structure, functions, coordination, and economic position of the many segments and participants of the wheat system. In addition to government programs that have been developed as major "shock absorbers" of the wheat system, there are many other government programs that provide: (1) much needed grade, communication, and educational services to permit the efficient flow of wheat products from the farmer to the ultimate consumer; (2) regulations to avoid the abuse of market position or misuse of market aids such as futures markets; and (3) meaningful domestic and international programs to improve the economic interrelationships between the U.S. wheat system and the total domestic and world economy.

A brief list of the variety of government programs that affect the wheat system was outlined previously in a general way on page 26 of this study. More specifically, these government activities include the following:

(1) Price support and export subsidies under specific programs such as wheat price supports set not only to provide minimum levels to wheat producers but also so as to be related to the price support levels of other crops; compensatory certificate payments; P.L. 480 concessional wheat export sales and export wheat market promotion, wheat storage programs including storage payment levels, withdrawals, or sales of government wheat inventories at varying price levels; the development of wheat reserves and policies for the use of reserves; price ceilings in wartime; allocations of wheat concessional sales in times of shortage and in relation to the economic development of a viable wheat economy for both the United States and the recipient country; the use or cancellation of acreage diversion and land retirement programs; wheat export subsidy payments, the use of wheat in domestic disaster areas, the use of special grain rates for government wheat shipments overseas.

(2) Economic and product research such as the development of special wheat varieties and special wheat products (bulgur, for instance), and the measurement and evaluation of various market structure relationships in the wheat system.

(3) Special regulations for major institutions in the wheat system such as the establishment of the Commodity Exchange Authority of the Department of Agriculture to supervise the futures markets for wheat at Minneapolis, Kansas City, and Chicago.

(4) The development of major service operations for other institutions in the wheat system, such as the advisory service provided by the Farmer Cooperative Service to various wheat cooperatives.

(5) The establishment of general regulations, including Pure Food and Drug standards, sanitation, grading, and antitrust laws.

(6) A variety of market services and educational programs provided by the Department of Agriculture and the Federal and State Extension Service.

Specific examples and effects of many of these government activities and their future trends will be discussed in Section V of this study, but a few of the more important activities and their effects on coordination will be noted here so that the reader will have a clear picture of how the wheat system developed and the governmental climate for future structural changes.

The tariff rates on wheat and wheat flour have been high enough to protect the U.S. domestic price support program for wheat and low enough to permit the importation of special "seed" wheat of unique varieties and wheat flour products that can be added to various animal feed preparations (wheat and flour that is "unfit for human consumption"). The rates as of 1966 are as follows:

Wheat: 21 cents per 60 lb. bushel [9] and a specific quota for Canada of 795,000 bushels for human consumption and a 5,000 bushel quota for all other countries combined.

Wheat, unfit for human consumption: 5% ad valorem.

Wheat flour: 52 cents a hundredweight for Canadian flour and $1.04 for other countries on a specific quota basis of a 3,815,000 lb. quota for Canada and 185,000 lbs. for all other countries combined.

Heavily damaged wheat flour unfit for human consumption: 2.5% ad valorem.

Other wheat flour unfit for human consumption: 5% ad valorem.

In addition to the above tariff rates under Section 22 of the Agricultural Adjustment Act of 1933, the President of the United States can take action to control imports of agricultural commodities and products thereof whenever he finds it necessary to prevent imports from materially interfering with any price support or other agricultural program or operation undertaken by the Department of Agriculture.

Price supports for wheat have been high enough to maintain the income level of the commercial wheat farmer, but so high that (except for wartime and 1965–1966 legislation) they have built up wheat inventories. Farmer wheat deliveries to the Commodity Credit Corporation for storage occurred in sizable quantities during the 1950s and early 1960s even with acreage reductions. With crop failures in Asia and parts of Europe, world wheat prices firmed and this fact, together with a new price support program that lowers the direct price support of wheat to "world

[9] In addition any wheat ground for flour must have a 75-cent a bushel certificate paid by the flour miller whether or not the wheat is U.S. or Canadian grown.

levels," has reversed the build-up of government owned inventories.

Reflected in Table IV-7 are some of the changing patterns of government policy that were used to meet various supply and demand imbalances. On the whole it was the unusual world situation which prevented wheat surpluses from becoming an unbearable burden (war, famine, drought, and population explosion) rather than any particular form of government price support program. On the other hand, it has only been since 1965 that farm programs have had a long-range focus (four years) and have taken into account the total agribusiness complex rather than just the producer segment of any particular commodity system.

The Agricultural Act of 1964 and the Agricultural Act passed October 12, 1965, allow producers to plant wheat on feed grain acreage if the farmer participates in both the wheat and feed grain programs. As of 1966, the world wheat situation allowed the Secretary of Agriculture to increase the wheat acreage allotment by 16.6 million acres to a national total of 68.2 million acres and to cancel the acreage diversion program that used to exist for wheat producers. On the whole the Agricultural Act of 1965 is a most farsighted and flexible program, geared to commercial agriculture, market-oriented, and aimed at reducing the role of the Commodity Credit Corporation; it relates agriculture to the broader objectives of national economic policy, it adapted to the growing importance of commercial world trade in wheat and other commodities, and it is an integral part of the U.S. food assistance programs and is directly interrelated with other facets of foreign policy.

Government price support programs in the wheat economy have performed coordinating activities since the days of the Agricultural Adjustment Act of the 1930s. The Commodity Credit Corporation utilizes a nonrecourse loan as a means of supporting the price of wheat. The CCC, under the direction of the Department of Agriculture, is empowered to make loans to wheat farmers who have complied with wheat crop control programs. The producer does not have to pay back the loan in cash but can deliver his wheat as payment when the loan becomes due. In essence, the price support programs provide an alternative market for the producers' wheat. The government "wheat market" is announced ahead of planting time and each wheat producer is informed of the wheat support price for his local agricultural area. These announcements also include the premiums or discounts, if any, that will be paid for higher or lower proteins, test weights, moisture content, and other qualities. The farmer is

TABLE IV-7. Price Supports, Price Ceilings, Deliveries to the Commodity Credit Corporation, and Average Prices Received by Farmers: Selected Years, 1942–1966 (In dollars per bushel)

Crop year	Support price	Ceiling price	Average price received	Net deliveries to CCC (1,000 bushels)
1942	$1.23	1.64[a]	$1.35	73,000
1944	1.38	1.64–1.79[b] (May 30, 1945)	1.49	200
1950	2.18	[c]	2.11	91,000
1956	2.00	—	1.93	193,500
1957	1.82	—	1.75	511,000
1958	1.81	—	1.76	181,900
1959	1.78	—	1.74	260,500
1960	1.79	—	1.83	119,900
1961	2.00	—	2.04	229,800
1962	1.82[d]	—	1.85	71,600
1963	1.30[e]	—	1.37	80,000
1964	1.25[f]	—	1.35	9,400
1965	1.25[g]	—	1.64 est.	—
1966	1.25[h]	—	—	—

[a] Based on soft wheat St. Louis Terminal Market.

[b] Based on soft wheat, St. Louis Terminal Market, raised to $1.79 on May 30, 1945.

[c] Similar legislation *discussed* during the 1951 Korean War but found not necessary to put into law.

[d] Does not include an 18-cent per bushel cash subsidy.

[e] Does not include marketing certificates paid to the farmers who have complied with the wheat program. Certificates were paid as follows: a 70-cent certificate per each bushel based on 45% of U.S. domestic wheat production reimbursed by a 70-cent certificate charged to the domestic flour miller, and a 25-cent certificate based on another 45% of U.S. domestic wheat production financed out of the U.S. Treasury.

[f] Does not include marketing certificates paid to the farmers who have complied with the wheat program. Certificates were paid as follows: a 75-cent certificate per bushel based on 45% of U.S. domestic wheat production and reimbursed by a 75-cent certificate charged to the domestic flour miller, and a 30-cent certificate based on another 35% of U.S. domestic wheat production financed out of the U.S. Treasury.

[g] Does not include marketing certificates paid to the farmers who have complied with the wheat programs. Certificates were paid on 45% of the domestic wheat production at a value at the difference between full parity in July 1966 and the $1.25 loan value. The loan value was $2.57 so the certificate values were $1.32 per bushel. Seventy-five cents per bushel for each certificate was financed by the flour miller and 57 cents per bushel came from the U.S. Treasury.

[h] The 1966 crop year had the same provisions as the 1965 crop year with the exception that the U.S. wheat allotment was revised upward so the certificates only cover 35% of U.S. domestic production.

SOURCE: *Wheat Situation*, October 1966. For additional details concerning the changes in recent price support and certificate programs, see p. 32 in that issue.

not committed to sell to the government, nor at the government's price; he may, up to a certain date, repay the loan and sell his wheat on the cash market if it is higher than the government loan value.

The wheat price support program in 1966–1967 (based on the 1965 Agricultural Act) has one additional feature important to wheat market coordination, namely, wheat marketing certificates. The wheat certificate program includes the provision for the market price of wheat to be supported at $1.25 a bushel (farm value and approximately "world wheat price levels") and a differential to be paid to the farmer to support his income potential from the domestic consumption of his wheat production. The value of this differential is based on the parity price of wheat versus the support price at the conclusion of the crop year; the July 1966 parity price was $2.57 a bushel, so the certificate was worth $1.32 a bushel. This certificate is issued on the proportion of the U.S. wheat crop used for domestic food consumption (45% in 1966 and 35% in 1967). The payment of this certificate is financed by a flour milling certificate of 75 cents a bushel and the remaining 57 cents comes from the U.S. Treasury. The certificates can be issued to the producer at the producer's pleasure because the certificates are based on his past normal wheat yield (five-year average) on the domestic percentage of his allocated acreage. These certificates may then be converted into cash at the local Agricultural Stabilization offices. The flour miller who converts wheat into flour must purchase domestic certificates from the Department of Agriculture at the end of each month on the basis of the wheat he has utilized in grinding wheat into flour or at a stated government conversion factor (the miller has the option to select either method).

The significance of the certificate program to the wheat farmer is that it lowers the cash market price support for wheat to a point where there are more market outlets domestically; for instance, wheat for feed and industrial uses. Because of the lower cash price for wheat, more of it moves into these broader markets, thereby reducing government wheat storage on and off farms. In addition, because most of the payment for the certificates is financed by domestic processors, part of the burden of supporting the wheat farmer is shifted from the Treasury Department (taxpayer) to the ultimate wheat product consumer.[10]

Table IV-7 summarizes wheat price support levels for selected crop years compared to average prices received by farmers for wheat as well as wheat ceiling prices where applicable. The first column indicates the average government price support for wheat at the

farm level. The second column indicates ceiling prices on wheat at a specific terminal market during wartime. The third column is the U.S. average price of wheat at the farm level. The fourth column shows the net deliveries of wheat made to the CCC by producers who preferred the price support level to the then current cash market. The footnotes attached to Table IV-7 describe other supplementary income payments available to the producer but not offered in terms of a price support level.

The farmer who participates in the wheat program not only improves his bargaining power in the marketing of his wheat and increases his time dimension alternatives, but he also is considered a better credit risk for those supplying him with industrial goods such as petroleum products, fertilizers, chemicals, and farm machinery, and those supplying him with consumer goods such as clothing and appliances. This is so because he has the government price support program as an alternative buyer of his crop, and thus those supplying him with goods know that he has an assured market and an assured price level.

Table IV-7 refers briefly to wheat ceiling prices during World War II, but the plentiful supplies and the willingness on behalf of the government to raise wheat ceiling prices as needed provided few problems to those buying and selling wheat. In essence the very fact that wheat price supports have been high and have heavily influenced the price level of wheat has provided such stability to the wheat market that those buying wheat (flour millers and exporters) have always looked to government inventories as an alternative source of wheat. This has made the procurement tasks of these firms much easier in the past than they will be in the future. "Round lots" in large quantities and of uniform quality of wheat were easily accessible.

The drastic change in the price support level for wheat and effective acreage restraint, coupled with increased foreign demand, has reduced government wheat stocks dramatically at a time when dollar demands and concessional sales are expanding. This change in the wheat pricing environment is having its effect on the entire wheat system. The major impacts are as follows:

(1) Less certainty of the market price of wheat has resulted in all participants using the wheat futures market much more than in the past as a hedging and basis device.

(2) Flour millers are paying higher prices for wheat because of the increased market price plus the necessity of paying for a 75-cent a bushel wheat marketing certificate.

(3) The government concessional wheat sale pro-

---

[10] Because of the small proportion of wheat cost in the total end products, a 50-cent change in a wheat certificate means less than a 1-cent change in a loaf of bread.

grams (such as P.L. 480) influence the free markets much more than they did in the past, and new restrictions and criteria for shipments are being developed and related to the domestic price level of wheat.

(4) The government storage programs that resulted from the build up of government owned stocks during high wheat price support years are becoming less important as "commercial" operations for various participants of the wheat system as wheat inventories decline.

(5) The pressure on U.S. domestic wheat prices has decreased the subsidies that must be paid to exporters so that they will be competitive in world wheat markets.

(6) The past and present wheat price support programs, based on acreage controls, have been rewarding to the most efficient user of the controlled acres who has in turn been encouraged to utilize all of the newest technologies to increase yields per acre with a guaranteed minimum return. In addition, the government wheat price support programs have been updated, and payments based on the historical production records of the participants in the program have provided an additional incentive for farmers to increase yields per acre, thus enabling U.S. production through improved technology to be in an excellent position to meet increasing domestic and export demands for agricultural commodities.

The impact of new price support programs and the increased demands for wheat are most dramatically expressed in the decline in the costs of storing and handling wheat by the Commodity Credit Corporation. As of August 1966, wheat storage and handling costs had been reduced by $223.5 million during the period 1961–1966. The peak storage and handling costs of all commodities owned by the CCC was reached in fiscal 1961 and costs averaged $1,162,000 per day compared with costs in fiscal 1966 of $643,-000 per day. These reductions in wheat storage payments have forced the closing of many large grain elevators that were in poor logistical locations for grain merchandising and were dependent on grain storage for income. The most recent closing was the large terminal grain elevator in Buffalo, New York owned by Cargill. Congressmen from that state pleaded with USDA officials to store grain in that location to avoid the closing of grain facilities in an already depressed and by-passed grain market.

The importance of wheat grain storage to the wheat system participants during high price supports and resultant surplus periods will be discussed in greater detail in the remaining portions of this chapter. Even with a decline in wheat inventories and wheat storage

rates, the existence of wheat storage programs has enabled many of the integrated firms in the wheat industry to rely on storage of wheat and other grain as an important source of storage income, as Table IV-8 indicates.

The change in the P.L. 480 provisions that broadens the purpose of the act from "surplus disposal" to "economic development" is also affecting the wheat system. The exporter of wheat is not only concerned with exporting wheat; he is also directly involved in the development of viable agribusiness entities in the recipient country. This means that export firms such as Continental Grain, Cargill, and Bunge not only are selling wheat but also are providing advisory services to their customers (e.g., wheat blends for local flour needs, building plans for the construction of flour mills and/or wheat storage facilities, and help in the development of alternative transportation policies in the procurement of wheat and the shipment of flour).

As of 1966, P.L. 480 provided for the sale of U.S. wheat (and other commodities) to developing countries on concessional terms (loans and grants, payable in local currencies). Such concessional sales are to be made *only* if they do not interfere with the *normal commercial* sales of wheat and other grain and help in the economic development of the recipient country. In order to participate in wheat sales, the exporter has to negotiate with the purchasing country or agent of that country that has received a U.S. Government P.L. 480 Authorization of Purchase. As previously stated, a subsidy is paid to the U.S. exporting terminal operator to make him competitive with other countries offering wheat. Armed with the knowledge of the current subsidy, the exporter offers his lowest price to the potential wheat customer of the importing country. Local currency provisions may induce the foreign buyer to favor a U.S. exporter in certain cases.[11] The exporter of wheat also has to be aware of the minimum and maximum export prices permitted under the International Wheat Agreement as well as the various provisions of the P.L. 480 program.

---

[11] If the exporter was successful in selling the wheat, the exporter *previously* had the option of taking the subsidy after he shipped the wheat, either in the form of cash or in Payment-in-Kind certificates which were redeemable in bushels of wheat on the basis of the dollar value of the certificates, or redeemable in a similar value of other agricultural commodities. The accumulation of Payment-in-Kind certificates was another way of carrying title to wheat without having to incur storage costs. On August 26, 1966, however, after a decade of use, the Payment-in-Kind certificates were discontinued except for outstanding authorizations because government wheat inventories had been substantially reduced and this program was intended to encourage additional sales of government wheat by using the wheat itself as an incentive.

TABLE IV-8. Storage and Handling Payments to Selected Leading Firms in the Wheat System: 1958–1963

	1963	1962	1961	1960	1959	1958	Total
C.G.F. Grain Co.[a]	$17,238,717	$19,376,218	$24,925,192	$28,313,848	$23,470,634	$14,787,434	$128,112,043
Cargill Inc.	5,831,757	6,335,499	9,474,404	9,808,744	12,103,615	13,226,341	56,780,360
Punta Alegre Commission Corp.[a]	4,884,202	5,277,319	1,233,023	—	—	—	11,394,544
Archer-Daniels-Midland	4,875,545	2,779,579	5,134,987	5,919,132	6,076,898	6,240,199	31,026,340
F. H. Peavey & Co.	4,690,655	4,064,223	4,169,304	5,389,505	5,528,810	5,623,702	29,466,199
Continental Grain	4,059,334	3,728,182	6,190,879	7,198,886	6,835,190	5,833,690	33,846,161
Farmers Union Grain Terminal Assoc.	3,700,543	2,390,665	3,945,877	4,089,595	4,781,426	3,328,488	22,236,594
Harvest Queen Mill & Elevator Co.	3,549,156	4,192,956	4,856,361	5,204,045	5,884,495	5,514,064	29,201,077
Seabord Allied Milling	2,806,792	3,060,487	3,299,454	1,435,573	1,139,311	517,396	12,259,013
Producers Grain Corp.	2,342,220	2,209,080	2,200,595	1,876,571	2,621,401	1,644,824	12,894,691
Bunge Corp.	1,821,093	1,852,199	1,696,717	1,992,720	2,318,773	1,839,525	11,521,027
Ross Industries	1,790,885	2,158,161	2,018,256	2,337,813	2,569,705	—	10,874,820
General Mills	1,613,513	1,245,985	2,086,142	2,642,146	2,776,898	1,634,936	11,999,620
Standard Milling	1,526,964	1,936,649	2,114,736	1,960,460	2,214,819	2,018,376	11,772,004
Pillsbury Co.	1,262,404	1,384,877	1,845,459	1,812,037	2,285,802	587,707	9,178,286
Kimbell Milling	1,139,162	1,607,697	1,611,101	1,628,315	2,181,374	1,570,497	9,738,146
Flour Mills of America	1,082,728	1,169,580	905,700	949,922	615,603	602,607	5,326,140
Louis Dreyfus Corp.	1,057,940	602,365	816,077	1,144,541	873,042	522,504	5,016,469
International Milling	916,330	910,118	1,638,625	2,059,948	1,544,132	1,698,514	8,767,667
Burrus Mills	632,845	802,503	979,529	2,575,778	2,787,837	2,176,166	9,954,708
Colorado Milling and Elevator Co.	—	545,873	852,616	1,012,049	1,217,058	800,843	4,428,439
Total	66,822,835	67,630,215	81,975,034	89,351,628	89,826,823	70,167,813	465,794,348

[a] Punta Alegre Commission Co. and C.G.F. became separate entities by agreement dated September 1, 1961.

SOURCE: USDA, Commodity Credit Corporation, *Annual Reports of Storage and Handling Payments in Excess of $500,000 under the Uniform Grain Storage Agreements.*

In essence the wheat exporter is not only dependent upon domestic government programs in planning his merchandising and storing activities, he is also dependent upon the successful utilization of government export programs if he plans to participate in this most important wheat market. One cannot ignore the variety of import restrictive programs developed by overseas customers (e.g., variable duties, percentage quotas) that also forcefully coordinate the movement of wheat from the U.S. terminal wheat markets.

One future government activity that will be especially important to the effective coordination of the wheat system is government action with respect to a wheat reserve policy. Much criticism has been leveled at the government for a constantly shifting policy that has made it difficult for participants in the wheat system to plan meaningful procurement and marketing strategies. The government has sold wheat for 105% of price support levels plus carrying charges, for 108%, and in some cases has withdrawn CCC wheat from the market completely. Several grain trade officials recognize the need for reserves, many of them favor the government maintaining and bearing the cost of such reserves while others feel that the "private trade" may wish to do so. Because the government,

through the price support and storage programs of the past, has carried most of the wheat inventories for the participants of the wheat system, this writer assumes that this burden will probably be continued to be carried by the government in the future because in a very uncertain world environment the existence of wheat reserves in this country may be both a public obligation and a national defense requirement.

Wheat reserves policies should be spelled out so as not to disrupt the efficient operation of the U.S. wheat system and so as to avoid the danger of putting the Secretary of Agriculture constantly in the position of trying to "outguess" the market. One set of recommendations on reserve policies was set forth on September 15, 1966, by Mr. Robert L. Searles, Chairman of the National Trade Council, before a hearing of the National Advisory Commission on Food and Fiber. He stated:

Prescribe a price and quantity scale for sale of government-owned grains, making such stocks available as market prices rise to predetermined levels. Such a scale might make 10% of existing CCC owned wheat stocks available at 120% of current low levels, plus carrying charges; another 10% at 130%, and so on. Disposition of a final 30% of reserves might be left for emergency determination suitable to the nature of the crisis at hand, as determined by the President.

The reserve policy, as formulated, will be especially important in a world where wheat supplies are more rapidly alternating between surplus and shortage. In a brief span of eight years U.S. wheat carryovers declined from 1,244 million bushels to 536 million bushels which is below the recommendation for a wheat reserve of 630 million bushels made by the National Agricultural Advisory Commission, Subcommittee on Farm Policy Review, on November 13, 1964.

TABLE IV-9. Recommended Wheat Reserves Compared with Average Wheat Carryovers from 1958 to 1962, Actual Carryovers for 1965 and 1966, and Estimated Carryovers as of 1967
(In millions of bushels)

Recommended wheat reserves	630
Average carryover, 1958 to 1962	1,244
Actual carryover, July 1, 1965	818
Actual carryover, July 1, 1966	536
Estimated carryover, July 1, 1967	400

Source: *Wheat Situation*, October 1966, p. 2.

In addition to these government programs and services that are affecting the coordination of the wheat system, there are several other governmental activities not previously mentioned such as the National Commission on Food Marketing, the National Advisory Commission on Food and Fiber, and special subcommittee Hearings on specific problems such as "Bread Price Increases" that have and will affect the interrelationships of the private and public managers in the wheat system.

CONTRACTUAL RELATIONSHIPS

There are many contractual relationships that exist in the wheat industry that help to integrate many of the industry's operations vertically in much the same way as that of actual ownership. In the case of the wheat producer, many farmers grow seed wheat or specialized wheat varieties for a specific market outlet. In addition, many producers contract ahead of time for their industrial inputs such as fertilizer, chemicals, seed, and machinery. Such contract buying may include not only the industrial items, but the actual labor of applying these inputs as well. Because of the seasonal nature of farm activities, it may be cheaper to hire someone to apply fertilizer and pesticides than to obtain part-time help or overstaff the farm the year round. In addition, specialized equipment needs and operating know-how encourage the producer to purchase his inputs on an applied basis.

Similarly, in marketing his wheat a farmer may agree to sell his wheat before harvest at a flat contract price, or he may have a contract with a country elevator operator to produce a certain variety of wheat for seed purposes. Such a marketing contract is like a government price support. In this case, however, the contractor is likely to be a country elevator operator, and the presumption is that the farmer does not have the right to change his mind.

Other contracts exist in the wheat economy such as to-arrive contracts and round lots that meet the time, location, quantity, and quality requirements unique to a particular processing or exporting firm. These quantity futures contracts for the cash commodity — wheat or flour — may be made in anticipation of a harvest movement, after a round lot is accumulated, or on an annual requirement of wheat or flour basis. Traditionally flour milling firms usually supply wholesale bakers on a 120-day contract basis although commitments have been made as far in advance as 6 months to a year. There is a general trade practice outlining charges to be made after a specified period (120 days) for holding the baker's flour inventories for him. Usually these fees are not large enough to cover the entire cost of inventory holdings, but the government storage program payments earned by the miller in the past have more than offset the inventory charges absorbed by the miller for holding the baker's future flour requirements (such may not be the case as wheat supplies and storage fees decline). In some cases, as much as 50% of a flour miller's flour production may be contracted for ahead of time. This is especially true when the location of the flour mill in relation to a major wholesale baking company's plant is at a distinct advantage over the locations of competitors. Flour millers usually are unable to cover these cash flour contracts with offsetting cash wheat purchases and therefore must resort to the futures market and try to obtain an advantageous trading basis.

The inventory carrying cost that has been shifted from the baker to the miller to the government storage program may also benefit the wholesale baker as he sells his national brand breads through major retail chains without receiving payment for 10 to 12 days. The retailer, having rapid turnover in his bread department, actually receives a cash flow into his business by not paying the wholesale baker for 10 days. The wholesale baker's inventory is ultimately financed by the government wheat price support program. In essence, the government wheat price support program may encourage the wholesale baker to make advantageous long-term purchase agreements with the flour miller and use these purchase contracts to provide his retail grocery customers not only with bread but with the use of funds at no interest.

One of the most prominent methods of contract coordination for the retailer in the wheat system is continuing purchase arrangements with a number of wholesale bakers. These purchase agreements include special discounts for promotional purposes, special provisions such as store deliveries, or special private label manufacturing arrangements. The growth of retail food chains and voluntary retail food store associations and the enormous size of these markets have placed competitive pressures on all segments of the wheat economy. Such pressures have made it possible for some chains to purchase private label bread supplies from wholesale bakers at a price below the manufacturing cost of the chains' own bakery plant.

Private label bread contracts are important to both those manufacturing only private label bread, as well as those who have advertised brands as well. In the National Commission on Food Marketing's special studies on food products,[12] 61% of the retail distributors who responded to the private label questionnaire purchased both their private label and their advertised brand from the same manufacturer, indicating the complexity of the private label and advertised brand contracted agreements.

There are many other contractual coordinating devices in the wheat economy that center around those institutions which, by their very nature, provide a coordinating service to the wheat system. Transportation firms have been in the forefront of long-term contractual relationships for the movement of wheat and flour products. Similarly credit institutions such as commercial banks, the Farm Credit Administration, and credit divisions of agribusiness firms have supplied capital to groups of firms in the wheat economy on a long-term contractual basis that has made contractual agreements among several segments of the wheat system possible.

SUMMARY

Thus far in Chapter IV we have noted:

(1) that a change has occurred in the organization, ownership and structure of the wheat system responding to change in the system's environment;

(2) that the existence of price support, storage, and P.L. 480 programs in the United States and a great variety of other wheat programs in other countries, as well as the International Wheat Agreement,[13] has not been a deterrent to domestic or international commercial wheat and wheat product trade, because businessmen have used these programs as procurement, marketing, and inventory tools; and government administrators, in turn, have wisely utilized the know-how and facilities of the private segments of the wheat system in the execution of these programs;

(3) that economies of scale have reduced the number and increased the size of each firm in each segment of the wheat economy;

(4) that independent firms in the integrated environment of the wheat system can succeed only if they have alternative ways of coordinating their activities with the total wheat system and if they take advantage of their singleness of purpose flexibility;

(5) that it is only recently that both government and private managers of entities in the wheat system have begun to take a broader and longer range view of the wheat system of which they are an integral part.

These changes in the structure of the wheat industry were triggered off by the basic underlying economic, political and social forces of change that encouraged the organizational and technological breakthroughs in production, processing, and marketing described in Chapter III.

Behind all the structural changes described thus far in Chapter IV are the business and government leaders who have helped to shape the newer types of corporate and cooperative firms in the wheat system, and who have helped to form the policies, actions, and administration of laws and programs through a great variety of public and private institutions both domestically and internationally. The author, of necessity, has had to concentrate on the development of the institutions and arrangements of the wheat system, but as Emerson so aptly put it, "The institution is but the shadow of the man." In order to complete our overall examination of the wheat complex, let us turn to an analysis of the behavioral and performance patterns of the changing market structure of the wheat system.

[12] Technical Study No. 10, June 1966.

[13] The International Wheat Agreement was first developed in 1933 when huge world surpluses developed. The agreement ended in 1935. It became a working agreement and has been extended for various time periods since 1948 and 1949. There are minimum price levels for producing countries and maximum purchase prices for importing countries that change from year to year. The United States has been a party to the agreement since its beginning. With the development of the Kennedy Trade Agreement of 1967, the International Wheat Agreement will probably come to an end.

V

Behavioral and Performance Patterns of the Wheat System

THE EMPHASIS on the structural and product flow analysis of the wheat system in Chapter IV is intended to force the reader to recognize the complexity of the wheat market structure. Such an analysis suggests that the private or public manager in an individual firm or institution must be an effective and useful participant in the *total* wheat system in order to function profitably and realistically within his own sphere of influence. The coordination of the various functions inside and outside a business in today's environment not only requires an awareness on the part of the individual businessman of the many coordinating devices available to him, but also requires a sophisticated organization that permits and encourages him to keep his firm to keep abreast of the rapidly changing outside influences. Such awareness requires new types of organization both within and outside the firm to improve communications among the participants in the wheat system and to keep top private and public policy leaders better informed. Furthermore, by seeing how company policies fit in such a broad environment, enables management to re-evaluate them in the light of the changing total system of the wheat economy.

The purpose of Chapter V is to analyze, in a highly selective manner, the behavioral and performance patterns of the wheat economy. The interplays that occur between the physical and market constraints and the entities of the wheat system will be used to highlight the main elements of this organism. What types of behavior and performance by firms and institutions characterize the overall behavioral patterns of the wheat system? What action results from the structural and performance patterns of the participants in the wheat system as indicated by the inventory management, profitability, price stability, competition, and adaptability of the parts and the system as a whole?

INVENTORY MANAGEMENT

In the wheat system we are faced with a typical agribusiness commodity pattern of year-round consumption for the end products of wheat (flour, bread, and bakery products) and twice-a-year harvests (in the spring for the winter wheat crop and in the fall for the spring wheat crop). Obviously storage of the crop in various forms takes place. Exhibit V-1 and Table V-1 represent two important time dimensions of storage activity in the wheat economy. Exhibit V-1 shows wheat stocks as of January 1, 1964, the end of a calendar year and the first quarter after the harvest "bulge" has had an opportunity to be absorbed into the wheat system. Approximately 309.7 million bushels of wheat or 19.2% of the wheat crop and carryover were being held on wheat farms. Of this 19.2%, 43.6% was stored for the Commodity Credit Corporation by the farmer, who was receiving storage payments for storing this government wheat on his farm. The overall grain storage capacity figures indicate ample storage with flexibility in the handling of all grains.

The 80.8% of the wheat crop and carryover that is in off-farm storage is stored primarily at country grain elevators and terminal grain elevators. (The reader should bear in mind that many of these country and terminal grain elevator operations are vertically integrated into flour milling and wheat export operations.) The off-farm wheat inventories are almost equally divided between country and terminal grain elevator positions. In both positions, it is the government that bears the cost of over two-thirds of the inventory holdings, although the terminal elevator operator seems slightly more dependent on government storage operation than does the country grain elevator operator. The 80.8% of the wheat crop and carryover that is in off-farm storage and that is primarily located at country and terminal grain elevator positions provides flexibility of location in satisfying the round lot wheat requirements of both large wheat processing firms and export firms. Although wheat inventories were fairly large as of January 1, 1964, they

were still stored in this type of facility on January 1, 1964.

Flour millers also store a small quantity of flour as part of their industry operations. Because of the perishability problem this amount is quite small and only amounted to a wheat equivalent value of 10.9

EXHIBIT V-1

Wheat Stocks in the United States: January 1, 1964
(In millions of bushels)

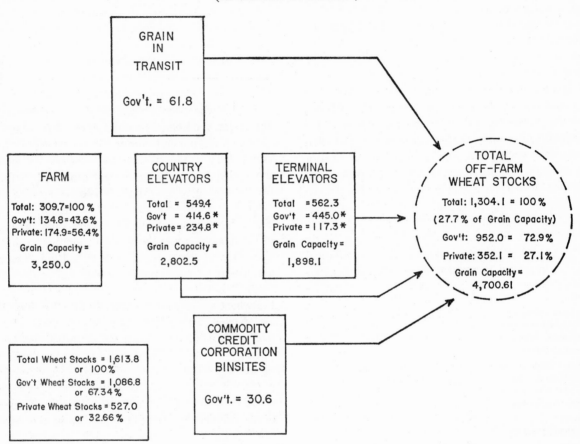

* The breakdown of off-farm wheat stocks among the separate holders has not been reported since the 1959–1960 crop. The figures shown here are based on the proportions indicated for the 1958–1959 and 1959–1960 seasons combined.

SOURCE: *Wheat Situation*, February 1966, p. 22.

still did not total the operating capacity of the grain elevators as may be seen in Exhibit V-1.

In addition to wheat stored in country and terminal grain elevators, there was a significant quantity of government owned wheat at various in-transit positions (e.g., railroad cars and barges) moving from one location to another and the government estimated this to be 61.8 million bushels. Also the government built its own storage facilities, called bin sites, in order to alleviate the shortage of commercial storage facilities in the late 1950s. Some 30.6 million bushels of wheat

million bushels as of January 1, 1964. This amount is not considered to be part of U.S. "wheat inventories."

Table V-1 indicates wheat stocks as of October 1, 1964, compared with the wheat stocks as of January 1, 1964. The October, 1964 on-farm levels represent after harvest peaks of on-farm wheat storage of 506.3 million bushels out of total wheat stocks of 1,799.4 million bushels, or 28.1%. The remaining 72.9% of wheat stocks were located in the two primary off-farm storage locations of country and terminal grain elevators. It may be noted that "free" or privately held wheat inventories increased in both locations while government stocks were reduced. Commodity Credit Corporation bin sites wheat stocks were also declining during this period. The increase in world demand for wheat has accounted for the rapid decrease in government-owned wheat stocks.

In the first place, this brief examination of wheat storage operations in the wheat system underscores the important but declining place that government wheat stocks play in the wheat system. In May 1967 U.S. government-owned wheat stocks were below the suggested minimum reserve levels. If the United States has a formal reserve policy, the location of such stocks becomes extremely important to the participants of the wheat system who have a surplus of storage space.

The second implication of these data is that as wheat stocks decline there will be greater competition between the processing and exporting segments of the wheat economy for control of or access to these inventories, thus encouraging more backward integration or additional contractual relationships with primary producing segments of the wheat system.

TABLE V-1. Wheat Stocks at Selected Locations in the United States: January 1, 1964, and October 1, 1964
(In millions of bushels)

	January 1, 1964	*October 1, 1964*
On farms	309.7	506.3
Off farms:[a]		
Country elevators		
Government owned	414.6	305.4
Privately owned	234.8	341.4
Terminal elevators		
Government owned	445.0	347.8
Privately owned	117.3	170.7
Commodity Credit Corporation (government bin sites)	30.6	12.6
Government grain in transit	61.8	115.2
Subtotal off-farm stocks	1,304.1	1,293.1
Total wheat stocks	1,613.8	1,799.4

[a] The breakdown of off-farm wheat stocks among the separate holders has not been reported since the 1959–1960 crop. The figures shown here are based on the proportions indicated for the 1958–1959 and 1959–1960 seasons combined.
SOURCE: *Wheat Situation*, February 1966, p. 22.

The third implication of storage patterns in the wheat economy is the location of stocks in relation to milling and export markets. The factors normally taken into consideration:

(1) The milling-in-transit privilege for wheat and wheat products.

(2) Rate differentials on wheat for export and for milling.
(3) Special rates on government wheat for disaster areas.
(4) The relationship between rates for different parts of the country.
(5) The relationship between rates on wheat and those on processed wheat products (flour).

Firms in the wheat industry that located their storage and processing facilities on the basis of a milling-in-transit privilege found themselves in a poor competitive position when railroads lowered *nontransit* rail rates in order to be competitive with trucking firms. The milling-in-transit "captured" customers of the railroads were at a distinct disadvantage, so much so that several railroads in the North Central States reduced their milling-in-transit rates as well as their nontransit rates. The pressure on the milling-in-transit rates is really only a symptom of a major factor in the location of wheat storage facilities — namely the competition of truck and water rates. The decisions of where to locate new wheat storage facilities in the future will have to take into consideration the advantages of having all three forms of transportation available in order to place wheat storage facilities in the most flexible position.

For U.S. exporters to be competitive in world wheat markets they have to have transportation procurement rates similar to those of other major exporting countries. Therefore, special export rail rates have been established in the past which favor the wheat exporter over the domestic flour miller. For example, in 1967 the wheat export rate from Kansas City to the West Coast is 82 cents per hundredweight and after the 100th meridian it is 70 cents per hundredweight. This compares with the domestic wheat rate between the same points of $1.34 per hundredweight. This occasionally places the exporter in an advantageous position as he competes with the flour miller for the producers' wheat. Also special rates on the shipment of government wheat and other grains affect the competitive procurement and wheat storage operations of the many segments of the wheat economy.

Finally the different regional "big John" railroad car rates for wheat adopted by various railroads and the lowered trainload rates on wheat as compared with those on flour have forced the closing of many flour mills in the midwest and the development of storage and milling complexes in the south and east. For example the single railroad car rate for flour and wheat has only a 0.5-cent differential from Minneapolis to the East Coast. However, the wheat trainload rate makes possible the delivery of wheat to an Eastern flour mill at 70.5 cents or 12.5 cents under the 83 cents per hundredweight rate for flour to the same destination because flour has not yet been able to be shipped in such loose bulk quantities.

PRICING

PRICE RELATIONSHIPS

Exhibit V-2 is a graphic presentation of the relationships of the price levels of wheat as related to flour and bread prices. The reader will note that the price level of wheat on the farm has remained fairly con-

EXHIBIT V-2

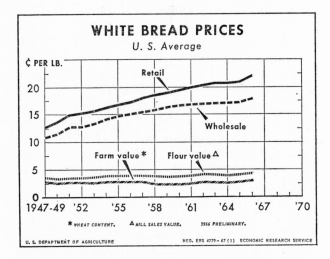

stant from 1947 to 1966. This was also true of the flour processed from this wheat as valued at the flour mill. On the other hand, the retail and wholesale value of a loaf of bread increased substantially during this same period. The increased labor and transportation costs of both the wholesale baker and the retailer partially accounted for this increase in price levels.

Exhibit V-3 sets forth the allocation of the consumer's bread dollar among the various segments of the wheat economy for the years 1964 and 1965 compared with the average allocations for the 1947–1949 period. Again the relative stability of the farm gross receipts between 1947–1949 and 1965 may be noted. On the other hand, all the other segments of the wheat system have had major changes in their gross receipts. The receipts to producers and handlers increased from 1.2 cents to 1.5 cents, or a 25% increase. Those of flour millers increased from 0.6 cent to 0.9 cent, which is a 50% increase, but this occurred on an exceedingly low base. Baker and wholesale gross receipts increased from 5.7 cents to 11.4 cents, or an increase of 100%. The retailer's gross receipts also increased by 100%, from 1.9 cents to 3.8 cents per one-pound loaf of bread.

The reader should also note the declining impor-

EXHIBIT V-3

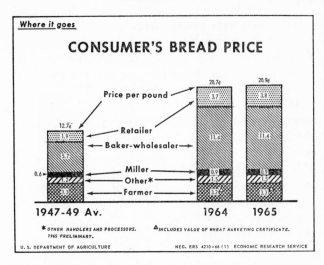

tance of wheat as a price factor in a loaf of bread. This decline in the relative value of wheat in a loaf of bread encouraged public policy makers in 1965 to utilize a high-priced domestic wheat certificate (75 cents a bushel as previously noted) to be paid by the flour miller as a partial offset to a cash subsidy to the wheat farmer. According to Exhibit V-3 there was no actual increase in the cost of wheat in a loaf of bread between 1964 and 1965.

The indicated general price levels for the products of various segments of the wheat economy represent national averages. Obviously, there is a great deal of price variability in different production and marketing operations. (The diversity of price operations in the wheat economy will be discussed in detail in the next portion of this chapter.) An example of price diversity is the retail price of a one-pound loaf of bread in Houston, Texas, and Los Angeles, California, compared with the U.S. average price for the same loaf of bread in 1947–1949 and 1963, as may be seen in Exhibit V-4, which shows that the U.S. average price for a one-pound loaf of bread increased 8.1 cents a loaf in the period from 1947–1949 to 1963, whereas in the same period the increase in the price of bread in Houston was 5.3 cents and in Los Angeles was 14.7 cents a loaf.

As we shall note later in this chapter, the price levels and the price spreads vary not only among geographical regions but from season to season, from year to year, and between types of retail outlet (chain, voluntary, and independent).

In the case of wheat, the Minneapolis, Chicago, and Kansas City cash terminal markets and futures markets have been the central price indicators. Wheat processors and exporters throughout the United States are dependent on these cash and futures markets to

EXHIBIT V-4

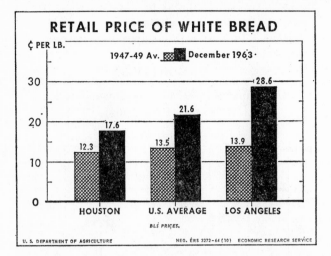

RETAIL PRICE OF WHITE BREAD

¢ PER LB.

1947-49 Av. ▨ ■ December 1963·

	HOUSTON	U.S. AVERAGE	LOS ANGELES
1947-49 Av.	12.3	13.5	13.9
December 1963	17.6	21.6	28.6

BLS PRICES.

U. S. DEPARTMENT OF AGRICULTURE   NEG. ERS 3272-64 (10)   ECONOMIC RESEARCH SERVICE

TABLE V-2. Wheat and Flour Price Relationships at
Minneapolis and Kansas City: 1948–1964

Crop year	Cost of wheat to produce 100 lb. flour (1)	Wholesale price of: Bakery flour per 100 lb. (2)	Millfeed obtained per 100 lb. (3)	Total products (flour + millfeed) Col. (2) + (3) (4)	Over cost of wheat (5)
		Minneapolis Spring Wheat			
1948	$5.41	$5.69	$0.80	$6.49	$1.08
1949	5.41	5.81	.75	6.56	1.15
1950	5.73	6.12	.85	6.97	1.24
1951	5.75	5.87	1.01	6.88	1.13
1952	5.72	5.74	.88	6.62	.90
1953	5.96	6.36	.79	7.15	1.19
1954	6.31	6.82	.72	7.54	1.23
1955	5.61	6.22	.68	6.90	1.29
1956	5.47	6.04	.70	6.74	1.27
1957	5.40	6.10	.57	6.67	1.27
1958	5.02	5.68	.64	6.32	1.30
1959	5.11	5.44	.61	6.05	.94
1960	4.92	5.36	.61	5.97	1.05
1961	5.43	5.70	.61	6.31	.88
1962	5.61	5.92	.68	6.60	.99
1963	5.20	5.52	.66	6.18	.98
1964	5.64	5.68	.70	6.38	.74
Average, 1948 to 1963	5.50	5.90	.72	6.62	1.12
		Kansas City Winter Wheat			
1948	$5.15	$5.24	$0.82	$6.06	$0.91
1949	5.13	5.36	.78	6.14	1.01
1950	5.38	5.59	.87	6.46	1.08
1951	5.66	5.64	.98	6.62	.96
1952	5.50	5.46	.93	6.39	.89
1953	5.52	5.93	.79	6.72	1.20
1954	5.87	6.14	.76	6.90	1.03
1955	5.34	5.73	.69	6.42	1.08
1956	5.29	5.68	.67	6.35	1.06
1957	5.18	5.64	.57	6.21	1.03
1958	4.81	5.14	.63	5.77	.96
1959	4.83	5.03	.60	5.63	.80
1960	4.77	5.04	.58	5.62	.85
1961	5.13	5.37	.58	5.95	.82
1962	5.47	5.65	.68	6.33	.86
1963	4.99	5.25	.67	5.92	.93
1964	5.33	5.41	.70	6.11	.78
Average, 1948 to 1963	5.25	5.49	.73	6.22	.97

NOTE: Col. (4) = col. (2) + col. (3); col. (5) = col. (4) − col. (1).
SOURCE: USDA, ERS.

give them a base for the relative value of their wheat and related flour and flour by-products. Of course the prices of wheat vary from one location to another as does the price of flour and the mill feed obtained as a by-product of the flour for the usual reasons of type of wheat, quality, transportation, storage, government price support differentials, and the complex demand factors present in the domestic and export wheat, flour, and millfeed markets.

Table V-2 shows the wheat and flour price relationships at Minneapolis and Kansas City from 1948–1949 to 1964–1965 for spring wheat and hard winter wheat respectively, which reflect in a summary fashion the varying price relationships of wheat and wheat products over 17 years.

The country or subterminal elevator, the terminal elevator, the local processor, the local exporter, and/or the government price support program are all sources of price quotations to the wheat producer. The boards of trade and terminal markets, through the cooperation of radio stations, and government market news programs, broadcast hourly changes of price at the local and terminal markets of Minneapolis, Chicago, and Kansas City.

To the wheat miller, wheat is a raw material to be converted into flour and millfeeds. Prices paid by the processor are related to his present and anticipated return from flour and millfeed. In the case of flour he has long term contracts on which to base his procurement of wheat, but he must take the risk of a fluctuating millfeed market which is tied to the poultry and livestock markets. The flour miller must also price his wheat in relation to his wheat inventory because his low unit cost of operations act as an incentive for the flour miller to buy enough wheat to keep his mill running at full capacity.

In general most flour millers when selling to their largest bakery customers do so on a negotiated basis. Price leaders in the past have been Campbell-Taggert Association Bakeries or Continental Baking Company and their prices have served as guides for negotiated prices between other firms. On the whole, smaller accounts are able to obtain lower prices from flour millers than such a firm as Continental Baking because they usually constitute an immediate cash sale and can take qualities of different types that may not fit into the formulas of continuous-mix bakeries. Day-to-day flour prices are strongly influenced by large day-to-day bakeries, such as Great Atlantic & Pacific Tea Company's operations.

Bread prices are also highly competitive with strong price cutting carried on by integrated private label manufacturers and retail food chain distributors.

The international markets for wheat and flour are heavily influenced by domestic policies. Many times millers have used foreign sales as low-priced "fill-in" sales and prices have sometimes been established on an out-of-pocket cost basis. Also the growing international demand for wheat has put price pressures on millers who are competing for that wheat with the exporter.

PRICE STABILITY

Price stability for the wheat portion of the wheat system has in large part occurred because of the Department of Agriculture's price support programs. The Commodity Credit Corporation's loan policies and disposal policies in the past established both a floor and a ceiling for most qualities of wheat at almost any location. The floor is usually set by the level of the loan price (or considerably below the loan price in years where there is a shortage of storage space and/or when the noncompliance by some producers makes them ineligible to use the loan). The ceiling price is established by the selling prices of the Commodity Credit Corporation which in 1966 was 108% [1] of the price support rate plus normal carrying charges or the "market," whichever was higher. From 1951 through 1964 the levels at which the government wheat programs "stabilized" *average* farm prices of wheat ranged from 17 cents per bushel below the loan rate in 1953 to an estimated 8 cents per bushel above the loan rate in the 1964 crop year (see Exhibit V-5). In the past, as long as government stocks of the quality, grade, and quantity needed were available to augment commercial supplies, the market price for wheat did not exceed the CCC formula price to any great extent. With an increased export market

[1] The grain trade in the past has requested that the selling price of the CCC be increased to 130% of the price support to provide more price flexibility. Department of Agriculture officials have said no because that would raise wheat prices to persons not complying with the program and would eventually mean a more restrictive and/or more costly government wheat program.

and a growing domestic market, however, wheat stocks have been reduced to a point where wheat prices are considerably above loan values. A more restricted P.L. 480 wheat shipment policy may be

EXHIBIT V-5

Government Price Support Operations for
Wheat: 1951–1964

Farm Price and Loan Rate

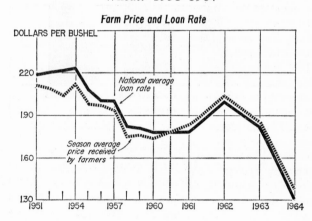

CCC Sales and Acquisitions

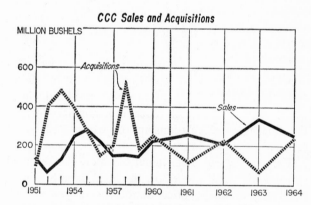

NOTE: Dotted line between 1960 and 1961 indicates approximate date when season average price received by farmers exceeded the national average loan rate. Please note that the years in the exhibit are *not* spaced evenly in order to emphasize the 1960–1964 sales of CCC inventories.

SOURCE: Testimony of the Honorable Secretary of Agriculture Orville L. Freeman on the Food and Agriculture Act of 1965 before the House Committee on Agriculture, April 6, 1965.

developed in order to maintain U.S. wheat reserves. Such a policy may permit more wheat to be available for the domestic market and keep wheat prices at present levels.

The potential authority given to the Secretary of Agriculture in the case of the domestic and international sales of government wheat stocks and their impact on wheat price levels together with the 1966 discussion on reserve grain policies, has caused a major concern to the participants of several segments of the wheat system as evidenced by the following cover article of the *Southwestern Miller*.

CZAR OVER PRICES, SUPPLIES?

Whether or not the present degree of freedom in markets for wheat and other grain under federal programs will be superseded by far more powerful domination depends on the outcome of a new bill, H.R. 12784, now before Congress. The bill, which proposes establishment and maintenance of reserves, leaves major decisions on accumulations and dispositions to the Secretary of Agriculture. The Secretary might thus become a czar over prices and supplies.

The National Grain Trade Council wisely recommends that the reserves should bear a fixed percentage relationship to total annual consumption and that private and commercial stocks be recognized as the most desirable and liquid source. Further it recommends clear stipulation of the conditions governing the holding of such reserves by the government and formulation of fixed and completely predictable obligations on the part of the government on acquisition and disposition, together with immediate disclosure of such activities at all times.[2]

Price rigidities undoubtedly have caused some poor allocations of resources, especially between wheat grades and qualities. On the other hand, without price supports a severe drop in the price of wheat would have occurred and the cost and hardship to the farming segment of the wheat economy might have resulted in a poorer allocation of both human and physical resources than that which occurred with price supports. In addition in the long run, the presence of

TABLE V-3. Commodity Credit Corporation Wheat Sales and Acquisitions: 1960–1965
(In millions of bushels)

Crop year	Total sales	Total acquisitions	Sales to Russia	Sales to India
1960	226	250	—	124
1961	255	113	—	93
1962	208	223	—	130
1963	342	67	64	163
1964	311	80	—	216
1965	379	7	—	262

SOURCE: Testimony of the Secretary of Agriculture before the House Committee on Agriculture, April 6, 1965, p. 18, and *Wheat Situation*, August 1961, p. 22; August 1962, p. 32; August 1963, p. 32; October 1965, pp. 26–27; October 1966, p. 27.

government stocks has improved the allocation of resources during times of unusual shortages, such as the Russian crop failure and famine in India (see Table V-3).

Even with domestic price rigidities, the wheat econ-

[2] *Southwestern Miller*, March 1, 1966, cover.

omy (as has been noted previously) has made many adjustments to changing wheat requirements. This suggests that it is possible to make adjustments with *small* variations in domestic wheat price levels.

World wheat prices have also been fairly stable until recently. A comparison between the prices received by United States wheat farmers and Canadian wheat farmers (No. 2 Northern Manitoba, the Canadian wheat price used by the International Wheat Agreement to indicate "world wheat prices") indicate fairly small year-to-year changes (see Table V-4).

TABLE V-4. Comparative Average Crop Year Cash Wheat Prices for U.S. and Canadian Wheat (Farm Level): 1951–1963
(In dollars per bushel)

Crop year	Received by U.S. farmers	Yearly change	% of yearly change	No. 2 Northern Manitobas, Winnipeg	Yearly change	% of yearly change
1951	$2.11	—	—	$2.28	—	—
1952	2.09	$−.02	−0.9%	2.21	$−.07	−3.1%
1953	2.04	−.05	−2.4	1.89	−.32	−14.5
1954	2.12	+.08	+3.9	1.72	−.17	−9.0
1955	1.99	−.13	−6.1	1.72	−0−	−0−
1956	1.97	−.02	−1.0	1.72	−0−	−0−
1957	1.93	−.04	−2.0	1.64	−.08	−4.6
1958	1.75	−.18	−9.3	1.68	+.04	+2.4
1959	1.76	+.01	+0.6	1.70	+.02	+1.2
1960	1.74	−.02	−1.1	1.65	−.05	−2.9
1961	1.83	+.09	+5.2	1.78	+.13	+7.9
1962	2.04	+.21	+11.5	1.82	+.04	+2.2
1963	1.87	−.17	−8.3	—	—	—

SOURCE: *Commodity Year Book*, 1964, p. 360.

The world wheat price has usually been substantially lower than the U.S. support level. During the week of January 25, 1965, the United States lowered its export wheat price 15 cents a bushel. The U.S. position was summed up in a news release by Secretary Freeman dated February 4, 1965, as follows:

U.S. wheat export price adjustments made last week reflect a drastically changed supply and demand picture from a few months ago.

The 1964 world wheat crop was a record and considerably higher than the 1963 crop. In contrast, current world wheat trade is estimated some 15% less than during the 1963–1964 year.

This imbalance between supply and demand has put tremendous pressure on world wheat prices. Other exporting countries with supplies considerably in excess of export demand have been offering wheat substantially below prices at which competing wheat from the United States could be purchased. As a result, the U.S. share of world commercial trade has been declining this year.

Current U.S. prices more fully reflect appropriate competitive relationships with wheat being offered by other exporting countries. The maintenance of this relationship should permit the United States to obtain a more equitable share of world commercial markets.

Importers have been anticipating adjustments in world price levels as the result of the exceedingly heavy supplies in exporting countries. These adjustments have now been made.

We see no reason for world wheat price levels to decrease further. The United States has always taken a leading role in working with exporting countries to maintain stable prices. We continue to have a major interest in promoting price stability, and will cooperate with other suppliers to attain that objective.

The implications of a more flexible world wheat price are such that this policy might cause some *reappraisals* of overseas operations of U.S. flour millers. For example, before Canada and the United States "pulled the plug" on international wheat prices, one president of a major flour milling concern expressed a belief that there would be more milling operations under joint sponsorship of U.S. firms and firms in developing nations, not only because of the nationalism that was evident in the developing countries, but also because the International Wheat Agreement, U.S. subsidy wheat payments, and the Canadian-American Agreement on price levels had tended to stabilize international wheat prices to a greater degree than domestic prices and had thus made price patterns less risky for overseas mill operations.[3]

The behavior and usefulness of the futures market pricing mechanism seem to have been considerably modified by government wheat programs in the past. Dr. Roger Gray has stated:

The loan program and the futures markets are, of course, competitive and basically incompatible mechanisms, each reflecting a different approach to price determination. In practice, they have not proven completely incompatible, although a substantial diminution in use of the wheat futures markets is attributable to the fact that the Commodity Credit Corporation owns most of the seasonal surplus, which is therefore not hedged in futures market.[4]

Gray also indicated that there is more seasonal variation in futures and cash prices for wheat with government programs. This is probably due to the heavy movement of wheat at harvest time (in some prior years farmers did not have access to storage facil-

[3] Interview with Norman Ness, President of International Milling Company.
[4] "The Seasonal Pattern of Wheat Futures Prices Under the Loan Program," p. 23.

TABLE V-5. Range of Monthly Average Prices of Wheat at Chicago, Kansas City, and Minneapolis: 1951–1962
(In dollars per bushel)

Crop year	Average	High	Low	Difference between high and low	Difference as % of crop-year average
No. 2 Yellow Hard Winter Wheat at Chicago					
1951	$2.48	$2.63	$2.33	$.30	12.1%
1952	2.29	2.39	2.05	.34	14.8
1953	2.09	2.32	1.91	.41	19.6
1954	2.25	2.40	2.11	.29	12.9
1955	2.13	2.38	1.97	.41	19.2
1956	2.26	2.43	2.09	.34	15.0
1957	2.18	2.28	1.95	.33	15.1
1958	1.97	2.13	1.84	.29	14.7
1959	2.09	2.21	1.94	.27	12.9
1960	2.02	2.14	1.88	.26	12.9
1961	2.09	2.21	1.98	.23	11.0
1962	2.17	2.22	1.98	.24	11.1
No. 2 Hard Winter Wheat at Kansas City					
1951	$2.43	$2.54	$2.32	$.24	9.9%
1952	2.32	2.46	2.25	.21	9.0
1953	2.27	2.45	2.09	.36	15.9
1954	2.37	2.53	2.19	.34	14.3
1955	2.18	2.33	2.10	.23	10.6
1956	2.21	2.36	2.09	.27	12.2
1957	2.15	2.27	1.90	.37	17.2
1958	1.94	2.09	1.84	.25	12.9
1959	2.00	2.12	1.94	.18	9.0
1960	1.94	2.05	1.89	.16	8.2
1961	2.05	2.19	1.98	.21	10.2
1962	2.25	2.37	2.03	.34	15.1
No. 1 Dark Northern Spring Wheat at Minneapolis					
1951	$2.51	$2.60	$2.44	$.16	6.4%
1952	2.51	2.56	2.45	.11	4.4
1953	2.58	2.67	2.44	.23	8.9
1954	2.71	2.76	2.58	.18	6.6
1955	2.50	2.62	2.43	.19	7.6
1956	2.42	2.50	2.37	.13	5.4
1957	2.41	2.47	2.36	.11	4.6
1958	2.25	2.43	2.17	.26	11.5
1959	2.26	2.30	2.24	.06	2.6
1960	2.18	2.29	2.12	.17	7.8
1961	2.43	2.50	2.30	.20	8.2
1962	2.48	2.53	2.41	.12	4.8

Source: *Commodity Year Book*, 1964, p. 360.

ities)[5] or movement of wheat that was not in storable condition. Eventually storage facilities became available and producers were in a better position to utilize the loan. Even though Gray's observations have valid-

[5] The increase in the use of harvesting machinery has resulted in shorter harvest periods in years when the price support has been in operation. This has created greater harvest bulges and more significant price declines when storage space has been limited.

ity, the crop-year price ranges in the three principal terminal markets for wheat (Minneapolis, Kansas City, and Chicago) and the crop-year price ranges in the largest wheat futures market (Chicago) indicate relatively minor price swings throughout a crop year (see Tables IV-5 and IV-6). These statistics also demonstrate that price ranges from year to year were also small. The year-to-year price adjustment revolves around the changes in the price support program.

TABLE V-6. Range of Highest and Lowest Prices of May Wheat Futures on the Chicago Board of Trade: 1951–1963
(In dollars per bushel)

Trading year June to May	*Range*		*Differential*	*Differential as % of lowest futures price*
1951	High	$2.60⅞	$.51	24.3%
	Low	2.09⅞		
1952	High	2.65½	.27½	11.6
	Low	2.38		
1953	High	2.49⅜	.38⅝	18.3
	Low	2.10¾		
1954	High	2.31¼	.44½	23.8
	Low	1.86¾		
1955	High	2.30¼	.29½	14.7
	Low	2.00¾		
1956	High	2.40¾	.52	27.5
	Low	1.88¾		
1957	High	2.44½	.36	17.3
	Low	2.08½		
1958	High	2.29⅜	.24⅝	12.0
	Low	2.04¾		
1959	High	2.12⅜	.29⅛	15.9
	Low	1.83¼		
1960	High	2.11	.18⅜	9.6
	Low	1.92⅝		
1961	High	2.15	.29⅞	16.2
	Low	1.85⅛		
1962	High	2.17	.16½	8.2
	Low	2.00½		
1963	High	2.28⅝	.28⅜	14.2
	Low	2.00¼		

SOURCE: *Commodity Year Book*, 1964, p. 359.

The prices for hard spring wheat that has a high percentage of protein (15% to 17%), as quoted on the Minneapolis market, have traditionally been above price support levels, and protein premiums are not hedgeable in futures market delivery descriptions. The prices of this higher protein wheat fluctuate a great deal indicating a "free market" above price support levels and no market control exercised by a relatively concentrated flour milling industry.[6] Domike's analysis of the price range of protein premiums at Minneapolis from 1947 to 1952 substantiates the nature of the fluctuation from a decrease of 5 cents a bushel to an increase of 6 cents a bushel for 12% protein; a decrease of 5 cents a bushel to an increase of 12 cents a bushel for 13% protein; and a range of a minus 10 cents to a plus 13 cents for 16% protein, all incurred in seven-day intervals. This writer's brief summary of 1963 variations in Minneapolis wheat proteins also verifies Domike's earlier work with fluctuations of from a minus 29 cents to a plus 4 cents for 16% protein during monthly intervals.

[6] Domike, *Procurement Strategies and Market Behavior of the Wheat Milling and Barley Malting Industries in the North Central Grain Market,* p. 154.

Flour prices. As noted previously in this study, flour prices follow the pattern of wheat price changes. Table V-7 indicates the small crop-year price ranges for flour at the Kansas City market.

TABLE V-7. Kansas City Flour Prices and Range of Monthly Average Wholesale Price of Wheat Flour:[a] 1951–1962
(In dollars per 100 lb. sack)[b]

Crop year	*Crop year average*	*High*	*Low*	*Difference between high and low*	*Difference as % of crop-year average*
1951	$5.64	$5.85	$5.33	$.52	9.8%
1952	5.47	5.68	5.15	.53	10.3
1953	5.94	6.15	5.28	.87	16.5
1954	6.15	6.33	6.00	.33	5.5
1955	5.74	6.03	5.60	.43	7.7
1956	5.61	5.79	5.43	.36	6.6
1957	5.64	5.80	5.35	.45	8.4
1958	5.12	5.47	4.85	.62	12.8
1959	5.03	5.17	4.82	.35	7.3
1960	5.04	5.09	4.98	.11	2.2
1961	5.37	5.68	5.22	.46	8.8
1962	5.65	5.93	5.23	.70	13.4

[a] Winter, hard, short patents.
[b] Beginning in January 1959 prices in bulk rather than in sacks as formerly.
SOURCE: U.S. Bureau of Labor Statistics.

Perhaps what is more important is how flour prices are determined in the absence of a "formalized" futures market for flour or its by-products.[7] Table V-8 shows a typical flour milling cost card somewhat expanded to make it self explanatory. The reader will note that it requires approximately 2.33 bushels[8] of wheat or 140 pounds of wheat to produce 100 pounds

[7] The futures market for the by-product of flour milling, "bran and midds," did exist in St. Louis in the early 1960s, but lack of participation made it an unsatisfactory market to utilize.
[8] One bushel equals 60 pounds.

TABLE V-8. Typical Flour Milling Cost Card

Mill **ANY**

Mix **A**

Date **March 31, 1964**

Mixture Cost	Lot no.	Formula % in mix	Prices	Cost	Pounds	Amount
	XM	75%	$2.34	$1.755		
	YM	25%	2.22	.555		
Mixture cost per bushel				$2.31		
Yield 2.33 bu. per cwt. (2 bu. + 20 lbs.)					140 lbs.	$5.39

Feed Credits Kind	lbs.	Value per ton	Amount		
Low grade (Red Dog)	4	$36.00	$.072		
Bran	18	35.00	.315		
Middlings	18	37.50	.338	40 lbs.	.73
				100 lbs.	$4.66

Material Cost of Straight Flour Clear Credits Kind	% of cwt.	Value per cwt.	Amount		
1st clear	15%	$3.90	$.585		
2nd clear	5%	3.15	.158	20 lbs.	.74
Material Cost of 80% Patent Flour				80 lbs.	$3.92
Cost per cwt.				100 lbs.	$4.90

Brand Grades Grade	Formula	Material cost	Production expense	Cost Bulk— f.o.b. Mill
A-1	100-0-0 (All Patent)	$4.90	$.50	$5.40
A-2	90-10-0 (90% Patent)			
	(10% 1st clear)	4.80	.50	5.30
A-3	80-15-5 (Straight flour)	4.66	.50	5.16
A-4	0-100-0 (100% 1st clear)	3.90	.50	4.40

NOTE: This mill requires a mixture of two types of wheat with an average cost of $2.31 a bushel (60 lbs.). It requires 140 lbs. of wheat to produce 100 lbs. of flour or 2 bushels and 20 lbs. Therefore, the wheat cost is $2.31 times 2.33 bushels, or $5.39 for 140 lbs.

Against this charge of $5.39 is the value of the by-products (Red Dog, bran, and midds) or 73 cents for 40 lbs. of this product.

Twenty pounds of the "first flour" removed in the sifting process has a slightly reduced value which is also subtracted from the $5.39 (the original cost of the wheat). The 80 lbs. of "patent" flour (first and second clears removed) has a residual value of $3.92. On a 100-lb. basis this is equivalent to $4.90 per cwt. By using different grade mixtures of flour, various varying material costs result (e.g., $3.90 to $4.90 per cwt. of flour). In this typical flour milling cost card production expense is estimated to be 50 cents per cwt. which is added to the various material costs to arrive at the bulk cost of flour of differing qualities f.o.b. the mill.

SOURCE: Private firm.

of flour. In this instance, 40 pounds of the 140 end up as by-products utilized in the mixed feed business; the other 100 pounds represent different qualities of flour. It may be seen from Table V-8 that by knowing the market price of Red Dog, bran, middlings, and various grades of flour in comparison to wheat prices one can assign the resulting residual cost to patent flour. Cash market prices for feed ingredients and flour qualities are published daily in trade publications. The baker has access to the same price information that determines the spread between wheat and flour and its by-products as does the miller. Most bakers use this information in arriving at an offering price for their flour. According to one report reflecting trade views, it is generally recognized that the bakery division of one major food chain is the day-to-day cash market barometer for flour prices.[9] The conversion or processing factor to process wheat into flour in essence becomes the bargaining point. According to one executive in the milling business, this firm in the past allegedly used a 65-cent processing margin as a formula for its price bids. Each year it has lowered *"its"* estimate" of the conversion factor until in 1966 it is approximately 60 cents per hundredweight.

The approximate production cost to run a "typical" flour mill is 40 to 50 cents per hundredweight made up of 28 cents of variable costs and the remainder of taxes and depreciation.[10] In the National Commission on Food Marketing survey costs for milling durum were 44 cents per hundredweight, 53 cents for soft wheat and 52 cents for hard wheat.[11]

The price pressure that is placed on the flour miller by the baker is, in turn, placed on the baker by the retailer and the food chain baker.

PROFITABILITY

As mentioned previously, there is really no separately definable wheat economy except in a theoretical sense. Practically every participant in the wheat economy is diversified into other agribusiness or nonagribusiness industries; i.e., other grains or crops, other services, or other sources of profit or loss. Therefore, the profitability of various segments and firms in the wheat economy must be arbitrarily extracted from integrated operations.

Farmers. If one uses input-output data obtained from the Department of Commerce and the Department of Agriculture and released in November 1964, one can obtain various statistics relative to the production and income aspects of the U.S. farmers' wheat crop for the year 1958. In that year gross wheat income for U.S. farmers was $2,331 million (includ-

[9] Interview with flour milling official, May 25, 1964.

[10] Cost figures for selected milling firms obtained by author.

[11] *Organization and Competition in the Milling and Baking Industries,* June 1966, p. 31.

ing government payments for wheat). Subtracting a variety of cost items of $1,531 million allocated to wheat production (a few of the major ones are set forth in Table V-9), the net income to farmers before

TABLE V-9. Major Expense Items in the Production of Wheat in the United States: 1958

Expense item	Millions of dollars
Petroleum products	$171.9
Farm machinery	31.1
Farm chemicals	80.7
Pesticides	19.5
Real estate lessors, agri. facilities	358.9
Federal, state, local government expenses	98.2
Interest	58.7
Repair shops and related services	81.5
General building contractors	44.4
Depreciation	350.0
Other	236.1
Total	$1,531.0

SOURCE: USDA, ERS.

taxes in 1958 was estimated to be approximately $800 million.[12]

If one adds depreciation of $350 million to the income before taxes of $800 million, then wheat farmers had a cash flow of $1,150 million on a crop of 1,457 million bushels or over 75 cents a bushel *with the aid of government price supports.* Without the aid of government price supports (the value of which were estimated to be $700 million[13]), then the cash flow would have been $450 million or only 31 cents a bushel. In the past, therefore, the wheat farmers' cash flow and income were especially dependent upon government price support program. This close relationship between the government price support and cash receipts from wheat is further demonstrated by Exhibit V-6.

The change in the world wheat markets has made the wheat farmer less dependent on government price supports, but nevertheless he required $1.32 a bushel cash subsidy on 45% of his production in 1966 in order to maintain fairly minimum returns on the wheat portion of his farming enterprise.

The economies of large scale farming also affect the income potential and vulnerability of the wheat farmer. Typical of the many economy-of-scale studies was that conducted by the Wyoming Agricultural Experi-

[12] Inevitably such a figure requires many arbitrary allocations which make it subject to criticism as a precise income figure. However, an examination of assorted income and cost data from other sources makes this figure seem reasonable as an order of magnitude of farm net income from wheat.

[13] Wilcox, *Farm Programs and Dynamic Forces in Agriculture*, p. 21.

EXHIBIT V-6

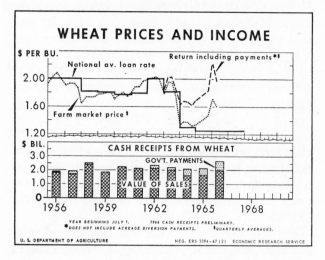

ment Station for 1959. Table V-10 indicates the declining per acre cost of producing wheat on farms of increasing size from $16.39 per acre for a 120-acre farm to $8.10 per acre for a 2,000-acre farm. Such

TABLE V-10. Per Acre Costs[a] of Wheat Farms in Southeast Wyoming by Size of Farm, including Fallow Costs: 1959

Total crop (acres)	Wheat-Fallow[b] (per planted acre of wheat)
120	$16.39
280	12.60
420	11.68
680	10.90
1,100	9.42
2,000	8.10

[a] Does not include costs of labor and management and costs of owning land.

[b] These farms were not necessarily farmed in exactly the same manner or did not produce the same per-acre yield.

SOURCE: Wyoming Agricultural Experiment Station, *Wheat Programs—Their Effects on Income*, March 1961, p. 5.

economic incentives to increase farm size still exist and are reinforced by the desires of wheat farmers to obtain reasonable standards of living. For example, a study by the Farm Production Division of the Economic Research Service indicates that for a wheat farmer to have received an annual income of $2,500 in 1959 a sales volume of from $14,000 to $26,000 would have been required.[14] To have obtained an annual income of $5,000 in the same year, a sales volume of from $20,000 to $62,000 would have been required.

A significant by-product of these economic pres-

[14] USDA, ERS, *Resource Requirements on Farms for Specified Operator Incomes*, pp. 6, 8, 9, and 10.

sures to increase size is that the wheat farmer, as he increases the size of his operation, becomes even more vulnerable to any change in the government price support programs, simply because the government pays a bigger part of his cash income, while his own expansion expenses are mostly frozen capital outlays.[15] (This statement is not true if one assumes government payments increase faster than the producer's out-of-pocket expenses. On the other hand, large capital investments in increased acreage are required for efficient farm operations. The dollar value of these additional acres is based on the price support values of wheat and, therefore, a dramatic change in price supports downward would result in major investment losses.)

Sixty-eight percent of the total number of nonrecourse government price support wheat loans in 1962 were made to producers who had loans of less than $3,000 in value. However, a large percentage (67% in 1962) of the *total dollar value* of these loans were issued to farmers having government price support wheat loans with values of $3,000 to over $50,000 on their wheat crops, according to USDA figures. In other words, price support wheat payments follow the pattern of wheat production — the operators with the larger more productive farms received the majority of the payments. Over two-thirds of the dollar value of all farm price support loans on wheat were issued to less than one-third of the number of farmers receiving such loans. The average size of loan to these larger farmers was over $6,000. The average size of loan to the more numerous but smaller farmers was $1,400.

The benefits derived from the government price support program tend to be capitalized into land values. Thereupon a vicious circle begins. As land values increase, return on "investment" decreases and land values can be maintained only if income from wheat or alternative crops is maintained. The wheat farmer looks upon the increase in the value of his land

as another potential source of income. The larger his farm holdings the more concerned he is about any change in farm programs. Table V-11 gives the wide range of increases in average value per acre of farm land in the principal wheat-producing states.

TABLE V-11. Changes in Average Value per Acre and Total Value of Farm Land and Buildings, Principal Wheat Producing States: 1960–1964

State	Average value per acre			Value per farm, 1964
	1960	1964	% change 1960–1964	
North Dakota	$53	$63	18.8%	$52,400
Kansas	101	114	12.9	61,000
Nebraska	90	104	15.6	61,100
Montana	35	42	20.0	97,900
Washington	133	145	9.0	57,800
Oklahoma	86	109	25.7	49,800
Total U.S. (48 states)	$116	$137	18.1%	$47,950

Source: USDA, ERS, *Farm Real Estate Market Developments*, October 1964.

In analyzing the income data for "typical" wheat farmers in the United States, if one ascribes any reasonable cost of labor to the manager of the farm, then return on investment seems low (from 1% to a high of 6%) even with government aid. If one assumes a 5% return on farm investments, however, then farm "wages" would be considerably less than the average urban worker's. The conclusion one reaches is that without government aid the wheat farmer would be in serious financial difficulty or at least his land values, and hence his net worth would decline. But with government aid (and in some areas where the crop is limited to wheat, possibly without) the price level of wheat has been so attractive, compared with other practical crop alternatives, that wheat farmers have developed or maintained a wheat capacity far in excess of that needed to satisfy the nongovernment wheat market in the past. For the immediate present (1966–67), demands for wheat commercially and in the concessional markets are so great that all the diversion acres have been put back into use and a portion of the acreage control land. How much land to "free up" for wheat is a major problem in a constantly changing world market.

The farmer's income problems, as summarized above, are these: (1) heavy dependence on government programs, especially when one compares wheat farm income with the estimated dollar contributions from government wheat programs; (2) the economies of scale and the urge to improve gross income increases the size of wheat farms and adds to the de-

---

[15] This point was emphasized by Dr. George L. Mehren, Assistant Secretary of Agriculture, at the Ninth Federal Reserve District Farm Forum, sponsored by the Minneapolis Chamber of Commerce, March 8, 1965. He stated: "Take an extreme case, the specialized cash grain farm with gross sales of over $40,000. In the past three years, with price supports and acreage diversion in effect, these farms had net receipts averaging over $10,000 a year. Without these programs, and with prices dropping to world levels, the average specialized farm would have lost more than $10,000 a year instead of netting $10,000.

"In contrast, commercial farms with sales ranging from $5,000 to $39,000 had net receipts averaging about $5,700 over the past three years. Without the support programs, many of these farms would have suffered net losses . . . but net income for the *average* farm would still have been $3,000."

pendence of the farmer on the government; and (3) the changes in world and domestic wheat demands have permitted new long range agriculture programs to be established that give the farmer much more freedom in his production alternatives and enlarge the market for the sales of the ultimate wheat products. The nagging question facing the Department of Agriculture is how to "unfreeze" wheat production acres in the "right proportion" to satisfy domestic and world needs, provide realistic wheat reserves, and provide incomes to encourage flexible farm production in the wheat system.

As the government wheat program becomes more permissive and allows farm resources more mobility, better utilization of these agricultural resources may be expected. The problem is that the potential domestic and export market in the near term may not expand as much as production increases, and "free market" prices may fall to government loan values or slightly below.[16] In summary, the wheat farmer welcomes greater freedom and is willing to produce wheat of the type and quality demanded by domestic and foreign consumers, but he feels that he cannot afford to let go of his dependence on the government for income support and for the development of subsidized wheat export sales.

On the other hand, government policy makers now recognize that it is unrealistic to expect to turn "excess production capacity into higher farm incomes, lower government program costs, lower food prices and less production control." [17] Dr. Cochrane, former Director of Agricultural Economics in the U.S. Department of Agriculture stated: "Frankly, I find those multiple objectives impossible of simultaneous achievement." [18] The compromise that was suggested in April 1965 in the wheat economy between the income needs of the producer and the budgetary requirements of the taxpayer and consumer involved a small increase in prices on consumer wheat products,[19] the maintenance of current gross income levels for wheat production, and a partial shift in program costs from the taxpayer to the consumer. The producer, because of crop rotation policies and capital investment problems, prefers a five-year program rather than the present two-year program. The U.S. Bureau of the Budget prefers one-year programs to give government administrators maximum fiscal flexibility. On the other hand, the Bureau could still maintain its year to year budget program under a four-year agricultural authorization. Irrespective of the time requirements of programs, it would seem that *both* major political parties advocate *less* government participation in the wheat economy at all levels.[20] Therefore, the producer is currently being encouraged to change his structure and improve his market position with less reliance on the government and the maintenance of a simpler control structure. Most of this encouragement has taken the form of increased aid to the farmers' purchasing and marketing cooperatives.[21]

The wheat producer is also aware of the present political environment and is quite concerned about his future. He is anxious to take advantage of the increasing size of his enterprise by building storage facilities on his farm and shipping directly to country subterminal or processing and/or export markets. But as he expands his business enterprise to become more efficient, he does not want to lose the government support which has enabled him to improve his economic and operational position. The wheat grower of the future may be one who is more concerned with ultimate wheat product requirements of domestic and export consumers and less concerned with the non-recourse loan price support activities of the government. His major public policy problem will be how to shift from a government to a private market structure without losing the operational and income benefits of the government wheat program. Furthermore, as stated above, his technological success may be indeed a mixed blessing as he increases production and improves technology in the face of an inelastic demand.[22]

[16] Production increases for wheat based on projected increases in demand made by Dr. Rex F. Daly of the Department of Agriculture in 1964 indicated a 33% increase over 1962–1963 levels for 1970 and a 42% increase over 1962–1963 levels for 1980. Both of these increases could be met by the current rate of improvement in wheat production and/or the utilization of idle wheat resources. Even so, many flour millers in the United States are quite concerned about any major decrease in wheat stocks.

[17] Cochrane, "Some Observations of an Ex-Economic Advisor; or What I Learned in Washington," p. 15.

[18] *Ibid.*

[19] From 21 cents to 21.5 cents on a one-pound loaf of bread.

[20] A more detailed analysis of government programs is presented in Section V of this study, pp. 181–213.

[21] Statement by Secretary Freeman.

[22] Boulding, *Economic Analysis,* p. 778, Comments on "Unprofitability of Industries Faced with Inelastic Demands":
"Some interesting corollaries follow from these propositions. The first is that in a progressive society industries whose commodities suffer from an inelastic demand always tend to be relatively unprofitable, and technical progress in these industries if anything accentuates this unprofitability. In a progressive society the proportion of resources employed in such industries continually undergoes a relative decline. The way in which society brings about such a relative decline, however, is by making the unfortunate industry relatively unprofitable and so squeezing resources out of it. The case of agriculture is an important example of this tendency. Agriculture is chronically unprofitable in a progressive society. Even though the past two centuries have seen an enormous

The wheat farmer of the future will require some voluntary or mandatory acreage or production controls to help him maintain some overall production and supply balance during the short run as world imbalances change from year to year. Government programs that allow the farmer maximum freedom in selecting overall crop production programs (such as the current wheat and feed grain programs) and allow the market place and market price to allocate resources to a greater degree (such as the current government loan price of wheat in relation to feed grains) will have to have lowered support levels or more stringent production controls as the cost of these programs and/or the excess production they bring forth become increasingly large. The danger to the efficient wheat producer is that the wheat programs may become selective and a limit may be placed on his support compared with his smaller, less efficient competitor. This would indeed be economically harmful to the efficient performance of the overall wheat economy and especially disastrous to the larger wheat farmers who are so vulnerable to any great change in the level of wheat price support.

As previously stated, the government has encouraged wheat producers (and farmers in general) to make more use of their cooperatives in order to promote profit opportunities. This encouragement has taken the form of various favorable tax interpretations, antitrust exemptions, and farm cooperative managerial services.[23] As farmers have increased the size of their farm operations, they have tried to improve their buying and marketing power by expanding farmer cooperative activities. By doing so, they are diversifying their investments into farm procurement and farm marketing operations. Patronage dividends earned by farm cooperative members boost the income levels of participating wheat farmers by approximately $86 million[24] annually.

Approximately 20% of all industrial farm purchases (including wheat farm purchases) are made through farmer cooperatives. With 20% of the farmers' inputs obtained through farm cooperative supply firms, and 40% of the wheat farmers' output merchandised through farm cooperative elevators, the investment in off-farm facilities is fairly high. Thus far, the investments by wheat farmers in their cooperatives as measured by cash savings vs. savings retained by the cooperatives, in general have produced greater returns per dollar of investment than those obtained from farming.[25] The use of the cooperative form of enterprise has increased rapidly in the wheat economy. There is no reason to assume that this trend will not continue in the future. The independent wheat producer will continue to make greater use of his own cooperative enterprises unless competitive elements improve their marketing and supply firms that will serve the wheat producer better.

Country Elevator Operators. Even though the country elevator segment of the wheat economy has many diversified functions, it is almost as dependent on government wheat price support programs as is the farmer. During the investigation of the Commodity

TABLE V-12. Distribution of Revenue by Function of Country Elevators: 1960

Source of funds	% of revenue
Storage (practically all financed by the government)	30.1%
Handling (partially financed by the government)	9.4
Merchandising	21.7
Processing	21.0
Custom services	3.9
Other (farm supplies)	13.9

SOURCE: U.S. Senate, *Investigation of the Commodity Credit Corporation, Part III,* "Price Support and Storage Activities," p. 1093.

Credit Corporation storage activities in 1960, a commercial grain storage survey was conducted with the results shown in Table V-12.

From this table it may be seen that approximately

expansion of agriculture, the increase in other industries has been much more marked; the very fact of the 'drift to the towns' proves that agriculture has been less profitable, broadly than industrial occupations. Moreover, technical improvements in agriculture, although they benefit those who introduce them first, do not ultimately have the effect of making agriculture more profitable. They may even have the opposite effect, for by hastening the rate of progress they bring about a still greater pressure to force resources out of agriculture. This pressure is exercised through the price system; technical progress in agriculture brings about an increase in production. Then because of the inelastic demand for agricultural products, their prices are forced down until many of those who were previously engaged in agriculture are forced out of it. The forcing-out process may take a long time, and meanwhile the industry may be quite generally unprofitable, even for the innovators. Moreover, by the time equilibrium would have been reached and agriculture restored to normal profitability again, new technical improvements may start the process all over. In eras of rapid technical change, therefore, agriculture may be continuously unprofitable."

[23] See Section V of this study for a more detailed analysis of farm cooperatives.

[24] Estimated as 50% of total savings of 448 regional *grain* marketing cooperatives. The estimated net worth of the investment in wheat marketing facilities is $388 million. Does not include savings of local wheat cooperatives.
Unpublished nationwide finance study, USDA, Farmer Cooperative Service, March 9, 1965.

[25] A large portion of these savings earned by the producer are re-invested by the cooperative to improve and expand their marketing and procurement facilities.

30% of all country elevator revenue in 1960 was primarily dependent on government storage operations.[26] Because the government pays the country elevator operator for handling and storing government wheat, the elevator operator has had less of his own or borrowed capital tied up in grain inventories. When the government reduced the rate of wheat storage payments by 19% in 1960, a major source of the elevator operator's income was adversely affected. The recent decline in government wheat stocks has also reduced the income levels of some country elevator operators. In addition, as government wheat stocks decline, country elevator operators will require additional investment to handle the free stocks of wheat that will move through their elevators.

The country elevator operator's dependence on government wheat storage programs for a profit becomes even clearer if one analyzes wheat storage payments. In 1963, approximately $140 million was paid by the government for off-farm wheat storage. Of this $140 million, the author estimates $65 million was earned by country elevator operators. During that same crop year, country elevator operators handled approximately 900 million bushels of wheat on an average 3 cents a bushel margin or $27 million gross revenue.[27] If one compares the handling or merchandising wheat revenue of $27 million with the estimated gross government wheat storage revenue of $65 million, the dominant government position is self-evident. Just as a public commission sets rates for a public utility, so does the government set storage rates for government grain. Periodically the government reviews these rates with the industry. The last review was in 1960 and rates were cut 19%. The lowered rates and the decline in government wheat stocks have decreased off-farm wheat storage payments from $185 million in 1960 to $140 million in 1963.

Not only is the country elevator operator extremely dependent on wheat storage payments, but he is also dependent on the government for the timing and volume of wheat moving into and out of his facilities. The country elevator operator, therefore, is in con-

stant contact with the Department of Agriculture through the regional, state and local agricultural stabilization committees.

In May 1965 the government announced a 1-cent a bushel decrease on all grain stored by any firm after July 1, 1964. Grain to be stored for short periods of time would not have a reduction in storage rates. The grain trade maintained that increasing costs and lower grain inventory occupancy levels should have resulted in the raising of storage rates. The government, on the other hand, was trying to reduce the costs of price support programs by reducing not only the inventories of government grain but the grain storage rates as well.

Because 40% of the country elevator handling of wheat is by farm cooperative country elevators, the wheat storage gross income of these country elevators (approximately $26 million) could be considered as eventually directly benefiting the wheat farmer stockholders of these cooperatives. Both the cooperative and its wheat farmer members are anxious not to see any further deterioration in the gross revenue level of the government wheat storage operation that is such an important revenue factor in country elevator wheat operations.

Furthermore, to compete for the storage of the producer's grain, many elevator operators have cut handling margins on cash grain, thereby offsetting storage income by a decrease in wheat handling income. The judgment to maintain government storage inventories of wheat, to have wheat shipped out at harvest, and to replace that wheat with new government storage is not a decision that the country elevator operator makes. He may make requests of the Commodity Credit Corporation, but the government is the final decision maker. Furthermore, an administrative ruling effective in 1966 permits the CCC to sell the country elevator's government wheat stocks to a third party without giving the country elevator operator first opportunity to purchase this grain. This ruling permits greater market flexibility for the CCC but shuts the door on a previous opportunity of the country elevator operator.

The country elevator operator increased the size of his operations in order to serve his farm suppliers and his processing customers in a more efficient manner. Margins on grain handling are small and storage revenues are constantly decreasing. Many country elevator operators have attempted to take advantage of more direct shipments from country positions to processing and export firms and, at the same time, to find a way to overcome the difficulties of small-scale operations by constructing country subterminals. These country subterminals handle large grain volumes at small mar-

[26] There is some country elevator grain storage paid for directly or indirectly by farmers, but the overwhelming percentage is government storage paid for by the government. This is true because of the large government stocks built up in the past under high government price supports. If there is a minimum reserve program presumably the storage of the reserve will be paid for by the government. The reserve stocks will probably continue to be higher than the commercial wheat stocks that may be financed by the farmer, elevator man, or miller.

[27] The 900 million bushels of wheat moving through country elevators is not all free market wheat, and to this extent the $27 million gross revenue from wheat handling is overstated.

gins yet provide enough income to attract top management. In addition, to provide more flexible market opportunities for their grain operations, many operators have developed "feeder" country elevators that may divert shipments to integrated country terminal elevators rather than shipping to terminal market positions during times of technical surpluses and unusual price declines. This change in the size of country elevator operations means additional investments of capital and management.

The growth of farmer-owned country elevators has been indicative of the favorable competitive position of these types of firms. The opportunity of retaining and using nontaxed "savings" to expand storage and handling operations at a time when such facilities were most needed by the wheat economy and at a time when economic incentives were provided by the government (guaranteed occupancies, rapid depreciation) are factors that partially explain the growth of cooperative country elevators at the expense of noncooperative firms. In addition, the normal preference for many farmers to do business with their own marketing agencies forces severe price and service competition among the noncooperative country elevator operators and results in low levels of profitability.

Other forms of vertical integration (common ownership) by integrated processing and export firms have been noted earlier. Because many of these firms look upon their country elevator operations as supply sources[28] rather than *profit centers,* these firms force down the profitability of the nonintegrated country elevator operators. Furthermore, such vertical integration can permit a wheat processor or exporter to utilize his country elevator facilities more efficiently and at higher rates of capacity than the nonintegrated country elevator operator.

The increasing size of country elevators, the development of country subterminals, and the vertical integration of farmer cooperatives, processors, and exporters have led the nonintegrated country elevator to develop contractual marketing arrangements with many processors and exporters for round-lot shipments of a uniform quality of wheat and other grains. These contractual arrangements have made it possible for the more progressive country elevators to survive as a coordinated but nonintegrated part of the wheat economy. Those country elevators that have not adjusted to the changes of the wheat economy have gone out of business or have been taken over by other firms in the wheat economy.

Another threat to the profitability of country elevator operations is their by-passing by some large

[28] Interviews with export and flour milling executives.

farmers who may truck their wheat directly to export or processing terminal or subterminal facilities.

Most country elevator operators believe that they can be efficient enough, have access to a sufficient number of broad market outlets, and provide a wide enough range of market and sales services to their farm suppliers and processing and export customers to maintain a profitable enterprise. Competition has been severe and gross margins on grain handling have gone down over the last decade (from a level of 5 cents to 3 cents a bushel of wheat), a decrease partially offset by wheat storage income. If there is a drastic change in the rates or levels of wheat storage, then country elevator operators will have to offset this loss by increasing the handling margins on wheat and other grains.

The country elevator operator, as the main link between the wheat producer and his processing and export markets, may be able to improve his profit position in the following ways:

(1) As wheat stocks are reduced and more "free grain" is available, both the wheat processor and the exporter will be more anxious to reach back in the vertical market structure to obtain their supplies. Now they can "call up" the Commodity Credit Corporation and "order" several million bushels by phone. In the future, buyers will have to deal with a great variety of country elevator sources for their wheat. The opportunity will be present for country elevator operators either to act as independent agents of these processors and exporters or to merge with them.

(2) The country elevator operator may bring the wheat producer closer to his market by by-passing terminal markets. The development of the country subterminal has simultaneously led to the "destruction" of small inefficient country elevators and out-of-position terminal elevators. The country subterminal is emerging as the most important and profitable assembling center of wheat.

(3) Although some large wheat producers by-pass country elevators and ship directly to processors and explorers, country elevator operators have maintained their position as vital organisms in the wheat market structure by constantly searching out a variety of markets and tailor-making their wheat shipments to meet their customers' needs.

(4) The government, in order to have its stocks in the most flexible position for both national defense and for economic reasons prefers to have them held on the farm or as close to the farm as possible, e.g., country elevators. Such a policy would indicate that country elevator operators will be in a favored position for being not only chief wheat merchandiser but chief

wheat warehouseman for the government as well. This is in contrast to a substantial storage of wheat at terminal positions in April 1965.

(5) Because most country elevator managers became used to rising grain prices after World War II and then had the government price support program to maintain price stability, they did not make maximum use of the wheat futures markets. With the exception of the processing, export, and cooperative integrated firms, most managers are not properly trained in "basis" hedging. The declining role of the government should force many operators to make greater use of this important business tool.

(6) The decline in the role of the commission merchant in the wheat economy means that country elevator managers do not have "interpreters of the wheat economy" available to them. They therefore, like the producer, must be oriented to the dynamics of the total wheat economy if they are to maximize their profit potential.

(7) The competition among country elevator operators is intense. The tax advantage of farm cooperative operators and the market advantage of processor and export integrated firms leaves only the ability to be flexible and anticipate changes in the wheat economy as an offsetting advantage to the independent country elevator operator.

(8) The country elevator operator is not only the main market for the producer's wheat, but is one of the principal suppliers of purchased inputs, such as fertilizers, pesticides, and seed. He is in an excellent position to provide information and supplies that will enable his producer customers to produce a crop of quality and quantity.

(9) Finally and most important of all, the government, as a full-time partner of the country elevator operator, has carried out its functions by giving the country elevator operator major directives but has placed maximum reliance on the individual decision-making activities of the elevator operator and other managers in the wheat economy. The government has done this by encouraging the private grain trade to request times of movement for wheat and other grains and the government has tried to honor as many of these requests as possible, consistent with overall policy.

Contrary to many public statements, the grain trade does not want the government out of business; what it really wants is the government in the grain trade *at its* (the grain trade's) *convenience.* It is true that the government has made many mistakes, e.g., unrealistic grade changes, inappropriate price differentials between grades and geographic locations, some

minor favoritism to different groups at local administrative levels, and a nonconsistent government program for any length of time. In spite of these minor faults, the government program did finance an important expansion in grain storing and merchandising country elevator facilities. The Uniform Storage Agreement did improve the cleanliness, bookkeeping procedures, and grain-handling techniques of the country elevator operator. Having accomplished these major improvements (primarily as a by-product of maintaining the producer's wheat income) the government now is attempting to withdraw slowly from country elevator operations. Actually complete withdrawal will probably never become a reality because of the need of emergency food stocks somewhere in the world. What the country elevator operator wants is a government program that does not change radically in format from year to year and some consistent policy as to the use and nonuse of government wheat stocks. With such specific guidelines, the country elevator operator will not be preoccupied with government programs as such and will invest in facilities and operations that are flexible enough to meet the changing demands of the wheat economy.

Terminal Elevator Operators. The exact same profitability pressures that exist for country elevator operators also exist for terminal elevator operators. In addition, the change in transportation media (from rail to barge and truck) has destroyed the profitable use of some terminal elevators. In a recent unpublished doctoral thesis on the northeastern grain economy,[29] the abandonment of several of these terminal elevators was noted. Furthermore, the development of country subterminals (having many of the same attributes of a terminal elevator) and the movement of grain directly from these subterminals to port or processing facilities have also hastened the decline in the value of certain terminal elevators.

The commercial grain storage survey mentioned previously indicated that terminal elevator operators are even more dependent on government storage operations than country elevator operators. Table V-13 shows that slightly over *half* of all revenue earned in 1960 by terminal elevator operators was derived primarily from grain storage operations.

As government wheat stocks declined and when government storage rates were lowered some 19% in 1960, the terminal elevator operators were faced with declining wheat storage revenues. The decline in all off-farm wheat storage payments was from $185 mil-

[29] Heid, "The Changing Structure and Performance of the Northeastern Markets for Grain."

TABLE V-13. Distribution of Revenue by Function of Terminal Grain Elevators: 1960

Source of income	*% of total*
Storage (practically all financed by the government)	50.4%
Handling (partially financed by the government)	9.8
Merchandising	21.9
Processing	15.0
Customer services	0.7
Other	2.2

SOURCE: U.S. Senate, *Hearings on Investigation of the Commodity Credit Corporation: Part III*, "Price Support and Storage Activities," p. 1093.

lion in 1960 to $140 million in 1963. The author's estimates of the terminal elevator's portion of the total storage payments is $111 million in 1960 and $75 million in 1963.

The country elevator operator has many operations that may offset a portion of his loss in wheat storage income (e.g., fertilizers, feeds, and chemicals). A terminal elevator, on the other hand, is more of a one-purpose grain handling and storage operation and therefore more vulnerable to any change in government wheat storage programs.

The government wheat storage program encouraged many terminal elevator operators to become merely custodians of government wheat stocks. Those terminal elevator operators who recognized the presence of the nongovernment market opportunities of the domestic and international wheat economy as well as the storage activities are now the most profitable, and seem to be in the best position geographically and administratively to meet the new challenges of a changing wheat economy.

Exporters. There are about 20 firms regularly engaged in the export of U.S. grain. The delicacy of international negotiations, the split-second risk decisions, and the impeccable reputation of the principals are all factors that account for the type of firms that handle an overwhelming percentage of U.S. exports. Four of the 20 major export firms handle up to 90% of the export volume. In order of dollar sales volume they are Cargill, Continental, Bunge, and Dreyfus. These firms are all owned by single families, have been in business for over 100 years, and are fiercely competitive. It is rare that at any one specific moment in time will an export sale be made at full replacement cost. This does not mean that export firms habitually take a loss, but rather a profit is made on other aspects of the business, such as transportation, financial arbitrage, and domestic grain handling.

Each of the four major export firms has a unique competitive advantage. Cargill, for example, has invested in country and terminal elevators, trucks, barges, and seaboard loading facilities and can usually deliver grain at a somewhat lower cost to port locations than can firms without interior facilities.[30] In 1967 most export grain is sold delivered to the export port (f.o.b.). Hence, an export firm such as Cargill with excellent domestic grain handling facilities may earn a profit on the export grain as it moves from country elevator to port facility.

Other export firms such as Dreyfus, Bunge, and Continental which had their origins in the original surplus and deficit areas of Europe, have other advantages. They have concentrated on supplying grain to importing millers and processors that have been their customers for a century. Cargill may have a domestic procurement advantage, but the three other major firms probably operate more economically in those countries receiving the grain. Typical of the growth of these export firms that have expanded with U.S. export activity is Continental Grain. In 1926 it had 13 employees and sales of $5 million. In 1965–1966 it had 2,000 employees in the United States and sales were $1.3 billion.

Each of the export firms has had important advantages in owning (or not owning) shipping lines or in having unique banking arrangements and the ability to conduct arbitrage among many forms of currencies. The exporter may not make money on the grain that he handles as such, but he more than offsets this by freight or financing that is profitable enough to overcome any grain handling loss. Cargill and other international firms that own facilities in the United States also have the advantage of making money on the domestic movement of the grain even if the export grain movement breaks even, or results in a "commodity loss."

The four firms that dominate the export industry have estimated dollar sales (that obviously vary from year to year) as follows:

Firm	Millions
Cargill	$1,250
Continental	1,100
Bunge	1,000
Dreyfus	750

In terms of commodities handled:

Firm	Wheat	Corn	Soybeans	Misc.
Cargill	40%	30%	15%	15%
Continental	40	30	20	10
Dreyfus	40	25	20	15
Bunge	35	30	20	15

Typically these export firms have a net worth from

[30] Interview with Wallace W. Hyde, Cargill Export Representative, New York City, March 12, 1964.

$40 million to $60 million and average a return on investment of from 5% to 15% after taxes.[31] On a sales volume of over $1 billion, and average earnings of $5 million, the earnings stated as a percent of sales are approximately 0.5% after taxes.

A typical export company uses loans to leverage both its inventory and its fixed asset investments. The importance of hedging institutions such as the futures market is all important to the banking community responsible for lending export firms huge sums of money to handle the billion dollar sales volumes indicated above.

The profitability of export firms is also very dependent on government programs. The growth of government wheat export programs has enabled these export firms to participate in wheat sales to the developing countries (concessional market). The government storage program for wheat (and all other grains) provided *gross* storage revenues for the major export firms for the six-year period 1958 through 1963 and annual average gross revenues as follows:[32]

Firm	Gross revenues (millions)	Annual average (millions)
Cargill	$56.8	$9.5
Continental	33.8	5.6
Bunge	11.5	1.9
Dreyfus	5.0	.8

Again, the theme is dependence on the government in terms of storage revenue and/or the opportunity to earn revenue through increased wheat exports.

The wheat exporter's dependence on the government for important export trade volumes is indicated by the fact that in the past over 70% of normal wheat exports from this country utilize concessional programs (e.g., P.L. 480) and the remaining 30% receive export subsidies. Furthermore, the changing pattern of world wheat markets (Table V-14) indicates a growth in the concessional and Sino-Soviet Bloc wheat markets and a relatively stable European wheat market that is encouraging production within the common market rather than relying on imports from the United States and Canada. The first two markets require specific government programs to be effective; the latter just requires government subsidies.

Factors that will affect the profitability of the wheat export segment in the future are as follows:

(1) The major challenge to the supremacy of the big four exporting firms is the rapid increase in cooperative exporting operations. As long as most ex-

---

[31] There are some years when unusual circumstances may reduce profit substantially below the 5% to 15% range.

[32] See Appendix Table V-1 for all major firms' storage earnings in the wheat economy.

TABLE V-14. World Wheat and Wheat Flour Imports from All Countries by Market: 1951–1963

Crop year	Commercial market			
	Sino-Soviet Bloc	Free world	Concessional market	Total
	(In thousands of bushels)			
1951	18,733	799,100	149,233	967,067
1952	29,967	826,533	39,100	895,600
1953	15,467	685,633	96,267	797,333
1954	35,300	700,933	144,867	881,067
1955	43,333	682,567	216,167	942,033
1956	136,967	725,967	342,133	1,205,067
1957	130,100	697,933	251,833	1,079,867
1958	165,267	741,533	291,567	1,198,400
1959	141,833	715,333	347,567	1,204,700
1960	163,800	792,167	421,833	1,377,800
1961	272,300	848,900	451,433	1,572,633
1962	261,567	729,400	441,533	1,432,533
1963	576,667	780,000	466,667	1,823,333
	Each market as percent of total			
1951	1.9%	82.6%	15.5%	100.0%
1952	3.3	92.3	4.4	100.0
1953	1.9	86.0	12.1	100.0
1954	4.0	79.6	16.4	100.0
1955	4.6	72.5	22.9	100.0
1956	11.4	60.2	28.4	100.0
1957	12.0	64.6	23.4	100.0
1958	13.8	61.9	24.3	100.0
1959	11.8	59.4	28.8	100.0
1960	11.9	57.5	30.6	100.0
1961	17.3	54.0	28.7	100.0
1962	18.3	50.9	30.8	100.0
1963	31.6	42.8	25.6	100.0

Source: USDA, Foreign Agricultural Service

port sales are made f.o.b. the U.S. port rather than c.i.f. the importing port, cooperative and other smaller exporting firms can compete successfully. (Movement to port facilities is primarily a domestic function.) Once export operations involve overseas shipping, financing, storing and import provisions, then the experience and common ownership of overseas firms enable the big four to have tactical and profitable advantages.

(2) As government programs decrease in importance domestically, export firms will have to follow Cargill's lead in developing sources of farm grains. This may not be in the form of direct ownership but rather in agent contracts with cooperating country subterminal operations. The handling margins will also have to increase to offset the loss of government storage earnings.

(3) The projected increase in world wheat trade should result in an increase in the volume of business handled by all grain exporters and increase the profitability of these firms.

(4) The major profitability problems facing the

exporter are (a) the creation of regional marketing arrangements in the developed countries that act as flexible tariff walls to keep wheat out, and (b) the inability of the developing countries who desire U.S. wheat to pay for it, store it and distribute it once it arrives. The major challenge for future profitability may be an aid and assistance program by exporters (with the help of the government) to help importing countries set up grain storage and distribution facilities to better utilize wheat shipments from the United States and other exporting countries. The weakness and strengths of the U.S. wheat economy, as evidenced by this study, should be of some help to these countries in developing their internal wheat marketing arrangements.

(5) Because the United States Government has provided subsidies to exporters to meet competitive "world wheat prices," the exporter has not used the futures markets to any great extent. However the change in world wheat demands and in the U.S. market make the cash market less certain and more futures market activity probably will take place. As long as the world wheat price is a "bargained one" based on "related subsidies," there does not seem to be any great need to improve the exporters' price protection except to maintain proper price hedges to satisfy the requirements of the principal lending institutions. The exporter will continue to have the government as its major decision-making partner for the next several decades as a means of selling to developing countries.

(6) As the exporter continues to work with the government for short- and long-range planning, the establishment of market sharing principles suggested by the United States and other governments will have to take into account the internal wheat market machinery in this and other countries as plans develop. If the international government plans can provide for as much flexibility and individual initiative as our domestic programs, then the exporter will be able to continue to use his expertise as chief merchandiser of wheat for the world markets.

The "market sharing" proposal was outlined in a speech prepared for delivery by Secretary of Agriculture Orville L. Freeman in Houston, Texas, before the Rice Millers Association on January 31, 1964.

The germane quotes are as follows:

We recognize, however, that for many commodities the fixed import duty is not the principal form of protection used. Variable levies, quantitative restrictions, and state trading are different, and they require different methods. There are these and a host of other devices which, singly or in combination, give the protection which was once required and which we all seek to reduce in these nego-

tiations for our common good. Nontariff barriers cannot be excluded from negotiations simply because they are not tariffs. The most sensible way to include them in the negotiations is to negotiate market share arrangements for products covered by such systems. Even here I see no need for any one form of arrangement. It should fit the needs of the countries and commodity with which we are dealing. The International Wheat Agreement and the market-sharing arrangements proposed by the United Kingdom in meats and cereals are important precedents.

The essence of each arrangement, however, would be an assurance given by the importers to efficient outside countries that these producers would have the opportunity to compete with domestic producers for a fair share of the domestic market. This market share would be based upon imports in a recent representative period, and it would provide for expanded imports as the total market grows. It does not admit exclusion from markets, either by direct quotas or by adoption of domestic policies which have that effect. For some commodities . . . cereals and meat and dairy products come immediately to mind — these market share arrangements may have to be quite elaborate. They may require new multilateral agreements involving all major importers and exporters. They may cover areas of national policy not now subject to international commitments — such as support prices of non-commercial sales. They might require all the developed countries of the world to make substantial contributions to the less developed countries by way of food aid.

The core of such arrangements, however, would be the assurance given by importers to exporters that they will not be shut out of the dollar import markets through the application of restrictions at the frontier.[33]

As of the summer of 1967 market sharing as attempted in the United Kingdom wheat market has not worked well for the United States because of the inability of the British Government to improve its domestic political environment so as to be consistent with the "market sharing objectives."

(7) The International Wheat Agreement will probably continue to exist but without much impact on either exporter or importer.

The International Wheat Agreement was signed by 48 countries in 1949 and has been extended for various time periods, the latest being to July 31, 1967. The purpose of the Agreement was to provide wheat importers who are parties to the Agreement first access to wheat at a maximum price (in times of short supply) and to provide exporters with a wheat market at a minimum price level during times of wheat surplus. In practice the Agreement has been somewhat meaningless. As Wallace W. Hyde of Cargill stated in the *Northwestern Miller*, September 30, 1958: "We still have the IWA with us today but buy-

---

[33] Pp. 11–12.

ing quotas are not and have never been enforced. Some countries choose to record their purchases within the IWA; others do not. In any event, it is difficult to see what either a buyer or seller can accomplish within IWA that he cannot equal or perhaps improve, and more simply, outside IWA."

More recently Loren Johnson, Executive Vice President of Continental Grain Company, stated at the Farm Forum at Spokane, Washington, February 10, 1964: "International Commodity Agreements of the traditional type have proved incapable of dealing with the problem of surpluses. The IWA effectively established a wall around U.S. wheat supplies and we had to crawl over that wall by using our P.L. 480 program. We had so much wheat that we had to sell it at a price, and we found the way, in spite of the Agreement. Canada has given nonsignators the same treatment as those who have signed the Agreement, and one of its largest customers, China, is not a member of the IWA."

Flour Millers. The flour miller segment is no exception to the diversified nature of the internal structure of the wheat economy. Firms in this industry are not only in the flour milling business; they are also engaged in country, terminal, and export wheat and flour merchandising; feed manufacture; institutional and consumer prepared flour mixes and packaged goods; cereal manufactures, snack goods, and peanut business.

In previous governmental analyses of the profitability of the flour milling segment of the wheat economy, the diversified and integrated nature of these firms was not taken into consideration, except for the recent publication of the National Commission on Food Marketing.[34] Typical of such analysis is the government publication entitled "Spreads in Farm-Retail Prices of White Bread." [35] In this study the analyst states "Profits (after taxes) for four major milling companies, in comparison, declined from 11.9% of stockholder equity during 1947–1949 to 8.4% in 1962." The National Commission on Food Marketing report showed flour milling profits in 1964–1965 to be 0.22% of sales *before taxes*.

This writer, with the cooperation of the industry, presents the following financial analysis of the flour milling industry as an isolated segment of the wheat economy. Because this segment of the wheat economy has not had a historical and *separate* profitability anal-

ysis before, the author has attempted to go into greater detail in the examination of the profitability of this segment of the wheat system. The flour milling companies that are only in flour milling operations are included as a complete unit in the flour milling statistics. The diversified firms in this study are represented only by their flour milling divisions and related financial information allocated from the total firm's operation.[36] Instead of an 8.4% on net worth after taxes or a 0.22% on sales before taxes for 1962, as stated above, these major *flour milling* companies and/or divisions (representing approximately 40% of the flour volume of the United States) actually had a 0.06% *loss* on sales and a 0.03% *loss* on net worth after taxes in 1962 (the latest year used in the USDA study of white bread prices) as shown in Table V-15. The profit figures for 1961 and 1963 were slightly better, averaging approximately 0.5% on sales and 3% on net worth.

When one analyzes Table V-15 in greater detail, the following important observations stand out:

(1) During the 1958–1963 period examined, net income from flour milling as a percentage of total flour milling assets (combined average of the selected firms) ranged from a *minus* 0.19% in 1962 to a high of 2.43% in 1959—an indication of a very low profit industry to say the least.

(2) Fixed assets increased from $51.3 million to $74.3 million indicating some acquisitions by these firms and major capital improvements, neither of which seems to improve the level of earnings.

(3) Working capital increased from $62.3 million to $88.8 million which may suggest changes in inventory policies in the face of relatively stable dollar sales.

(4) Long-term debt increased from $14.9 million to $29.2 million, increasing the leverage of this industry. The ability to attract funds must be attributed to confidence in the "stability" of the industry or perhaps unused debt capacity.

(5) On the other hand, net profit after taxes has had a pattern of alternating up and down: e.g., $937,000 in 1958; $3,934,000 in 1959; $932,000 in 1960; $3,482,000 in 1961; $376,000 *loss* in 1962; and a $3,291,000 profit in 1963. No one can explain this "roller coaster" profit pattern except to assume that after a "good" year, one hopes to increase volume by lowering flour prices.

The combined data of Table V-15 mask the wide range of operating results of individual firms and in-

---

[34] *Organization and Competition in the Milling and Baking Industries,* June 1966.
[35] USDA, Economic Research Service, Miscellaneous Publication No. 969, September 1964.

[36] See Notes to Table V-15 for an explanation of flour milling financial allocations. The reader is cautioned that accounting procedures were reconciled for those firms and divisions represented. However, the problem of a "transfer price" from the flour division at market or cost to the grocery products division presented many allocation judgments.

TABLE V-15. Financial Data[a] for Combined Flour Milling Operations of Selected Flour and Food Processing Firms: 1958–1963

Year[b]	1958	1959	1960	1961	1962	1963
Bushels of wheat ground (thousands of bushels)	190,593	229,778	234,559	226,143	231,901	222,711
Operations Data (thousands of dollars)						
Net sales	$544,532	$607,220	$611,912	$601,750	$630,574	$650,974
Cost of goods sold	515,890	567,749	578,490	562,438	599,232	613,174
General sales and administration	27,111	30,947	31,279	31,750	31,234	30,882
Gross profit	28,642	39,471	33,422	39,312	31,342	37,800
Net profit before income taxes	1,531	8,524	2,143	7,562	108	6,918
Income taxes	594	4,590	1,211	4,080	484	3,627
Net profit after taxes	937	3,934	932	3,482	(376)	3,291
Working capital	62,325	73,079	72,294	73,471	76,631	88,837
Fixed assets	51,295	57,289	60,981	63,812	71,675	74,344
Long-term debt	14,860	15,940	19,145	22,251	24,259	29,191
Net worth (net assets)	87,540	100,418	102,564	107,642	113,418	120,897
Total capitalization	102,400	116,358	121,709	129,893	137,677	150,088
Total assets[c]	137,703	161,824	167,148	170,410	201,680	197,072
Combined Flour Milling Operations Net Income After Taxes as Percent of:						
Sales	0.17%	0.65%	0.15%	0.58%	(0.06%)	0.51%
Net worth (net assets)	1.07	3.92	0.91	3.23	(0.33)	2.72
Total assets	0.68	2.43	0.56	2.04	(0.19)	1.67

[a] These statistics treat the flour divisions of major firms as separate entities. Those firms that have flour milling as the sole operation are included without allocations. (See Notes for bookkeeping procedures.)

[b] Fiscal years: represent a wide range of year-end dates.

[c] Total assets exceed total capitalization by the amount of current liabilities.

SOURCE: Flour milling operations of selected major food firms.

NOTES TO TABLE V-15.

1. Net sales include all flour sales after discounts.
2. Cost of goods sold includes all raw material costs and manufacturing costs for the net sales stated above.
3. General sales and administration costs include all costs except income taxes that can be attributable to the net sales figure above. An appropriate basis of allocation would be a value added concept or the margin over a materials cost basis. This would apply to all costs including basic research, company overhead, and similar expenses.
4. Gross profit is the net difference between sales less cost of goods sold less general sales and administration costs.
5. Income taxes are determined on the same percentage tax basis as utilized throughout the company.
6. Net profit after taxes is a simple subtraction of income taxes from net profit before taxes.
7. Long-term debt was determined on the average opening and closing of the books for all long-term debt. The proportion attributable to the flour milling division was measured by taking the net fixed assets after depreciation of this division compared with the total fixed assets of the company after depreciation and using this same proportion in allocating long-term debt to the flour milling division.
8. Total assets include all the assets on the balance sheet used in the flour milling division. Fixed assets include the plant and equipment less depreciation in the flour milling division.

dividual flour milling divisions. Table V-16 gives the results of the most profitable and least profitable firm or division as measured by net income after taxes as a percentage of sales, net worth, and total assets. From this table the reader will note that the least profitable firm and/or division in three out of the six years had a *net loss*. The most profitable firm and/or division had as high a return as 5.62% net income as a percentage of total assets utilized in flour milling operations. Even this top performance indicated, at the most, a 1.7% return on sales for the same year, 1959.

Wide operational variations existed among the major flour milling firms and divisions. For example, the highest average selling price for a firm was $3.12 a bushel in 1963 and the low was $1.98 a bushel in 1960 — a spread of over $1 a bushel. Part of this variation can be explained by changes in the price support of wheat, another part by the different types of flour sold by individual flour milling firms and divisions, and the mixing and blending services provided to the baker. Another example of extreme variation among the firms in the survey is the net profit and loss after taxes expressed in dollars per bushel, the high being a profit of 4.2 cents a bushel in 1961 and the low being a loss of 2.5 cents a bushel in 1962.

The low profitability of the flour milling segment of the wheat economy has taken place in spite of a slowly rising increase in the miller's flour spread. This spread

TABLE V-16. High and Low Individual Firm Flour Milling Operations as Measured by Net Income After Taxes as a Percent of Sales, Net Worth, and Total Assets: 1958–1963

		1958	1959	1960	1961	1962	1963
Sales	High	1.03%	1.70%	0.93%	1.79%	1.29%	1.16%
	Low	(0.43)	0.43	(0.28)	0.01	(0.85)	0.07
Net worth (net assets)	High	6.63	11.42	6.13	11.67	9.46	10.34
	Low	(2.79)	2.62	(1.59)	0.04	(3.72)	0.27
Total assets	High	4.21	5.62	2.93	4.98	3.95	4.93
	Low	(1.72)	1.49	(0.97)	0.03	(2.29)	0.16

SOURCE: Flour milling operations of selected major food firms

represents the spread between the sales value of flour and the cost of wheat to the miller. The increase in the flour miller's spread as represented in a one-pound loaf of bread went from 0.8 cent to 1.0 cent from 1957 to 1963. This increase was partially due to a 25% increase in labor costs in the flour milling industry (from 1948 to 1963), and an increase in the amount of flour extracted per bushel of wheat.[37] The sharply increasing and decreasing spreads that took place in 1964 were due to the special change-over provisions of the new domestic wheat certificate price

to the profitable operation of the flour milling segment of the wheat economy. If the $6.9 million profit before tax figure in Table V-15 represents 40%[38] of the industry's profits in 1963, then the estimated total profits before taxes for the U.S. flour milling industry would be $17.3 million. The integrated flour milling firms receiving $500,000 or more of wheat storage payments in 1963 obtained $24.4 million in gross wheat storage revenue (see Table V-17).

Once again the government is an important, if not dominant, factor in determining the profitability of another segment of the wheat economy.

There are other economic factors that affect the profitability of the flour milling segment of the wheat economy such as the problem of excess capacity. Even though the number of flour mills with a capacity of over 400 hundredweights per day had declined from 377 in 1950 to 282 in 1963, excess capacity still persisted, but it was declining as Table V-18 indicates. (The writer believes that there was perhaps more excess capacity than is shown in Table V-18 because of the modernization of mills.) On the other hand, the closing of 9 of General Mills 17 flour mills in 1965 reduced excess capacity significantly. One should also note in Table V-18 that the large mills were running

TABLE V-17. Commodity Credit Corporation Storage Payments to Primarily Flour Milling Firms by Specific Categories of Operation: 1958–1963

Firm	1963	1962	1961	1960	1959	1958	Total
Archer-Daniels-Midland Co.	$ 4,875,545	$ 2,779,579	$ 5,134,987	$ 5,919,132	$ 6,076,898	$ 6,240,199	$ 31,026,340
F. H. Peavey & Company	4,690,655	4,064,223	4,169,304	5,389,505	5,528,810	5,623,702	29,466,199
Harvest Queen Mill & Elevator	3,549,156	4,192,956	4,856,361	5,204,045	5,884,495	5,514,064	29,201,077
Seaboard Allied Milling Corp.	2,806,792	3,060,487	3,299,454	1,435,573	1,139,311	517,396	12,259,013
Ross Industries Inc.	1,790,885	2,158,161	2,018,256	2,337,813	2,569,705		10,874,820
General Mills, Inc.	1,613,516	1,245,985	2,086,142	2,642,146	2,776,898	1,634,936	11,999,623
The Pillsbury Co., Inc.	1,262,402	1,384,877	1,845,459	1,812,037	2,285,802	587,707	9,178,284
Kimbell Milling Co.	1,139,162	1,607,697	1,611,101	1,628,315	2,181,374	1,570,497	9,738,146
Flour Mills of America	1,082,728	1,169,580	905,700	949,922	615,603	602,607	5,326,140
International Milling Co.	916,330	910,118	1,638,625	2,059,948	1,544,132	1,698,514	8,767,667
Burrus Mills	632,895	802,503	979,529	2,575,778	2,787,837	2,176,166	9,954,708
Colorado Milling & Elevator Co.		545,873	852,616	1,021,049	1,217,058	800,843	4,437,439
Kansas Milling Co.					562,482		562,482
Montana Milling Co.					535,881		535,881
Salyer Grain & Milling Co.					510,655		510,655
Hunter Milling Co.						520,105	520,105
Total	$24,360,066	$23,922,039	$29,397,534	$32,975,263	$36,216,941	$27,486,736	$174,358,579

SOURCE: Commodity Credit Corporation, *Annual Reports of Storage and Handling Payments in Excess of $500,000 under the Uniform Grain Storage Agreements.*

support program, and the cost squeeze placed on the miller once the program became law.

The current price support program and previous governmental programs have been extremely important

at greater capacity and, therefore, presumably at less per unit cost than the smaller mills. (Even with operations at higher levels of capacity, profits had not increased as was shown in Table V-15.)

[37] USDA, ERS, *Spreads in Farm-Retail Prices of White Bread*, p. 7.

[38] Firms in the financial sample accounted for approximately 40% of the industry's flour milling operations.

TABLE V-18. Number, Production, and Production as a Percent of Annual Capacity by Capacity Groups of U.S. Flour Mills for Selected Years: 1950–1963

Capacity group (cwt.)	1950	1953	1957	1959	1961	1962	1963
Number of mills							
400 and under	651	n.a.	n.a.	n.a.	n.a.	n.a.	n.a.
401–4,000	310	247	204	201	199	191	190
Over 4,000	67	73	82	81	85	91	92
Total over 400	377	320	286	282	284	282	282
Total all sizes	1,028	n.a.	n.a.	n.a.	n.a.	n.a.	n.a.
Production of flour in millions of cwt.							
400 and under	6.2	6.1	7.1	7.9	7.8	7.9	9.1
401–4,000	98.6	82.5	68.3	72.4	72.0	65.0	62.5
Over 4,000	120.2	133.6	163.4	168.2	180.5	189.2	191.4
Total	224.9	222.2	238.9	248.5	260.3	262.1	263.9
Production as % of estimated annual capacity							
400 and under	23.6%	24.4%	26.4%	28.8%	53.1%	54.3%	73.0%
401–4,000	72.8	71.9	72.4	74.6	73.5	70.3	68.4
4,000 and over	89.4	92.0	100.1	99.2	101.6	100.8	100.0
Total	78.6	81.2	86.6	86.9	93.3	92.4	92.6

n.a. = not available.
SOURCE: Bureau of the Census.

The flour milling industry is one suffering from excess capacity and severe competition. Low profitability in flour milling, in addition to the cost advantages of vertical integration, has encouraged flour milling firms to diversify into other but related lines (grain merchandising, feed manufacturing, institutional and consumer cake mixes) or to close down their commercial flour milling operations as General Mills did. The price support program remains an important determinant in profitable operations, affecting grain storage income and the price levels of various classes of wheat.

Typical of the impact of government programs on integrated grain and flour milling operations is the following comment from the *Southwestern Miller* on the Seaboard Allied Milling Corporation's annual report for the fiscal year ended May 28, 1966.

The report shows storage and other operating revenues in 1965–66 totaling $1,373,290, compared with $1,744,343 in the preceding year and $2,658,893 in 1963–64. The report observes:

"The past year was not a successful one for our grain operations. U.S. stocks of wheat and other grains have been reduced within the past several years from a condition of 'surplus' to one of near scarcity, and genuine concern is being voiced in many quarters over the adequacy of supplies. Our grain operations, particularly in the storage area, were affected by this change.

"At the same time, our extensive grain merchandising and handling system gives our milling operations the advantage of being able to draw wheat from the most desirable areas. Also, your management looks for improvement in the grain division from recent shifts in government policy, most notably the decision to increase the wheat acreage allotment for the 1967 crop to the highest level in a number of years." [39]

Government policies to help guarantee overseas investments were also important to the development of a joint venture between Seaboard Allied Milling and Continental Grain in Ecuador in 1966 and for Seaboard Allied's flour mill in Sierra Leone, Africa.

The surprising finding of the current study is that even with this dependence on government programs and the urge to diversify domestically and internationally, the most profitable firm represented in the flour milling survey is neither diversified nor does it store a bushel of government grain.

In this low profit competitive jungle of flour milling several alternative strategies are utilized by flour milling firms:

(1) Some of the larger flour milling firms have diversified into grocery product items that lend themselves to product differentiation; e.g., General Mills and Pillsbury and their various consumer cake mixes and institutional cake mix products. With excellent product innovation and advertising to bring these products to the attention of the consumer, profit margins have been improved. In these cases, flour milling is

[39] *Southwestern Miller*, August 16, 1966, p. 33.

primarily a procurement operation and usually a low profit phase of the overall business operation.

Other firms do not have the funds or the know-how to enter the franchised retail cake mix industry. It is estimated that it cost one well-known firm in the United States over $57 million over a three-year period to enter the cake mix field. This firm had the advantage of a well-known brand, excellent retail distribution, and consumer product management.

(2) Those flour milling firms that wish to diversify into the cake mix product line but do not have the resources or know-how to do so have looked to the institutional cake mix market as a possible diversification. This institutional prepared mix market is estimated to be over $100 million. Some 15 to 25 firms averaging sales of $4 million are active in this industry. In order to buy technological innovation and market penetration in this area several mergers have occurred between flour millers and institutional cake mix manufacturers. Undoubtedly more such mergers will take place.

(3) Most flour millers are attempting to provide special pre-mixes to their customers in order to differentiate their flour products. Many discussions with industry leaders leads this writer to the conclusion that imminent technological breakthroughs will permit greater product differentiation by flour millers, although several millers are skeptical as to the exclusiveness of any flour franchise.

(4) Other flour millers have built up their operations on price alone. Many of these firms specialize in one or two qualities of flour and have developed unique and cheap transportation arrangements for their products. They represent the "discount house" of flour milling.

(5) Another strategy has been to utilize government wheat storage to the exclusion of the flour milling business. With few exceptions (as has been noted above — a profitable exception) most flour milling firms have utilized government storage programs to provide funds and upgrade their wheat inventory management operations. Many of these firms did not properly allocate these earnings to their inventory management operations and used these inventory profits to cut flour prices (this was especially true in the Southwest). Those firms that relied *primarily* on government storage operations have been hurt financially by the lowered storage rates and the decline in the utilization of their warehouses for government storage operations. Many of these firms are now for sale. The government storage earnings that still exist for some of these firms have become the "times earnings" evaluation of the property. The flour mill is just thrown in

for goodwill. The short-sighted approach of relying primarily on government storage rather than on a combination of enterprises (including government storage) has added to the current low profit difficulties of many flour millers.

(6) Transportation changes mentioned in preceding chapters of this report have led to the building of new mills closer to population centers and the closing of by-passed interior mill operations that were running at below capacity levels. As long as freight rates continue to favor wheat shipments in relation to flour shipments, such a trend will probably continue. The dynamics of the wheat economy provide competitive pressures and opportunities for the flour miller. Certainly no one firm has been immune to these changes. Most favorable rail rates can best be utilized by big firms. This "rail favoritism" places the small flour mill at a distinct disadvantage.

(7) The severe competition in this industry and the low profit levels have led to alleged attempts at price agreement, which, if they did exist, have been dramatically unsuccessful.

(8) Many flour mills have gone out of business or have been sold at low prices that have enabled *new* owners to make higher returns on investments than that which is "normal" for the industry.

(9) The flour milling industry *privately* is divided in its opinion of the usefulness of current government wheat programs. The domestic certificate program may encourage the production of high yielding but poor milling wheats. On the other hand, the low price support level of wheat does permit the "remaining free wheat market" to allocate wheat qualities and quantities in a realistic manner.

(10) In spite of low levels of profitability in this industry, there are many ways that profits can be improved as indicated above. Furthermore, many firms find that the "stability" of this portion of the wheat industry has attracted investment funds for the total firm's use in other divisions as well as in flour milling. In addition, depreciation schedules have permitted cash flows to be fairly significant to several firms (a kind of *planned liquidation* of the flour milling portion of the business)[40] Other firms find that flour milling by itself may be unattractive but it complements wheat merchandising, feed merchandising, and grocery product operations to the point where the "sum of the parts" is greater than an allocated evaluation of the "flour milling division."

(11) Some flour mills have kept integrated family

[40] A few long-range plans of flour millers outline a policy of purposely keeping capital expenditures well below depreciation rates.

flour and cake mix consumer portions of their flour milling operations and closed or sold off the remaining mills (General Mills, for example).

Bakery Operators. The bakery industry is characterized by four major types of operators: (1) independent bakers who are members of cooperatives which furnish management, purchasing services and a national advertising program, (2) major interstate wholesale bakers, (3) independent local operations, and (4) bakeries operated by chain stores or cooperative groups of independent supermarkets.[41] Sales of this industry are over $4 billion annually;[42] and sales of one product, white bread, account for over 60% of all bakery products sold in the United States.[43]

The net income of most of the *major* bakers in the industry, the wholesale bakery operators, has been declining. Profits after taxes of six leading baking companies declined from a high of 18.9% of stockholders' equity in 1947–1949 to 5.9% in 1963.[44] This decline has taken place because of the competitive pressures of high distribution costs and the "ability of food retailing organizations to undercut wholesalers' distribution costs sufficiently to have a lower selling price, in spite of equal or slightly higher production costs." [45]

Bread marketing margins have risen faster during the postwar period than margins for most of the other major food items. In a recent market structure analysis of the baking industry during the 1947–1958 period,[46] Walsh and Evans found that margins on white bread were markedly higher than would prevail if optimum sizes of plants were utilized and if distribution was by drop delivery rather than by driver-commission men. The potential savings were estimated to be approximately one-third of the 1958 price of 19.3 cents per one-pound loaf. This poor performance reflected inefficient operation and union pressure.

Because of the high perishability of bread and bread products, as well as the freshness expected by the consumer, this industry is made up of many local markets.

Each market has its own distributive pattern of product type, weight, size, price, determined by local costs, local customs, and consumer preferences, collective bargaining at local levels with local unions, local competition between bakers, and in many cases, local chain stores manufacturing and marketing private label products.[47]

These local markets extend in distance for about 60 miles and another 60 miles can be used for "depot" shipments to allow for a wider geographical distribution pattern and production cost savings of a larger baking plant.

Even though local markets are an important element in describing this industry, there is some degree of concentration. The four largest companies in 1963 accounted for 23% of the total value of shipments, the next four accounted for another 12%, and the next dozen averaged less than 1% of the market apiece. Three of the top firms — Continental Baking, General Baking, and Ward Foods — own and operate their own bakery facilities, whereas Campbell Taggart Association Bakeries (the industry's most profitable large firm) is primarily a holding company operating a great variety of separately incorporated operating subsidiaries.

To meet the competition of a flexible national bakery organization that maintains a national advertising program and has the ability to adapt to the uniqueness of each local bakery market, three cooperative enterprises have developed. These three cooperatives (Quality Bakers of America Cooperative, American Bakers Cooperative, and W. E. Long Co.) assist in the management of over 200 operating units with a combined dollar volume about half as large as the total of the eight major bakery wholesalers.[48]

In addition to cooperative competition, there has been a rapid development of grocery chain baking operations supplying "private label" bread to their captive retail outlets. Some experts claim that 20% of all bread volume sold is baked and sold under private label.[49] Other studies estimate this to be lower — approximately 8% to 10%.[50] Table V-19 gives a comparison of the sales of the 8 largest wholesale baking companies with the value of shipments by the 10 largest chain bakery operations[51] in 1954 and 1958. This indicates that chain store bakery production was increasing slightly more than that of the major wholesale bakeries. This growth was substantiated by the Federal Trade Commision's report, *Economic In-*

[41] U.S. Senate, *Administered Prices of Bread,* p. 231.

[42] National Commission on Food Marketing, *Organization and Competition in the Milling and Baking Industries,* p. 1.

[43] *Is Distribution the Major Problem in the Wholesale Baking Industry?* speech by Nicholas M. Thuroczy, November 18, 1963.

[44] USDA, ERS, *Spreads in Farm-Retail Prices of White Bread,* p. 13.

[45] Arthur D. Little, Inc., *Distribution: The Challenge of the Sixties.*

[46] Walsh and Evans, *Economics of Change in Market Structure, Conduct, and Performance: The Baking Industry 1947–1958.*

[47] Quotation by Russell J. Hug, President of the General Baking Company, *Administered Prices of Bread,* p. 225.

[48] *Ibid.,* p. 232.

[49] *Ibid.,* p. 101.

[50] *Ibid.,* pp. 103–104. See also *Baking Industry,* June 1964, p. 29.

[51] Private label and manufacturer's label are discussed in greater detail on p. 88 of this chapter.

TABLE V-19. Comparison of Sales of the Eight Largest Wholesale Bakers with Value of Shipments by the Ten Largest Chain Grocery Companies: 1954 and 1958
(In thousands)

Companies	1954	1958	1958 as % of 1954
8 largest wholesale baking companies sales:			
Continental Baking Co.[a]	$210,762	$297,204	141.0%
General Baking Co.	122,093	166,104	136.0
Campbell Taggart Association Bakeries	133,921	162,435	121.3
American Bakeries	134,768	152,114	112.8
Total 4 largest	601,544	777,857	129.3
Interstate	94,210	116,873	124.0
Ward Baking Co.	95,241	104,594	109.9
Langendorf-Winter	50,712	69,932	137.9
Southern Bakeries Co.	24,821	25,059	101.0
Total 8 largest	$866,527	$1,094,314	126.2%
10 largest grocery chain companies, value of bakery product shipments:			
Great Atlantic & Pacific Tea Co.	$142,622	$180,534	126.6%
Kroger Co.[b]	30,144	43,713	145.0
Safeway Stores, Inc.	27,820	33,939	122.0
American Stores	14,465	19,719	136.4
First National Stores	15,247	15,344	100.0
Colonial Stores	5,100[c]	8,560	167.8
National Tea Co.	6,639	8,495	128.0
Winn-Dixie Stores, Inc.	2,762	8,051	291.5
Food Fair Stores, Inc.	2,000[c]	2,077	103.8
Grand Union	200[c]	723	361.5
Total 10 largest	$246,999	$321,155	130.0%

[a] Excluding in 1954 Paniplus sales ($1,700,000) and in 1958 Paniplus, Morton Frozen Foods, and Stewart sales (estimated $30,800,000).

[b] Includes for Columbus plant (classified in industry 2052) only bread and related products.

[c] Estimated.

SOURCE: *Moody's Industrial Manual* and companies' replies to subcommittee questionnaire. See also *Administered Prices of Bread*, p. 103.

TABLE V-20. Comparison of Profits before Taxes of the Six Largest Wholesale Bakers with Profits before Taxes of Selected Categories of Members of the Quality Bakers of America Cooperative: 1962 and 1963
(Categories determined by asset value of companies)

Company	Total assets	Profit before taxes	Profit before taxes as % of total assets
1963			
Continental Baking	$147,017,237	$18,314,534	12.4%
American Bakeries	53,617,271	3,570,903	6.7
Campbell Taggart	80,265,108	9,625,000	12.0
General Baking	58,709,317	2,474,131	4.2
Ward Foods, Inc.	37,571,161	(2,264,248)	(6.0)
Interstate Bakeries	52,199,934	6,286,588	12.0
Quality Bakers of America (large)	$3,500,000		10.91%
Quality Bakers of America (medium)	1,300,000		16.09
Quality Bakers of America (small)	600,000		11.02
1962			
Continental Baking	$140,496,106	$16,272,020	11.5%
American Bakeries	51,481,937	3,339,681	6.5
Campbell Taggart	77,650,136	8,245,000	10.6
General Baking	58,600,197	585,563	1.0
Ward Foods, Inc.	35,430,306	(283,276)	(0.8)
Interstate Bakeries	49,236,217	5,531,246	11.2
Quality Bakers of America (large)	$3,500,000		10.20%
Quality Bakers of America (medium)	1,300,000		16.72
Quality Bakers of America (small)	600,000		7.01

( ) = loss

SOURCE: *The Southwestern Miller* and Quality Bakers of America Balance Sheet Studies, 1962 and 1963.

quiry into Food Marketing.[52] In spite of this growth, brands of the largest wholesale bakers on a "preference" basis still indicate strong market dominance for their products.[53]

The burden of strong union pressure and the resulting high distribution costs for bread have put the major wholesalers at a distinct cost disadvantage[54] (see Table V-23). On the other hand, one leading

bakery authority maintains that if there is any competitive advantage as between wholesale bakers in a particular local market area, it is likely to be the result of a *favorable* union contract.[55] Some unions will allow "drop delivery" by the baker to the chain or supermarket door and others will not. If the baker gets a drop delivery contract with no commission involved for the driver of the bakery delivery truck, he has a distinct competitive advantage. Unions have been known to give such a contract to one bakery in an area and not to another even though both bakeries have the same union.

From a competitive position, those bakers that belong to a cooperative, such as Quality Bakers of America, have on the *average* shown better profit results than the big six major wholesalers (see Table V-21).

[52] Federal Trade Commission, *Economic Inquiry into Food Marketing*, Part I, pp. 284 and 295.

[53] *Administered Prices of Bread*.

[54] *Ibid.*, p. 113.

[55] Interview with George N. Graf, President of Quality Bakers of America, May 29, 1964.

TABLE V-21. White Bread Sales from Large, Medium, and Small Wholesale Bakers and from Chain Stores with Own Bakeries (X & Y) to Different Sized Chains, Cooperatives, Voluntaries, Independents, and Firms Outside Market Area: Six-Month Period, 1959–1960
(Average weekly sales and prices per one-pound loaf)

Sales from bread manufacturers	Chain V (large stores)	Chain W (large stores)	Chain W (medium stores)	Chain X (large stores)	Chain Y (large stores)	Cooperative I (large stores)	Cooperative I (medium stores)	Cooperative I (small stores)	Cooperative II (medium stores)	Cooperative II (small stores)
Large wholesale bakery	—	—	—	—	—	—	—	—	—	—
Selling price	$0.190	$0.185	$0.185	$0.180	$0.180	$0.185	$0.190	$0.190	$0.200	$0.200
Number of loaves	22,000	25,000	25,000	10,000	7,000	38,000	38,000	38,000	38,000	38,000
Medium wholesale bakery	—	—	—	—	—	—	—	—	—	—
Selling price	$0.190	$0.185	$0.185	$0.180	$0.180	$0.185	$0.190	$0.190	$0.200	$0.200
Number of loaves	15,000	18,000	18,000	8,000	3,000	24,000	24,000	24,000	24,000	24,000
Small wholesale bakery	—	—	—	—	—	—	—	—	—	—
Selling price	$0.190	$0.190	$0.190	—	—	$0.190	$0.190	$0.190	$0.200	$0.200
Number of loaves	3,000	7,000	7,000	—	—	8,000	8,000	8,000	8,000	8,000
Large food store Chain X (own bakery)										
Selling price	—	—	—	$0.155	—	—	—	—	—	—
Number of loaves	—	—	—	162,000	—	—	—	—	—	—
Medium food store Chain Y (own bakery)										
Selling price	—	—	—	—	$0.165	—	—	—	—	—
Number of loaves	—	—	—	—	90,000	—	—	—	—	—

Sales from bread manufacturers	Voluntary I (large stores)	Voluntary I (medium stores)	Small local chain (medium stores)	Independent supermarkets (large stores)	Independent supermarkets (small stores)	Sales outside market	Total sales per week — Loaves	Total sales per week — Dollars	Output Per hour	Output Capacity
Large wholesale bakery	—	—	—	—	—	—	—	$75,560	6,500	6,500
Selling price	$0.190	$0.190	$0.200	$0.200	$0.200	—	—	—	—	—
Number of loaves	22,000	38,000	22,000	11,000	22,000	—	394,000	—	—	—
Medium wholesale bakery	—	—	—	—	—	—	—	$49,660	4,000	6,000
Selling price	$0.190	$0.190	$0.200	$0.200	$0.200	—	—	—	—	—
Number of loaves	15,000	24,000	15,000	8,000	15,000	—	259,000	—	—	—
Small wholesale bakery	—	—	—	—	—	—	—	$18,025	2,500	3,000
Selling price	$0.185	$0.185	$0.200	$0.200	$0.200	$0.180	—	—	—	—
Number of loaves	3,000	8,000	3,000	1,000	3,000	20,000	95,000	—	—	—
Large food store Chain X (own bakery)										
Selling price	—	—	—	—	—	—	—	$25,110	2,700	3,000
Number of loaves	—	—	—	—	—	—	162,000	—	—	—
Medium food store Chain Y (own bakery)										
Selling price	—	—	—	—	—	—	—	$14,850	2,400	3,000
Number of loaves	—	—	—	—	—	—	90,000	—	—	—

SOURCE: Private firm.

For example, in 1963 the largest Quality Bakers of America members (average asset value $3,500,000) had net profits before taxes as a percentage of return on investment (total assets) of 10.91% in 1963. This compares with 10.20% in 1962. The medium-sized member (average asset value of $1,300,000) had net profit before taxes as a percentage of return on investment of 16.09% in 1963 and 16.72% in 1962. The smaller sized firms (average asset value $600,000) had net profit before taxes as a percentage of return

on investment of 11.02% in 1963 and 7.01% in 1962.[56]

These figures would indicate no appreciable economic advantage in the size of bakery operations. However, this does not seem to be the case when one examines a specific cost and price relationship in a specific market structure over a specific period of time. Tables V-22 and V-23 represent an attempt to

[56] Quality Bakers of America Balance Sheet Studies, 1962–1963.

TABLE V-22. White Bread Production, Distribution, and Administration Costs for Large, Medium, and Small Wholesale Bakers and for Chain Stores with Own Bakeries (X & Y), and Miscellaneous Distribution Variables: Six Months, 1959–1960

Type of firm	Production costs Fixed	Variable	Distribution costs Fixed Other	Routes	Variable Other	Routes	Administration costs	Total cost per unit	Average sales price per unit[a]	Weekly profit
Large wholesale bakery	—	—	—	—	—	—	—	—	—	$8,413
Cost per 1-lb. loaf	$0.01094	$0.09642	$0.00578	$0.00442	$0.01114	$0.03073	$0.01100	$0.17043	$0.19178	—
Cost per total production	$4,310	$37,989	$2,277	$1,741	$4,389	$12,107	$4,334	—	—	—
Medium wholesale bakery	—	—	—	—	—	—	—	—	—	$2,705
Cost per 1-lb. loaf	$0.01441	$0.10546	$0.00673	$0.00552	$0.01116	$0.02929	$0.00873	$0.18130	$0.19174	—
Cost per total production	$3,732	$27,314	$1,743	$1,429	$2,890	$7,586	$2,261	—	—	—
Small wholesale bakery	—	—	—	—	—	—	—	—	—	$258
Cost per 1-lb. loaf	$0.01457	$0.11094	$0.00566	$0.00588	$0.01122	$0.03007	$0.00907	$0.18701	$0.18974	—
Cost per total production	$1,384	$10,501	$538	$559	$1,066	$2,857	$862	—	—	—
Large food store Chain X (own bakery)	—	—	—	—	—	—	—	—	—	$4,072
Cost per 1-lb. loaf	$0.01202	$0.10211	$0.00216	—	$0.00586	—	$0.00771	$0.12986	$0.15500	—
Cost per total production	$1,947	$16,542	$350	—	$950	—	$1,249	—	—	—
Medium food store Chain Y (own bakery)	—	—	—	—	—	—	—	—	—	$1,824
Cost per 1-lb. loaf	$0.01281	$0.11253	$0.00306	—	$0.00722	—	$0.00911	$0.14473	$0.16500	—
Cost per total production	$1,153	$10,128	$275	—	$650	—	$820	—	—	—

[a] See Table V-21.

SOURCE: Private firm.

construct a sales and cost matrix of the principal factors that determine the profitability of the major types of competitive wholesale and chain store bakery operations.

The significant factors illustrated by Table V-22 are as follows:

(1) The large wholesale baker has sales prices for his bread that vary from 18 cents to 20 cents a loaf. The lowest sales prices are offered to the chains that have their own bakeries indicating the competitive pressure of the chain to force the price of the branded bread down closer to the private label price of the chain store's own bread. Also Chain X may be a very large customer and obtain annual quantity discounts, utilize different services, and so forth.

(2) The medium wholesale baker also provides bread to the chain stores with their own bakeries at a cheaper price, first, to meet the competition of the private label of the chain, and second, to meet the price competition of the large wholesale baker.

(3) The small wholesale baker is not able to sell to the chains that have their own bakeries, and he is unable to get rid of his production in his normal local market. He therefore may sell outside of the market at a low price so he does not disturb the price of the products he can sell in his local market.

(4) Large food store chain sells all of its output to its own retail outlets at the lowest selling price in the market, 15.5 cents a loaf.

(5) Medium food store chain sells all of its output to its own retail outlets at a slightly higher price than Chain X because of the lower volume and higher costs involved. Both Chains X and Y now have the lowest cost bread in the market.

(6) Table V-22 also indicates that the bakery wholesalers are selling a high proportion of their output to a great number of smaller sized stores which add to their distribution costs. The wholesale bakers are forced into this position by the retail chains who sell on the average about 65% of their bread volume under their own private label. The Arthur D. Little report[57] also indicates that 18% of U.S. bread business is handled by small retail food stores. These same food stores account for approximately 29% of the bread business of the wholesale bakers.

The significant factors illustrated by Table V-21 include various cost and profit analysis derived by comparing the costs in Table V-22 with the sales prices in Table V-21. These factors are as follows:

(1) The lowest production costs in the market are those of large wholesale bakers. The second lowest are those of large retail food Chain X. The third lowest are those of the medium-sized wholesale baker. These cost figures indicate that in terms of production costs the large wholesale baker serving a broad market area is in the most favorable position.

[57] Arthur D. Little, Inc., *Distribution: The Challenge of the Sixties*, p. 21.

(2) When one examines the distribution costs, the competitive positions change. Both Chain X and Chain Y have extremely low distribution costs from their bakeries to their own retail chains. (This production cost disadvantage and distribution cost advantage is illustrated on a national basis in Table V-23.)

TABLE V-23. Cost per Pound of White Pan Bread, Four Largest Wholesale Bakers and Five Major Grocery Chains with Baking Operations: 1958 (In cents)

	4 largest wholesale baking companies	5 major grocery chains' baking operations[a]
Production costs:		
Ingredient costs	5.14	5.72
Packaging and wrapping materials	1.09	1.08
Compensation, bakery plant employees[b]	2.62	2.68
Compensation, company officers	.06	.01
Depreciation expense	.35	.17
Taxes, other than income and social security	.11	.05
Other costs and expenses	1.26	1.01
Total production cost	10.63	10.72
Distribution costs:		
Compensation, delivery employees[b]	3.21	.06
Delivery expense other than wages and salaries	.60	.94[c]
Advertising and promotion	.66	.08
Total distribution cost	4.47	1.08
Total cost per pound	15.10	11.80

[a] As reported and without adjustment for costs borne by non-bakery departments.

[b] Includes wages, salaries and employer contributions to fringe benefits and social security.

[c] Includes wages for one company and costs of contract carriers for another. None of the other three, however, was below the wholesale company average.

SOURCE: Computed from companies' replies to subcommittee survey. See also, *Administered Prices of Bread*, p. 113.

(3) The low distribution costs of the chain stores more than offset any disadvantage in high production costs that they may have.

(4) The high production and distribution cost structure of the small wholesale bakery is the major reason why so many of them have gone and are going out of business.

(5) The chains do not translate their bread cost savings into large profits, but rather keep their selling

prices very low, as we shall note later on in this chapter.

In addition to the severe competition of the bakery chains noted above, the bakery industry also suffers from excess capacity. The Arthur D. Little survey[58] also indicated excess oven-capacity for bread manufacturers in most cities.

The wholesale bakery industry is one of low profits for most participants. The high cost distribution pattern[59] of the bakery industry provided an incentive for retail chains to cut these costs by manufacturing their own private label bread. In addition, the Robinson-Patman Act that attempted to maintain uniform bread prices at the wholesale level could best be challenged by a retail chain's producing its own bread and reducing the price to its retail outlets. There is no doubt that the growth of retail chain store bakeries has forced many cost-cutting programs to take place among wholesale bakers. These have included production efficiencies through bulk handling. On the other hand, other costs such as promotion and advertising, and packaging, as well as distribution, have forced the cost of bread up and have placed a squeeze on bakery profits.

Most of the institutions utilized in improving the profitability of this industry involve vertical integration of operations to cut distribution costs, or coordination of advertising, promotion, and procurement policies through association and cooperative efforts.

The small baker must be a specialist and provide a unique product and service to exist in this highly competitive segment of the wheat economy.

Several alternative strategies have been developed by bakers, including the following:

(1) The development of new products and of technologies that differentiate their products from the staples manufactured by the food chains: frozen pies, cakes, tarts, and doughnuts.

(2) The utilization of freezers for dough and finished products to reduce the problem of perishability and broaden their available markets.

(3) Contract flour procurement practices that maximize the locational advantages of various mill-bakery relationships.

(4) Reduction of labor costs through the development of continuous baking procedures.

(5) Greater specialization by the small retail bake shops

[58] *Ibid.*, p. 22.

[59] *Ibid.*, USDA, ERS, *Spreads in Farm-Retail Prices of White Bread*, p. 14. Vehicle expense and a portion of the driver's commission often make the cost of moving a loaf of bread from a west-side city bakery to an east-side grocery store greater than the cost of transporting the wheat equivalent to the bread from North Dakota to the East Coast.

to provide unique products with quality and taste appeals.

(6) The development of low cost bakers — "discount bakers" — who cater to the private label manufacturing requirements of some chains.

(7) Increasing cooperation of labor unions with bakers to provide more drop delivery systems of distribution.

(8) The growth of cooperative associations that upgrade the management and functional operations of their members as well as providing procurement bargaining power and national promotion.

(9) The development of conglomerate companies that handle other food items that are not necessarily wheat-oriented.

Retailers. The retailer as a participant in the wheat economy is perhaps the most diversified of all. A typical supermarket carries over 6,000 items. Therefore, to measure the *general profitability* of retail outlets as a measure of a typical profit pattern in the *wheat economy* would be extremely misleading. In order to examine the retailer's profit position in the wheat economy, various financial data for white bread sales and costs were obtained from a selected group of major food chains representative of the major geographical areas in the United States. Corporate chain stores were selected rather than voluntary or cooperative chains or independent stores in order to simplify the task of reducing individual accounting systems to a common pattern and to require as few accounting adjustments as possible.

Before turning to these selected data, a general outline of how important bakery (wheat) products are to the retailer will be presented in order to provide a realistic setting for the individual bread data.

According to a preliminary announcement of its plans, the National Commission on Food Marketing stated, "Grocery store food margins have increased 4% over the last ten years, and of the $69 billion[60] the nation's consumers spent for food in 1964, about $2.5 billion represented that increase." [61] Undoubtedly there are many reasons for this increase. In general, there have been increased operating costs and an increase of promotional devices, such as trading stamps. Even though gross margins of grocery stores have increased, net operating profits of food chains declined from 1.35% of sales in 1955 to 1.12% in 1963–1964.[62] A maturing retail food industry that once

lowered margins as volume increased has currently raised them as food retailing has become more complex and operating and promotional costs have increased. Increased competition has led to various forms of price and nonprice competition, and advertising and promotion are a growing part of the food bill, now totaling around $2.5 billion a year.[63] The severe price and nonprice competition has resulted in ownership and retailing innovations. The biggest chains have not increased their share of the food retail dollar. The smaller chains have grown, and *total* corporate chain store share of the market has risen slightly (from 37% in 1947 to 41% in 1963).[64] Affiliated stores (wholesale-sponsored and cooperative retail store chains) have increased rapidly from 29% of total retail food sales in 1948 to 49% in 1962. Independents, although more numerous than chain and affiliated stores have declined in total dollar sales volume from 34% in 1948 to 10% in 1962.[65] Discount food stores have increased their overall share of the grocery market to 5% in 1964.[66] These statistics provide a general background of retail food store variations.

The corporate chains selected for the author's special study represent 6 out of the 24 largest chains in the United States, and account for approximately $4.3 billion of retail food store sales (about 7% of total food store sales). The author believes these firms represent an important cross section of all corporate food chain firms that handle 41% of the U.S. total grocery store dollar sales volume.

Although retail margins have increased during recent years, returns on net assets for food chains have *decreased* slightly to an average of approximately 12%.[67] This return is higher than the return on investments in other segments of the wheat economy and supports the comments by Mueller and Garoian[68] that retailers, *in general,* who integrate into manufacturing enterprises and develop their own brands and labels, would lower their profit rates. "Profits of the affected grocery-manufacturing industries would decline relative to grocery retailing. Available empirical data support this hypothesis." [69]

[60] Civilian expenditures for food originating in the United States.
[61] National Commission on Food Marketing, news release, May 5, 1965.
[62] Harvard Business School, *Operating Results of Food Chains in 1955;* Cornell University, *Operating Results of Food Chains in 1963–1964.*
[63] *The Food Marketing Outlook and the Consumer,* speech by Kenneth E. Ogren, November 19, 1963.
[64] *Progressive Grocer: Annual Report for 1964,* p. F20.
[65] USDA, ERS, *Changes in Total Market Structure and Implications of these Changes,* "Project 1964", February 1, 1965.
[66] Testimony of Robert Montgomery, Vice President of Kroger Co., before National Commission on Food Marketing, May 7, 1965.
[67] First National City Bank of New York, *Net Income of Leading Corporations,* 1963 and 1964, p. 4.
[68] Mueller and Garoian, *Changes in the Market Structure of Grocery Retailing.*
[69] *Ibid.,* p. 149.

How do bakery goods profits of retail corporate and cooperative chain stores fit the general description of grocery retailing above? From three specific studies — the Super-Valu Study (a cooperative chain) of 1957 (North Central states); the Dillon Study of 1959 in Kansas (Mid-Central states); and the Colonial Study of 1963 (the South) — one is able to extrapolate some general characteristics of bakery product sales as a percentage of total store dollar sales volume.[70]

Super-Valu (1957)	5.76%
Dillon (1959)	6.62
Colonial (1963)	4.63

All three studies indicate that bakery products are a significant portion of a store's 6,000 item dollar sales. Gross margins on bakery products have remained fairly constant averaging slightly over 18%.[71] In addition over 50% of all bread sales in food chains are private label and 23.7% of all foods manufactured by food chains are bakery products.[72]

The Colonial Study went on to separate bread and rolls as a special category and indicated that this group represented 3.88% of weekly dollar sales and had a margin of 17%, but had an annual turnover rate of 363.3 times which enabled this product category to return $74.17 for each dollar invested.[73] (This compared with total store returns of $7.14 for each dollar invested or *ten times* the average.) As indicated earlier in this study, national brand bread that is not paid for until sold (stale bread is returned to the baker) and that has a high turnover actually permits a cash inflow for the retailer which partially accounts for the excellent dollar return on investment.

Other general studies point out that retail grocers, on an average, received about 4.2 cents gross margin on a one-pound loaf for their services in 1963.[74] Trade reports for 100 cities in 1957 indicated that prices of bread sold under a store's own label were about 4 cents per pound loaf below retail prices of wholesale bakery brand bread.[75] One might assume that the private label bread would have lower margins as well as a lower retail price structure. Keeping the above general descriptions and assumptions in mind let us turn to a specific analysis of several major food

chain firms all of which manufacture and sell their own private label bread.[76]

In the absence of any information on retail food chain private label operations in comparison with manufacturers' branded breads, the author undertook to obtain some cost and price information with respect to this. As indicated on page 87, six corporate retail food chains cooperated in this study and were selected from the top 24 retail food chains in the United States (as measured by dollar sales volume). The selected chains, collectively, are represented in each of the major geographical areas in the United States. A single statistic was obtained from each corporate food chain for each sales and cost item noted in the following tables. These statistics consisted of weighted average of all the divisions (and individual store data within each division) of each of the food chains represented. The *collective* data as utilized in the following analysis represents a weighted average of each food chain's statistical information. The *range* data, as presented in Tables V-26 and V-29, indicate the high and low of the individual statistics obtained from the six chains.

Elsewhere in this study it was estimated that from 10% to 20% of all white bread sold in the United States was manufactured and sold by food chains under their own private labels. In the special sample from which we received data for the present study, 70% to 75% of all white bread sales were private label bread sales (see Table V-24).

TABLE V-24. Dollar Volumes and Percent of Private Label and Manufacturers' Brand Bread Sold by Selected Food Chains: 1959–1963
(In millions of dollars)

		Private label bread		Manufacturers' brand bread	
Year	All bread sales	Sales volume	% of total bread sales	Sales volume	% of total bread sales
1959	$237.1	$177.7	75.0%	$59.4	25.1%
1960	259.7	190.9	73.5	68.8	26.5
1961	259.2	189.3	73.1	69.8	27.0
1962	264.6	187.6	70.9	77.1	29.1
1963	275.2	196.9	71.6	78.3	28.6

SOURCE: Six corporate food chains.

Each food chain management in this study had a slightly different policy with respect to the manufacture and sale of its private label white bread. One chain management believed in a mathematical balance

---

[70] *Progressive Grocer: Colonial Study*, 1963, p. C43.
[71] *Ibid.*
[72] National Commission on Food Marketing, *Organization and Competition in the Milling and Baking Industries*, p. 56.
[73] *Ibid.*, p. C26, column 29, row 2.
[74] USDA, ERS, *Spreads in Farm-Retail Prices of White Bread*, p. 14.
[75] *Ibid.*

[76] Some retailers have been optimistic about bread manufacturing operations and sell private label bread to other retail outlets as well as their own. Those chains in this study sell their manufacturer private label *only* through their own retail outlets and purchase additional private label bread from other bakeries.

TABLE V-25. Operating Data of Bakery Divisions of Selected Food Chains:[a] 1958–1963

Bakery statistics	1958	1959	1960	1961	1962	1963
Baked food sales[b]	$74,578,707	$83,033,191	$90,418,329	$93,642,065	$103,517,760	$108,253,121
Cost of goods sold	67,738,217	75,674,337	82,333,586	84,913,484	92,851,157	96,326,157
Profit before taxes	6,840,490	7,358,854	8,084,743	8,728,581	10,666,603	11,926,964
Net profit after taxes	3,297,879	3,550,157	3,918,015	4,226,666	5,169,419	5,773,952
			% of sales			
Baked food sales	100.00%	100.00%	100.00%	100.00%	100.00%	100.00%
Cost of goods sold	90.83	91.14	91.06	90.68	89.70	88.98
Profit before taxes	9.17	8.86	8.94	9.32	10.30	11.02
Net profit after taxes	4.42	4.28	4.33	4.51	4.99	5.33

[a] All the food chains in this study charged the cost of distributing bakery products to their retail outlets, as follows:

	1958	1959	1960	1961	1962	1963
Amount	$6,912,381	$7,403,601	$7,903,545	$8,279,647	$8,928,706	$9,067,398
% of sales	9.27%	8.92%	8.74%	8.84%	8.63%	8.38%

[b] "Baked food sales" are sales to the chains on a transfer price basis laid down at the retail store.
SOURCE: Six corporate food chains.

(50% manufacturers' brand and 50% private label).[77] Another chain operator believed in an all-out effort to sell his private label bread and carry a minimum of manufacturers' brands for customer satisfaction. Over 94% of all white bread sales by this chain were private label sales. This same firm, although currently manufacturing all of its own private label, was debating whether or not it would be more efficient to purchase its private label bread. At the other extreme was another food chain which manufactured and sold approximately 35% of its bread volume as private label.

age (4.28% of sales[78] after taxes in 1960 and 5.33% in 1963) than the typical 1.3% of retail sales[79] for all sales of food chains. (These results also contradict Mueller's and Garoian's earlier statement that retailers entering manufacturing would reduce profit levels.) On the other hand, this manufacturing "success" may be a bookkeeping one because the transfer price to the retail store may provide an excellent return to the bakery manufacturing operations but a very low return on the retail sales of the private label bakery products.

TABLE V-26. Range of Operating Data of Bakery Divisions of Selected Food Chains as a Percent of Sales:[a] 1958–1963

Bakery statistics		1958[b]	1959[b]	1960	1961	1962	1963
Cost of goods sold	Low	89.67%	87.94%	84.53%	85.80%	85.70%	86.13%
	High	97.39	97.78	97.83	97.64	97.11	96.88
Net profit after tax	Low	1.33	1.12	1.08	1.12	1.25	1.55
	High	5.08	6.03	7.74	7.10	7.15	6.81
Cost of distribution	Low	4.75	3.71	3.45	3.45	3.02	2.72
	High	12.35	11.07	10.67	10.90	10.80	10.60

[a] All the food chains in this study charged the cost of distributing bakery products to their retail outlets. The firms representing the low and high ratios were not the same for each of the years analyzed, nor were they the same in any one year for the various categories.
[b] In 1958 and 1959 one or more firms were unable to provide data either because private brands were not produced or because statistics were unavailable with respect to the private and/or national brands under consideration.
SOURCE: Six corporate food chains.

The combined operating data of bakery divisions of selected food chains for 1958–1963 given in Table V-25 shows the results of these various policies. The significance of these results is that bakery division operations are considerably more profitable on the *aver-*

The weighted average statistics discussed above prove misleading. If one examines the same data presented in Table V-25 as a range of combined bakery division results for *individual* firms expressed as a percentage of sales, the profitability of manufacturing

---

[77] This balance was accomplished by estimating weekly bread sales and manufacturing enough private label bread to cover 50% of total sales and priced competitively enough to sell out the private label.

[78] Bakery sales are defined as the "sales" value of bakery products laid down at the retail store.
[79] Retail store bakery sales are "sales" value of bakery products sold to the consumer.

private label bread varies considerably among individual corporate chains (see Table V-26). One chain bakery had as low a manufacturing profit as 1.08% after tax in 1960. Another chain bakery operation in that same year had a net profit after tax of 7.74% of sales. The chain with the lowest net manufacturing profit would appear to be penalizing the overall profit potential of the firm unless its retail bakery sales of private label compensated for the low return in manufacturing bakery products.

The major significance of these data is that operators may add to their profitability in the food retailing segment of the wheat industry by manufacturing their private label bakery products *provided* they have *low distribution and production costs*. (Some firms maintain that even with high production and distribution costs it pays to manufacture their own private label to add to the competitive market structure of the manufacturers of brand bread.)

Let us next turn to an analysis of white bread prices and margins for private label and leading manufacturers' brands in these same selected food chain retail operations for 1959 through 1963 in order to analyze the *combined* bakery and retail operations. Table V-27

TABLE V-27. White Bread Prices and Margins for Private Label and Leading Manufacturers' Brands in Selected Food Chains: 1959–1963
(Companywide averages, annually in cents per one-pound loaf)

Private label	*1959*	*1960*	*1961*	*1962*	*1963*
Cost of 1-lb. loaf of white bread delivered to store and placed on the shelf	14.13	14.64	14.96	15.19	15.35
Average price of bread sold	16.00	17.10	17.32	17.89	17.77
Cost of stales[a]	.44	.45	.47	.49	.48
Gross margin	1.43	2.01	1.89	2.21	1.94
Cost allocation to this item	1.19	1.39	1.46	1.54	1.56
Net margin	.24	.62	.43	.67	.38
Leading manufacturers' brands					
Cost of 1-lb. loaf of white bread delivered to store and placed on the shelf	16.26	16.83	18.33	19.01	19.05
Average price of bread sold	20.27	21.35	23.28	23.31	23.35
Cost of stales[a]	—	—	—	—	—
Gross margin	4.01	4.52	4.95	4.30	4.30
Cost allocation to this item	1.27	1.65	1.76	1.86	1.97
Net margin	2.74	2.87	3.19	2.44	2.33

[a] Cost of stale bread to the retailer for private label is dependent upon the amount of bread left over at the end of the day in relation to total private label bread sold. There is no "cost of stales" to the retailer for manufacturers' brands because the wholesale baker takes back stale bread (day-old bread) and replaces it with fresh bread at no cost to the retailer.

SOURCE: Six corporate food chains.

represents companywide averages on an annual basis.

The reader will note that private label sales and cost data indicate that, *on the average, net* margins before tax on private label bread were extremely meager (0.24 cent in 1959 to a high of 0.67 cent in 1962 per one-pound loaf). These data also indicate that *gross* margins were also minimal, varying from a low of 1.43 cents in 1959 to a high of 2.21 cents in 1962 per one-pound loaf.

The data for the leading manufacturers' brands suggest that the retailers were able to maintain a gross margin of 18% to 20% and a net margin of from 2.33 cents per one-pound loaf in 1963 to a high of 3.19 cents in 1961. Without taking into consideration the profit on bread *manufacturing*, these data indicate that it is much more profitable to sell manufacturers' brands of bread than private label through these selected retail food chains. Table V-27A, extrapolated

TABLE V-27A. Net Margins for Private Label and Leading Manufacturers' Brands of White Bread: 1959–1963
(In cents per one-pound loaf)

Year	Private label	Leading manufacturer
1959	0.24	2.74
1960	0.62	2.87
1961	0.43	3.19
1962	0.67	2.44
1963	0.38	2.33

from Table V-27, shows the net margin advantage of the manufacturers' brands.

When one compares the data for private label bread with those of the leading manufacturers' brands (see Table V-27 and Exhibit V-7), one notes a widening differential between private label and manufacturers' brand costs of a one-pound loaf of bread delivered to the store. Similarly, there is a widening differential between private label retail bread prices and manufacturers' brand retail prices in these selected food chain stores, and between private label and manufacturers' brands. The cost and sales differentials extrapolated from Table V-27 are given in Table V-27B.

The significance of these statistical relationships in the selected food chain firms suggests that an appeal is made to the consumer on a price basis that is evident by the low selling price for private label bread. These statistics also indicate that the reduced billing price of private label bread to the retailer is passed on to the consumer in the form of a reduced selling price. The wide differentials in billing price and sales price between private label and manufacturers' brands suggest that the retailer has to cut his price substantially to obtain a major sales volume of his private label

EXHIBIT V-7

White Bread Prices and Margins for Private Label
and Leading Manufacturers' Brands in Selected
Chain Stores: 1959–1963
(Companywide averages annually)

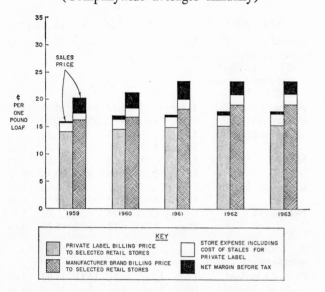

consumer,[81] the sales volume data for this study of
selected food chain stores show that approximately
two-thirds[82] of all bread sales by these stores are
private label sales (see Exhibit V-8). Exhibit V-8
also indicates that national brands have retained approximately the same percentage of total white bread
sales in these selected food chains from 1959 through
1963. The consumer is given a wide range of choice
in his selection of bread in these selected chain stores
and overwhelmingly chooses the private label on the
basis of price and store reputation.

EXHIBIT V-8

White Bread Dollar Sales and Net Margin as a Percent
of Sales for Private Label and Leading Manufacturers'
Brands in Selected Food Chains: 1959–1963
(Companywide averages annually)

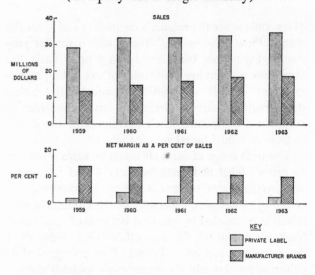

product over the manufacturers' brand bread.[80] In
addition, these data from the selected firms point to
strong price competition that limits the private label
bread profits to the retailer even though he has a cost

TABLE V-27B. White Bread Cost and Selling Price
Differentials for Private Label and Manufacturers'
Brands: 1959–1963
(In cents per one-pound loaf)

Year	Private label	Manufacturers' brands	Differential
		Cost delivered to store shelf	
1959	14.13	16.26	2.13
1960	14.64	16.83	2.19
1961	14.96	18.33	3.37
1962	15.19	19.01	3.82
1963	15.35	19.05	3.70
		Selling price	
1959	16.00	20.27	4.27
1960	17.10	21.35	4.25
1961	17.32	23.28	5.96
1962	17.89	23.31	5.42
1963	17.77	23.35	5.58

advantage. It also provides an extremely competitive
market in which the manufacturer must operate. Although some studies indicate a strong preference for
the leading manufacturers' brands of bread by the

As evaluated in terms of profitability, the retailer
would, on the average, seem to be better off handling
manufacturers' brands rather than private label bread
(see Exhibit V-8). However, if the *combined* manufacturing and retail profit for private label bread provides a greater return on investment than does manufacturers' brands, then the retailer's net margin results
on private label sales are not indicative of overall
profit opportunity and the retailer would attempt to
increase private label bread sales (Table V-28). Second, the low sales price of private label bread pro-

[80] The reader is cautioned that the author has not taken into
consideration any *quality* differentials that may exist among
the private label bread and manufacturer brands used in this
limited statistical analysis.

[81] A consumer bread preference study made in 1957 by
E. T. Sperry states, "In 19 of the 27 communities at least five
times as many consumers preferred the leading wholesale company's bread as the leading chain store brand." *Administered
Prices of Bread*, pp. 122–123.

[82] The actual percentage in the selected food chain study
varied from a high of 74.95% in 1959 to a low of 70.88%
in 1962. The most current figure was 71.55% for 1963 operations.

TABLE V-28. Comparison of Net Margin and Bakery Operations' Dollar Contribution of Bread Sales for Private Label and Manufacturers' Brand Bread Sales in Selected Food Chains: 1959–1963
(In thousands)

Year	Net margin private label bread sales	Net margin private label bakery sales	Total net margin for private label bakery and retail sales	Net margin[a] manufacturers' brand bread sales
1959	$ 426	$3,298	$3,724	$1,627
1960	1,184	3,550	4,734	1,975
1961	814	3,918	4,732	2,228
1962	1,257	4,227	5,484	1,880
1963	748	5,169	5,917	1,824

[a] Note that net margin on manufacturers' brands is on volume less than two-thirds of private label sales and therefore return on investment might be much higher.
SOURCE: Six corporate food chains.

vides savings for the retailer's customers and gives the store a "low price image." Third, with a retailer promoting his private label largely on a price basis, the arrangements that are made with others selling manufacturers' brands are inevitably affected by either downgrading quality or foregoing services in order to maintain a competitive shelf movement or the development of a dual brand sales policy.

The wide range of costs allocated by store managers to private label and manufacturers' brand bread operations indicates some differences in overhead accounting procedures, especially in the charge for rent which is overstated in one firm because of specialized lease arrangements. On the other hand, there does seem to be a consistent internal firm policy of allocating approximately the same costs to both private label and manufacturers' brand bread. This consistency provides some validity to the overall comparison of private label and manufacturers' brand bread operations among the selected food chain companies. (The problems of allocating costs to individual products still plague the industry as the McKinsey and Pet Milk Studies demonstrate.[83]

As in our previous analysis of bakery operations of retail food chains, averages are misleading. Table V-29 and Exhibit V-9 set forth the high and low margin ranges for individual food chain operators' private label and leading manufacturers' brand bread operations for the six corporate food chains in the study.

The high-range and low-range data suggest three observations:

[83] McKinsey, *The Birds Eye Study;* Buzzell, Salmon, and Vancil, *Product Profitability Measurement and Merchandising Decisions.*

TABLE V-29. Range of White Bread Costs, Prices, and Margins for Private Label and Leading Manufacturers' Brands in Selected Food Chains: 1959–1963
(Based on one all-store average for each company covered in cents per one-pound loaf)

Private label		1959	1960	1961	1962	1963
Cost of 1-lb. loaf	Low	12.73	11.65	12.04	12.37	12.74
of white bread delivered to store and placed on the shelf	High	18.68	18.69	18.72	18.76	18.77
Average price of	Low	15.63	16.57	16.49	16.90	16.68
bread sold	High	24.00	24.00	26.00	26.00	26.00
Cost of stales[a]	Low	.31	.33	.33	.34	.33
	High	1.13	1.17	1.24	1.28	1.26
Margin	Low	.98	1.16	.83	1.17	.89
	High	4.84	10.08	9.69	8.38	9.63
Cost allocation to	Low	.76	.83	.94	1.00	1.08
bread	High	4.79	4.79	5.18	5.12	5.10
Net margin	Low	(.07)	.04	(.30)	.03	(.25)
	High	2.99	6.78	6.38	5.27	6.19
Leading manufacturers' brands						
Cost of 1-lb. loaf	Low	15.97	16.10	16.11	16.97	17.03
of white bread delivered to store and placed on the shelf	High	20.80	20.80	22.40	22.40	22.40
Average price of	Low	19.17	19.84	19.45	20.63	20.37
bread sold	High	26.00	26.00	28.00	28.00	28.00
Cost of stales[a]		—	—	—	—	—
Margin	Low	3.20	3.37	3.34	3.66	3.70
	High	5.20	6.58	6.58	6.58	6.58
Cost allocation to	Low	.94	1.04	1.13	1.14	1.14
bread	High	5.18	5.19	5.58	5.51	5.49
Net margin	Low	.02	.01	.02	.09	.11
	High	3.06	3.85	3.84	3.91	3.86

[a] Stales are returned to wholesale bakers for manufacturers' brands and are a cost of doing business for private label operations.
SOURCE: Six corporate food chains.

(1) Even though the *weighted average* net margin realized from private label bread sales is very small (Exhibit V-7), there are chain store operators who are able to maintain very profitable private label operations (net margins before tax as high as 6.78 cents per one-pound loaf).

(2) There is a wide range of performance in individual company private label cost and sales operations. There is also a wide range of operational performance in individual cost and sales prices of leading manufacturer brands. It was possible for the author in examining the confidential data to identify geographical and local trade patterns even though the data were not comprehensive enough to present statistics to support such a generalized statement. The broad range of individual company op-

EXHIBIT V-9

White Bread Net (before taxes) Margins Realized for Private Label and Leading Manufacturers' Brands in Selected Chain Stores: 1959–1963
(Range and weighted average of companywide annual net margins realized for the year)

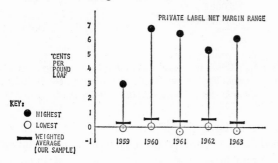

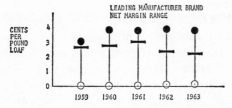

erating results for private label and manufacturers' brands of bread is summarized in Table V-29A.

Because the author's figures are *annual companywide averages,* they tend to dampen the high and low price and margin statistics that exist within a particular food chain at any one particular time period. Eventually the

TABLE V-29A. Individual Grocery Chain White Bread Cost, Price, and Margin Ranges: 1959–1963
(Lowest and highest figures in cents per one-pound loaf)

Bread costs and sales information	Private label (lowest)	(highest)	Manufacturers' brands (lowest)	(highest)
Cost to retailer	11.65	18.77	15.97	22.40
Sales price to consumer	15.63	26.00	19.17	28.00
Cost of stales[a]	.31	1.28	a	a
Gross margin	.83	10.08	3.20	6.58
Costs allocated	.76	5.18	.94	5.58
Net margin before tax	(.30)[b]	6.78	.01	3.91

[a] Stales are returned to wholesale bakers for manufacturers' brands and are a cost of doing business for private label operations.
[b] Loss.
SOURCE: Six corporate food chains.

variations that may exist between divisions of a firm at any one time tend to average out. For the most part those stores and geographic regions that have high profit margins have a pricing pattern of frequent price specials which lower overall annual margins. On the other hand, those stores that have low margins for their bread operations seldom, if ever, have price specials and hence tend to have comparable margins when compared with other regional or individual store bread departments.

(3) The wide range in the "cost of stales" statistics indicates two types of food chain policies. One policy encourages the stores to stock private label bread heavily and therefore to overstock and sell more. The other policy wants stale costs held to a minimum but expects stores to produce large bread sales (the higher the sales, the lower the percentage of stales). The latter policy may encourage the store manager to under-order private label bread to keep cost of stales relatively small.

The retailer has been one of the most important factors in maintaining competition in the wheat economy. The development and growth of private label operations have forced a reappraisal of pricing, procurement, and distribution policies by managers in every segment of the entire wheat industry. The retailer has benefited indirectly (less risk for him in procurement and inventory costs) from government price support programs which have stabilized wheat and flour prices and have also assumed much of the inventory investment burden of the producer, assembler, processor, and retailer. There are many alternative strategies that the retailer is currently formulating as expressed in interviews with the author. They are as follows:

(1) Many retailers are planning increases in the manufacturing of or purchase of private label bread and other bakery products (a) to avoid the high costs of distribution of wholesale bakers, (b) to operate manufacturing plants at 100% capacity in supplying their own retail outlets, and (c) to keep competitive price pressure on wholesale bakery suppliers.

(2) Many retailers are developing a more balanced program between the "questionable" profitability of manufacturing and selling primarily private label bread vs. the handling of more manufacturers' brands.

(3) Severe competition in bakery operations may mean that it may be more profitable for retailers to *purchase* private label bread rather than manufacture it themselves.

(4) Most retailers tend to specialize in the production of one or two basic baking products (e.g., the one-pound loaf of white bread) in their own captive bakeries and leave the specialty product sales and development to wholesale baker suppliers.

(5) Some retailers use and understand the futures market for sugar in their bread manufacturing-selling operations, but have made little use of the wheat futures market primarily because of the price support program that has lessened wide swings in wheat and flour prices. If wheat prices become less tied to price support levels, retailers should have more occasion to make use of the wheat futures market.

(6) Because of the requirement of daily freshness, which, in turn, leads to localized manufacturing, most private label manufacturing will probably be limited to the larger food chains that have enough local retail outlets to warrant a bakery manufacturing plant of efficient size.[84]

In summary, the profitability of individual firms in the wheat economy seems to be quite dependent on the policies a top manager adopts with respect to utilizing his firm's human and physical resources in the broad perspective of the total wheat system. The most effective manager is aware of and a party to the technological and structural changes of his industry system. He also provides leadership in creating new coordinating arrangements that make it more possible for his firm and industry to be more efficient and competitive in domestic and world markets.

COMPETITION

Thus far it has been shown that low profit levels, responsiveness of prices, the development of new products and competitive contractual relationships, the prominent position of farm and nonfarm cooperatives in the industry, and the development of private label consumer products at sharply reduced retail price levels result in many types of product and price competition in the wheat system. We shall now consider other measures of competition in this industry.

EASE OF ENTRY AND EXIT

The capital investment required to build or buy flour milling facilities utilizing the latest technologies and to build adequate storage and grain elevator facilities gives an economic advantage to larger flour milling units. The processing cost advantages seem to be associated with the size of the *milling unit* rather than the *daily capacity of a plant* as shown in Table V-30. This indicates that smaller flour milling plants with *large milling units* can be competitive with larger plants that have high capacity but smaller operating units. Furthermore, many flour mills have been closed and are for sale at extremely low prices. The growth of such firms as John Vainer, Dixie Portland, Bay State, Allied Seaboard, and others was made possible in part by a writedown of the fixed asset value of flour milling plants. Such a writedown was still occurring in the spring of 1967. In addition, several flour mill-

[84] Even though many retailers are not able to *manufacture* their own private label bread, a good many have been able to *purchase* their private label bread at considerable cost savings when compared with the distribution costs of some of the major manufacturers' brand bread suppliers.

TABLE V-30. Flour Milling Costs by Size of Plant: Crop Year 1964

Daily capacity (cwt.)	Total manufacturing costs (dollars per cwt.)
12,500 and over	$0.3746
10,000–12,499	0.3574
7,500–9,999	0.3042
5,000–7,499	0.3009
2,500–4,999	0.3385
400–2,499	0.4214
Average	0.3366

SOURCE: Based on reports from 78 plants milling hard wheat from National Commission on Food Marketing, *Organization and Competition in the Milling and Baking Industries.*

ing firms have developed joint ventures with grain firms in the United States and overseas to improve procurement operations and to do so at limited investment levels.

It is fairly easy to enter other segments of the wheat system. Any person may become a wheat producer as the Department of Agriculture makes available additional wheat allotments for new acres of production. Also any producer who grows wheat in one out of three years maintains his wheat allotment priority.

The cost of a country subterminal or small terminal elevator is approximately $1 million for each million bushels of capacity, but older facilities are available for much less. In addition the cost of such facilities has not prohibited the growth of many farmer cooperative facilities. In essence, entry though costly is not prohibitive.

Entrance into the export business requires (in theory) a telephone and a desk. But from previous analysis in this section of the study, it is quite apparent that large amounts of capital are required to handle huge volumes of grain at minute margins (even though capital can be borrowed against hedged inventories). More important, the knowledge of the intricate, complicated, and in many cases highly personal ways in which export trade takes place puts a premium on experience and trust built over many decades. New firms are constantly entering the export business, however, but few have yet succeeded in becoming a major firm (with the important exceptions of Cargill and Producers' Export) able to challenge the leadership of century old firms.

It is also fairly easy to enter the bakery and retail food chain businesses. Perhaps the one exception is the retail food chain-bread manufacturer combination. In this case, the freshness that is required of the product limits the area of delivery and thus only the food chains with numerous retail outlets in a compact area can operate a bakery plant of economical size. However, there is the alternative of purchasing private label, which in many cases may have advantages over manufacturing one's own private label bread.

Ease of exit from the industry is also apparent by the decline in the number of many small size operating units at each segment of the wheat economy. The presence of the government's wheat price support and storage programs may have delayed some adjustments, but on the whole these programs have been most beneficial to the larger more efficient segments of the wheat system; and at the same time they have permitted a less painful departure of many participants in the wheat system.

CONCENTRATION

The previous structural analysis of the wheat system has indicated that, in most segments, the number of firms is declining and those that remain are growing in terms of dollar volume of products produced and/or sold and in terms of capital invested. In several segments ownership is highly concentrated, and vertical and conglomerate mergers are increasing among the various sectors of the wheat economy. Yet, competition (price and nonprice) is severe. Even within a single vertically integrated firm competition exists. For example, the procurement division and the processing and marketing divisions many times find themselves at opposite positions in the futures market or bidding against each other in the spot market.

No one firm in any one segment of the wheat industry is of such size as to dominate any portion of it. As one examines each segment of the wheat industry in greater detail, it is apparent that different types of functions and business strategies require different sized firms. It is a heterogeneous group of large and small firms. The large firms have counterparts in size among firms engaged in similar operations and in firms supplying goods and services to them or purchasing from them.

Summarizing, segment by segment:

(1) Wheat farming is still atomistic, and even though 40% of the wheat volume is handled by farm cooperatives, these cooperatives consist of many individual regional and local farm cooperative groups. They compete with one another domestically and internationally. For example, although farmer cooperatives own a cooperative export company — Producers' Export Company in New York — in an interview on February 29, 1964, Mr. Alcone, the manager, estimated that "less than 50% of the wheat for export shipped by cooperatives is shipped through Producers' Export." The remainder is shipped through other export firms.

(2) Country elevator and terminal firms also compete vigorously. The presence of equally strong farmer cooperative, wheat processing, export, and flexible independent operators, together with declining margins on wheat and storage handling, is evidence of this competition.

(3) Flour milling is an industry that is both concentrated and vertically integrated but the indication of flexible pricing of wheat and the pressures exerted by the bakers on one side and the cooperatives and export firms on the procurement side (plus government programs) certainly suggests competition among the flour millers. The flour milling industry seems to meet the tests of competition: (a) buyers and sellers do have choices, (b) firms are seeking to be chosen, (c) firms do try to improve their appeals and effectiveness in responding to customers' requirements, and (d) firms are constantly trying to reduce costs. There is also competitive pressure exerted by those supplying them with raw materials and by those purchasing flour. Table V-31 shows a slight decline in the percent of value of shipments of flour and meal by the four and eight largest companies in the industry.

TABLE V-31. Flour Milling Capacity Ownership Patterns: 1951, 1958, and 1965

	% of U.S. capacity		
Firms	*1951*	*1958*	*1965*
4 largest	28.6%	32.1%	23.9%
8 largest	41.1	45.3	39.0
12 largest	48.8	52.1	49.9
16 largest	53.9	56.9	56.5
20 largest	57.7	61.3	61.1
U.S. total daily capacity	1,124,943	1,101,342	1,094,000

SOURCE: U.S. Bureau of the Census.

The 20 largest wheat flour milling firms as of 1965 are listed in Table V-32. The reader will note that General Mills is third in the country with the closing of 9 of its 17 flour mills; it was formerly first. The reader will also note that two of the top three firms are now primarily in the consumer end product business and that flour milling is continually declining in importance in their overall business operations.

In the 1966 annual report of Pillsbury, it was noted that consumer products as a percentage of sales had increased from 28.5% in 1949 to 55.4% in 1966.

A recent study of the market organization of grain industries in the North Central Region of the United States also indicates a flour milling pattern of diversification into other products.

Competition among wheat exporters is also intense as well as concentrated. The presence and importance

TABLE V-32. Twenty Largest Flour Milling Firms in the United States: 1965

Company	No. of mills	Daily capacity (cwt.)
The Pillsbury Co.	7	79,000
International Milling	14	75,100
General Mills, Inc.	8	56,300
Peavey Co. Flour Mills	8	52,000
Colorado Milling & Elevator Co.	8	43,950
Seaboard Allied Milling Co.	7	43,500
National Biscuit Co.	3	31,600
Vanier Group	6	29,800
Bay State Milling Co.	5	31,200
Nebraska Consolidated Mills Co.	8	27,800
Dixie Portland Mills Co.	3	29,500
Ross Industries Inc.	4	29,000
Archer-Daniels-Midland	3	24,000
Flour Mills of America	2	16,400
Burrus Mills	2	15,900
Sunshine Biscuits Inc.	4	15,650
Fisher Flour Mills	1	15,000
Centennial Mills	2	13,900
Montana Flour Mills	4	11,750
Mennel Milling Co.	1	10,000

SOURCE: National Commission on Food Marketing, *Organization and Competition in the Milling and Baking Industries.*

of the government in all of its activities places this portion of the wheat economy under constant surveillance by the Commodity Credit Corporation, the State Department, Commodity Exchange Authority, and similar agencies. A high concentration of volume in the hands of four family-owned firms has existed for many decades and there has yet to be any sign of market sharing or price collusion (with the exception of the Russian purchase of wheat, when the government stated that no one firm could handle more than 25% of the sales of wheat to Russia).

The bread and related products segment of the wheat economy presents a wide range of firm sizes as demonstrated by Table V-33.

TABLE V-33. Percent of Shipments Accounted for by Largest Companies in the Bread Baking Industry: 1947, 1954, 1958, and 1963

Year	Number of companies	Value of shipments (in thousands)	% of value of shipments 4 largest firms	8 largest firms	20 largest firms	Coverage index
1947	6,796	$2,403,589	16%	26%	36%	.99
1954	5,407	3,067,017	20	31	40	.99
1958	5,305	4,078,612	22	33	42	.99
1963	5,003	4,473,066	23	35	45	—

SOURCE: U.S. Bureau of the Census, *Concentration Ratios in Manufacturing Industries, 1958; U.S. Census of Manufactures, 1958*, Vol. 2, Industry Statistics.

Nine multistate corporations produced about 40% of all commercial bread in the United States in 1965, and seller concentration in the national wholesale baking industry has been gradually increasing.[85]

In spite of this implied concentration, the competition of the retail food chain manufacturer, the affiliated independent, and the regional independent all provide price and nonprice competition as illustrated elsewhere in this chapter. The regional independent has flexibility of decisions, pride of and incentive of local owner-management, unique product development, and local prestige. To meet the national competition of the large wholesale bakery chains, cooperatives composed of independent affiliated bakers have been formed, and they accounted for about 24% of production in 1965.[86] The leading such cooperative is Quality Bakers of America.

Quality Bakers of America acts as a purchasing agent and management consultant to its 120 members who have a bakery capacity of 453 million hundredweight.[87] This organization has established specific flour qualities and 17 different standard classifications of flour for its members. On the whole, it buys from most flour mills except those it feels are in direct competition in the sale of some bakery products. The independent, Mr. Graf feels, can compete with the large chain baker. He is worried about the bargaining power of the chain. He cited a price cut in May 1964 of 17% for bread in California as typical of chain power. Mr. Graf also believes that there are unethical procedures present in the purchasing of bread as suggested in the government report on *Administered Prices of Bread.* However, these unethical procedures (bribes, entertaining, and the like) seem to be the exception in this industry.

Quality Bakers of America was cited in 1940 by the government for violating the Robinson-Patman Act and for allowing price discrimination to take place. Since that time this organization, as well as other major bakery chains and cooperatives, has been especially cautious as to its pricing policies. The use of the Robinson-Patman Act probably encouraged retail food chains to develop their own bread manufacturing plants. Professor Adelman cites the Robinson-Patman Act as giving impetus to vertical integration because it thwarts the translation of cost differences into price differences.[88]

[85] National Commission on Food Marketing, *Organization and Competition in the Milling and Baking Industries.*

[86] *Ibid.,* p. 50.

[87] Interview with George N. Graf, Executive Director, Quality Bakers of America, Inc., May 29, 1964.

[88] M. A. Adelman, "Bases and Bounds of Integration of Firms and Functions," *The Frontiers of Marketing Thought and Science,* pp. 183–184.

In addition to the types of competition in the bakery sector cited above, a whole host of new products have been developed that have added to the total competition of this industry: for instance, doughnuts, cakes, pies, pastries; frozen, half-cooked, brown and serve bread and rolls.

The retail food chains also comprise a major competitive segment of the wheat economy as described previously. The retailer seemed to have passed on the cost savings of their private label operations to the ultimate consumers. (They probably were "forced" to give price concessions to consumers in order to meet the brand competition of the large wholesale bakers.)

ADAPTABILITY

The wheat industry, the oldest and most important food grain commodity system in the United States, has proved to be most flexible in adjusting to the many changes of its external and internal environment. It is true that the nature of the farming segment of the wheat system has required government transfer payments from other segments of the economy in order to insure adequate income incentives to wheat farmers to maintain and improve the functioning of that segment of the industry. In some cases the emergency or stop-gap nature of the program has encouraged excessive resource allocations to that segment of the wheat system which in turn has resulted in capitalization of wheat land values. On the other hand, all these programs have benefited the efficient and expanding wheat producer who responded to price supports and acreage controls with a more productive use of his measures. At the same time, the resultant government wheat stocks and set aside acreages have become important reserve supplies and revenue productive capacity during times of war and world food shortages.

Such programs have also encouraged the development of new and more efficient capital inputs of seed, fertilizer, pesticides, and farm machinery as well as freeing up a labor force necessary to meet the expanding needs of other segments of the national economy.

Many of the misjudgments of the past programs resulted in the excessive build-up of wheat stocks and resulted in the creation of other government programs such as grain storage operations and P.L. 480 which have also proved to be beneficial in the domestic and international development of the wheat system. Perhaps the most important reason for the fact that even the patchwork nature of these programs did not put the participants of the wheat system in a greatly disadvantaged position has been the attitude and the practical necessity of all political administrations to make maximum use of the private sector of the wheat system. The managerial talent and the multitude of institutions, arrangements, and facilities of the wheat system have all been utilized in the execution of these programs. These programs would have been even more effective if they had even more specific operating guidelines that the businessman could count on, and if they took into account the impact they would have on the long-run development of the *total wheat system,* rather than just the farming segment of it.

The participants in the wheat system have been extremely innovative, providing new types of wheat varieties, fine grinding, air classification milling, new transportation methods, new flour and bread products, new methods of freezing, storing and retailing products, new methods of corporate and cooperative organization, and new ways to cut costs through vertical and contractual integration. The participants have also been imaginative in developing overseas wheat and flour markets and in providing not only products but technical know-how and total market concepts to their customers in these foreign markets. Perhaps most important of all, the participants of the wheat system whose firms have been most profitable and efficient have been those who have been able to mesh government programs and services into their overall operations as they satisfy the requirements of their many domestic and international customers.

In spite of its great adaptability, the wheat system has not been too successful in building formal or informal networks of communication among the diverse participants. Many of the trade associations that have been developed for this purpose have been fairly narrow in their perspectives concentrating on only one segment of the wheat system and ignoring the broader relationships of that segment to the total.

SUMMARY

In summary, Chapter III of this study has described and analyzed the underlying forces of change that helped to shape the wheat system. Chapters IV and V have described the complex structure of the wheat system and the resultant behavioral and performance patterns of the participants of the system as they reacted to domestic and international market, technological, economic, political, and social changes. The interaction of the private and public manager with the total wheat system involves a whole bundle of arrangements and institutions created by and for the wheat system. It would be redundant to list again all these coordinating devices, but in every case they helped to:

(1) Improve the manner by which business and government managers fit together the necessary physical and human resources needed to supply the changing wheat food requirements of domestic and foreign consumers;

(2) Even out the imbalances between consumption and production in the wheat system at price levels that provided for viable business operations throughout the system and that provided for easing the exit of inefficient operations; and

(3) Develop a formal and informal communication network to enable management to systematize its industry intelligence system.

Throughout the long and detailed analysis of the wheat system, it has been apparent that the types of firms, institutions, government programs and unique personalities that helped to create the wheat system of today did so from a long historical evolution. The very complexity of the wheat system and its long-time presence in the U.S. economy from pre-Revolutionary days has made it difficult for decision makers to break away from historical prejudices and relate their individual entities, operations, and functions to that of the total wheat system.

Excess capacity exists in practically every segment of the wheat economy and an argument could be made that the wheat economy and its individual parts are suffering from "income anemia." The wheat producer, in particular, in the past has had excess resources committed to this crop as evidenced by former large wheat carryover stocks and export programs whose original aim was to reduce domestic wheat inventories. Yet, the wheat economy attracts long-term investments and in many instances could be considered a highly leveraged industry. At the same time, many in the financial community regard it as a low risk industry because bread is considered the "staff of life" by the consumer and the industry is dominated by proven and mature firms. In addition, the presence of government programs that have stabilized income levels of the total wheat economy is considered a stabilizer in the financial evaluation of the industry, since federal funds have been made available to support wheat producers and others. The price support programs also have become capitalized in land values and in the earning capacities of other segments of the wheat economy (e.g., country and terminal elevators).

In spite of its seeming maturity, the wheat economy, as has been noted above, is in a constant state of change and seems to be on the threshold of even greater innovations. New bakery products, the increase in consumer and institutional pre-mix products, flour product differentiation, the development of new separation processes that can tailor-make blends of flour from a great number of wheat varieties, the opening up of new wheat export markets and the dramatic decline in U.S. wheat inventories are but a few examples of dynamic product and market innovations and changes. Furthermore, the decline in the domestic per capita consumption of wheat products seems to have leveled off and is on the increase in many of the developing economies of the world. The maturity of the industry and the presence of a few large firms have not precluded competitive alternative sources of supply and markets for buyers and sellers within the wheat economy.

The problems of dealing with changing transportation, consumption, production, vertical integration, terms of trade, and domestic and international governmental relationships have afforded opportunities for the wheat system to improve its performance. The behavioral pattern of the wheat system today suggests that it is a vigorous industry ready to take advantage of opportunities. It is a more unified industry than ever before in terms of trying to improve the total market structure, as evidenced by the formation of the National Wheat Council and the excellent cooperation between it and the government.

The evaluation of how well the general wheat economy works would have to be a mixed one. Competition has created an environment that encourages change and efficiency of operations. On the other hand, the dependency of the wheat system on many government programs has meant that participants in certain segments of the wheat economy did not have the economic incentive to improve their operations; others have overextended their operations to satisfy a governmental market. Furthermore, the long-time freeze in the transportation network of milling-in-transit relationships provided a price umbrella under which new transportation methods developed to break an unrealistically high freight structure (e.g., captive freight companies for barge and truck shipments). The attempt of groups, whether they be labor unions or a dominant firm in the industry, to maintain a high cost and profit structure for any one segment of the wheat economy at the expense of another has brought forth new forms of competitive strengths, such as retail food chain bakery operations and farmer cooperative enterprises. Finally, the wheat economy has adjusted to the changes noted at the beginning of this section, namely: (1) changes in the diverse and manifold needs of domestic and foreign consumers; (2) changes in marketing and processing activities responding to these needs; and (3) changes in the way the raw product is presented to the marketing system.

In essence this chapter has presented an examination of how the general wheat market structure works and what are currently some of its physical and institutional limitations. In general, one may say the performance of the wheat system is an uneven one. The use of institutions such as government programs; the development of vertical ownership integration; and the development of large-scale enterprises in every segment of the wheat economy have created efficiencies and smooth product flows. However, these same programs and trends may have slowed down needed adjustments or they may have created centers of economic strength that may cause public policy problems in the future.

The next two sections of this study will examine two relatively newer commodity systems (soybeans and oranges) and the types of behavioral and performance patterns the participants of these systems have as they adjust to change and to their new roles within and outside of their respective commodity systems. The last section of the study will involve a comparative analysis of all these systems as related to the participants' ability to adjust to the probable major future trends facing them.

SECTION III

Soybeans

FROM 1948 to 1958 an industry with one of the fastest annual percentage growth rates in the United States was the soybean industry. Its growth, according to the National Industrial Conference Board, was 7.6% per year compared with the gross physical output of all U.S. industry of 2.6%.[1] The soybean supplies an important protein and vegetable oil ingredient to hundreds of types of industries from animal feed ingredients, and important vegetable food oil ingredient to paint products, plastics, lubricant, leather tanning ingredients, milk substitutes, and baby food. Its principal uses are as a major protein ingredient in the mixed feed industry and as a major vegetable oil in edible oil products, such as margarine, salad oils, cooking oils, and mayonnaise.

Recently new emphasis has been placed on soy flour and lecithin as important base ingredients for a low-priced high protein food that can be made available at reasonable cost to the protein-deficit regions of the world. One such product is a popular drink called "Vita-Soy." This beverage in February 1967 was outselling Coca-Cola in Hong Kong. Other dramatic uses of the soybean include the production of simulated foods made from protein extracted from soybean meal. Foods thus far produced include "artificial" ham, bacon, turkey, and steak.

This rapidly growing industry has benefited from the development of many institutions and arrangements that have enabled it to adjust to the rapidly growing and changing demands for soybean oil and soybean meal products. In order to encourage the production of soybeans guaranteed market outlets had to be developed. This led to producer-processor agreements that guaranteed a market for the producer at a specified price and provided a source of soybeans for the processor at a certain price level. As in the wheat system, the various participants were unwilling to rely completely on a "free market" system in order to move the product from soybean production, assembling, processing and distribution to the ultimate consumer. The participants of the system wanted prices at each transaction stage to be set by a market mechanism, but they wanted certain price, volume, and quality guarantees to reinforce the market system.

The effective combining of the production, processing and distribution functions is referred to throughout this study as "coordination." The instruments of coordination in the soybean system include vertical integration, various types of contractual arrangements, cooperative ownership plans, government price support programs, and P.L. 480 programs as well as various market aids such as future markets for soybeans, soybean oil and soybean meal. These instruments of coordination have the task of integrating the many functions to be performed in the soybean industry through specific contractual agreements, specific price support programs, and through the development of concessional overseas markets for soybean oil. The coordinating patterns have evolved over time from "arrangements" for the production, processing, and marketing of soybeans and soybean products through extension meetings sponsored by agricultural railroad agents or county agents to the more complex cooperative pool agreements of 1965.

One must keep in mind in reading this section that, as is true of wheat, at different functional levels people are engaged in the production, processing, and handling of many commodities and many food products, and that the soybean industry as outlined throughout this report is extracted from conglomerate entities —

---

[1] "Gross physical output is defined as the number of physical units for each year converted to 1929 prices by National Bureau of Economic Research." NICB, *Growth Patterns in Industry: A Reexamination*, p. 77.

from diversified farms to one-stop-shopping super-markets.

In the pages that follow, the dynamics of the soybean industry will be described and analyzed. Market and technological developments have (1) increased foreign and domestic consumption of soybean food products; (2) altered the marketing and processing activities of the industry responding to these needs; and (3) changed the way the raw product is presented to the marketing system. The dynamics and structure are set forth in Chapters VI and VII. Furthermore, the soybean industry has developed certain behavioral and performance patterns as a result of the interaction of management strategies and alternative uses of various coordinating institutions, and these are outlined in Chapter VIII.

VI

The Dynamics of the Soybean System

SOYBEANS are considered the "wonder crop" in the United States. It was not until 1924 that the Statistical Reporting Service of the Department of Agriculture first reported the size of the soybean crop which was then slightly less than five million bushels. Since that time there has been a phenomenal growth in the demand for the two major products of the soybean—soybean meal and soybean oil.[1] Soybean meal is the major source of protein for animal and poultry feeds. Soybean oil is the major ingredient in most margarine, shortening and salad oil products and an important element in paints and other industrial products. The increase in the demand for soybean end products has resulted in a rapid expansion of soybean acreage and production as Table VI-1 indicates.

TABLE VI-1. U.S. Soybean Production and Acreage: Selected Crop Years, 1924–1966

Crop year[a]	Annual production (thousands of bushels)	Acreage harvested (thousands of acres)
1924	4,947	488
1941	107,197	5,889
1958	580,250	23,993
1964	699,882	30,738
1965	845,608	34,449
1966[b]	931,491	36,644

[a] The soybean crop year began on October 1 until 1965 when it was changed to September 1.
[b] Estimated as of December 20, 1966.
SOURCE: *Soybean Blue Book*, March 1967, p. 32.

Historically the greatest increases in soybean production occurred during World War II and the two

[1] Soybeans are utilized in the form of two products obtained by crushing the soybean and extracting oil from it. The most modern and widely used method of extraction is the solvent method. For every bushel of soybeans (60 lbs.), the yield of product from solvent crushing is approximately 10.9 lbs. of oil, 48.1 lbs. of meal, and 1.0 lb. of waste.

decades that have followed. Before the war the United States was a net importer of oil seed crops for its animal feed and edible oil uses. The war cut off many of the Asiatic supplies to this country. At the same time rising incomes resulted in heavier demands for meat and poultry, which in turn meant a greater need of protein supplies to feed the expanding numbers of livestock and poultry. The demand for feed was further accentuated by the development of the mixed feed industry and its emphasis on new scientific formula feeds for all types of livestock and poultry. The oil market also was strengthened because of the need to replace imported oils during wartime. Furthermore, consumption changes in a diet-conscious, lighter meal, low cholesterol society encouraged the greater use of vegetable shortening and salad oils, and the replacement of butter by margarine. The war and postwar consumption patterns of our "affluent society" and the increasing income levels of other developed and developing economies, together with high government support prices, the absence of soybean acreage controls, increasing soybean yields, and improved technology in the use of soybean oil and meal in a variety of products, brought about the rapid rise of the soybean crop during the last 25 years.

CHANGES IN DOMESTIC CONSUMPTION

THE UTILIZATION OF SOYBEAN MEAL

Consumers spend over $5.4 billion annually for the retail value of soybeans utilized in a variety of products. In the case of meat and poultry products, soybean meal has been the major high protein ingredient used in the feeding of livestock and poultry. The expansion of the livestock industry has averaged approximately 4% per year resulting in an ever-increasing demand for soybean meal as a basic feed ingredient.

The poultry industry has almost doubled in the last decade, also adding to the demand for soybean meal used in mixed poultry feed.

Civilian per capita consumption of all meats has increased from 148.5 pounds per person in 1947–1949 to 174.0 pounds in 1964. The 1964 consumption figure expressed as a percentage of 1947–1949 was 117%. Similarly civilian per capita consumption of chickens increased from 18.7 pounds to 31.4 pounds or a 68% increase. The utilization of soybean meal in the domestic production of these poultry and livestock products more than doubled from 1947–1949 to 1965, increasing from 3.8 million tons to over 9 million tons in 1965. In addition, soybean meal exports increased from 150,000 tons in 1947–1949 to 2 million tons in 1965. Table VI-2 summarizes these meat and poultry product consumption changes. These changes, together with the growth in population, have resulted in an enormous increase in the utilization of soybean meal.

TABLE VI-2. Changes in Per Capita Consumption of Meat and Chicken, and Utilization of Soybean Meal in Animal and Poultry Feeds: 1947–1964 Average, 1957–1959 Average, and 1964

	1947–49 average	1957–59 average	1964	1964 as % of 1947–49
Civilian per capita consumption of total meats (lbs.)	148.5	156.6	174.0	117%
Civilian per capita consumption of chicken (lbs.)	18.7	27.5	31.4	168
Soybean meal utilization in domestic feed industry (1,000 tons)	3,761	8,450	9,132	243
Soybean meal utilization in overseas feed industry (1,000 tons)	173	406	1,484	858

SOURCE: USDA, ERS, and *Soybean Blue Book*, March 1965.

Even though the demand for soybean meal has greatly expanded, the increase in the soybean crop coupled with the competition from other oilseed meals (cottonseed and linseed) and chemical substitutes (urea) has enabled livestock and poultry producers to obtain soybean meal at prices varying from a high crop-year average price of $83.35 per ton in 1951 to a low average price of $47.45 per ton in 1956 (see Exhibit VI-1). As of December 1966 soybean meal (44% protein wholesale price per ton bulk at Decatur) was priced at $85 per ton.

EXHIBIT VI-1

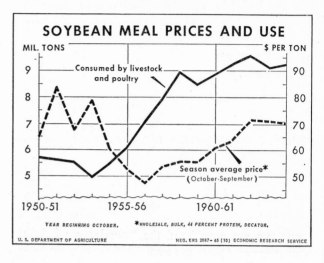

THE UTILIZATION OF SOYBEAN OIL

The domestic use of soybean oil, on the average, has increased each year in the United States. The increase in consumption has been in three major edible product categories: margarine, shortening, and salad oils. The per capita consumption of each of these products has increased significantly as Table VI-3 indicates. This

TABLE VI-3. Changes in Consumption of Soybean Oil and Soybean Oil Products: 1947–1949 Average, 1957–1959 Average, and 1964

	1947–49 average	1957–59 average	1964	1964 as % of 1947–49
Domestic soybean oil utilization (million lbs.)	1,445	3,080	4,130	286%
Overseas soybean oil utilization (million lbs.)	300	895	1,361	453
Margarine (lbs. per capita)	5.6	8.9	9.7	173
Shortening (lbs. per capita)	9.6	11.4	13.7	143
Other edible fats and oils (lbs. per capita)	7.3	10.8	13.7	188

SOURCE: USDA, ERS. Prepared at the request of the author.

table shows that per capita consumption of margarine increased 73%, shortening 43%, and other vegetable oils 88% in the period from 1947–1949 to 1964. During this same time U.S. civilian per capita consumption of all fats and oils increased only slightly from 42.4 pounds to 47.0 pounds, or 11%. In essence, what has occurred has been a minor increase in total fat consumption, a major increase in vegetable oil consumption, and a decline in animal fat consumption — primarily butter. Most of the increase in vegetable oil

EXHIBIT VI-2

U.S. Per Capita Consumption of Liquid Edible Oils: 1944–1965

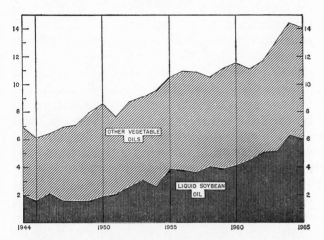

SOURCE: *Soybean Blue Book,* March 1966.

consumption increase came from soybean oil as Exhibit VI-2 indicates.

Table VI-4 sets forth the utilization of soybean oil by classes of products in the United States for selected years. From this table one can note the more recent increase in the importance of soybean oil in shortening and salad oil products and the maintenance of the dominant position of soybean oil in margarine products.

In addition to its utilization in edible food products, soybean oil is also used in various paint and other industrial products with an average annual volume of approximately 300 million pounds.

TABLE VI-4. Soybean and Cottonseed Oil versus All Other Oils Utilized in Margarine, Shortening, and Salad Oil Products: 1947–1949 Average, 1957–1959 Average, and 1964

(In millions of pounds)

	1947–49 average	1957–59 average	1964
Margarine			
Soybean oil	247	1,013	1,146
Cottonseed oil	402	169	101
All other oils	36	60	260
Total	708	1,248	1,507
Shortening			
Soybean oil	709	998	1,373
Cottonseed oil	451	277	378
All other oils	35	25	52
Total	1,195	1,300	1,803
Salad dressing, mayonnaise, and other vegetable oil food products			
Soybean oil	242	733	1,638
Cottonseed oil	458	638	868
All other oils	263	487	164
Total	1,063	1,858	2,670

SOURCE: *Fats and Oils Situation,* March 1965, pp. 24 and 26, and USDA, ERS.

Soybean oil has improved its competitive position in satisfying the domestic needs of the manufacturers of consumer food products because of the reasonable price level of the oil and improved technology in hydro-

TABLE VI-5. Wholesale and Retail Prices for Selected Fats and Oils and Fat and Oil Products: 1959–1964
(In cents per pound)

Item	1959	1960	1961	1962	1963	1964
Wholesale prices						
Butter, creamery, Grade A (92-score) bulk, N.Y.	60.5	59.9	61.2	59.5	59.1	59.9
Corn oil, crude, tank cars, f.o.b., Midwest mills	11.8	13.1	18.3	14.6	12.1	11.1
Corn oil, refined, tanks, New York	15.4	16.8	22.1	18.2	15.3	13.7
Cottonseed oil, crude, tank cars, f.o.b., S.E. mills	11.2	9.9	13.0	11.5	10.4	10.3
Cottonseed oil, refined, tanks, New York	14.5	12.9	16.4	14.6	13.1	13.0
Margarine, colored, delivered, Eastern U.S.	25.2	23.8	26.8	25.6	23.8	24.1
Margarine, yellow, quarters, f.o.b., Chicago	25.9	24.4	27.5	25.6	25.0	25.4
Soybean oil, crude, tank cars, f.o.b., Decatur	9.0	8.8	11.5	9.0	8.9	9.2
Soybean oil, refined, tanks, New York	11.2	10.8	13.7	11.2	11.1	11.4
Retail prices[a]						
Butter	75.3	74.9	76.3	75.2	75.0	74.4
Margarine	28.0	26.9	28.6	28.4	27.5	26.0
Shortening	29.4	27.3	30.0	29.6	27.8	26.3
Salad dressing	37.6	36.0	37.4	28.3	28.1	74.1[b]

[a] Leading cities. New series, Consumer Price Index revised January 1964.
[b] Italian only.
SOURCE: *Fats and Oils Situation,* January 1967, p. 41.

genization and deodorizing processes. Table VI-5 gives a brief summary of wholesale and retail price levels of soybean oil and related products. During the five-year period soybean oil remained the cheapest source of vegetable oil.

CHANGES IN EXPORT CONSUMPTION

SOYBEANS

In the 1930s U.S. soybean exports were negligible and, as has been stated earlier, the United States was a net importer of vegetable oil and oilseeds. China, including Manchuria, supplied over 90% of the soybeans entering the world market during this period.

TABLE VI-6. World Production of Soybeans: 1935–1939 Average, 1950–1954 Average, 1955–1959 Average, and 1965

(In thousands of bushels)

	1935–39 average	*1950–54 average*	*1955–59 average*	*1965*
United States	56,167	298,422	483,901	845,608
China	207,666	330,000[a]	344,000[a]	255,000[a]
Manchuria	151,214			
Brazil	—	3,471[b]	4,000	16,755
U.S.S.R.	—	4,825[b]	6,467	16,000
All other	48,853	46,937	55,332	59,042
World total	463,900	683,655	894,300	1,187,405

[a] China and Manchuria data combined.
[b] Average less than 5 years.
Source: *Soybean Blue Book*, March 1967, p. 26.

Tables VI-6 and VI-7 show the world production and export changes that have occurred during the last quarter century. China, faced with erratic agricultural output and a rapid growth in its population, has lost

TABLE VI-7. Exports of Soybeans from Specified Countries: 1935–1939 Average, 1950–1954 Average, and 1965

(In thousands of bushels)

	1935–39 average	*1950–54 average*	*1955–59 average*	*1965*
United States	4,793[a]	30,511	86,437	227,660
China & Manchuria	69,112	24,350[a]	44,240	22,000
Brazil	3	1,038	1,369	2,766
U.S.S.R.	—	—	—	—
All other	6,715	1,873	3,068	4,184
World total	80,623	57,772	135,114	256,610

[a] Average less than 5 years.
Source: USDA, Foreign Agricultural Service, Foreign Agricultural Circular, October 8, 1959, p. 37, and October 1966, p. 30.

its traditionally large exportable surplus.[2] On the other hand, the production of soybeans in the United States has climbed rapidly in recent years and has dominated the world soybean trade, accounting for over 90% of the soybeans entering world markets and two-thirds of the world's soybean production. What is equally important, the United States has never made an export subsidy payment on soybeans during this export expansionary period, but only on soybean oil. In fact soybeans and soybean products have become the number one dollar earner for the United States, accounting for $908 million of shipments during the 1964 crop year. The exports of soybeans, as beans, totaled 205 million bushels valued at $586 million during the 1964 crop year. The soybean exports for the 1966 crop year are estimated to be 275 million bushels which would set a new record for U.S. soybean exports, as Exhibit VI-3 indicates. Approximately 41% of the total U.S. soybean crop has been exported in recent years, partly in the form of soybeans and partly in the form of meal and oil.

EXHIBIT VI-3

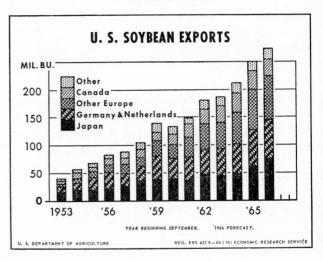

Exhibit VI-3 indicates that most of the world market for U.S. soybeans is located in countries with rapidly rising standards of living. Europe will probably continue to be an important buyer of U.S. soybeans because of its rapidly expanding livestock and poultry industry requiring an expanded mixed feed industry. Japan, too, has a rapidly expanding livestock and poultry industry requiring the importation of soybeans and soybean meal. The projections for the next decade indicate a continuing growth in the markets for soybeans in these areas. Japan, however, has attempted to

[2] China in recent years has exported soybeans to improve its balance of payment position even though domestic food supplies were in short supply.

obtain more soybeans from China because of its proximity and has a long-term contract with that country for approximately 10 million bushels of soybeans per year.

SOYBEAN MEAL

Export demand for soybean meal is generated essentially by the same factors as soybeans. Demand for oilseed meals is strong and continues to expand in both Western and Eastern Europe where U.S. soybean meal has established a reputation for high quality. The expanding demand for protein concentrates in Europe and Japan reflects an increasing demand for poultry and livestock products along with rising incomes. In addition, increased knowledge of the feeding value of soybean meal and continued improvement in feeding practices are additional factors that have led to an increase in soybean meal exports. Exhibit VI-4

EXHIBIT VI-4

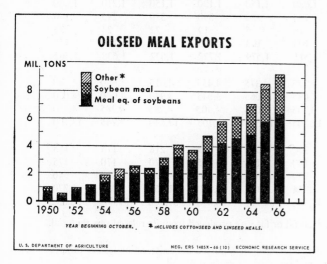

summarizes the increase in U.S. soybean meal exports with a new high being reached in the 1965 crop year of 2 million tons of soybean meal (approximately 19% of total U.S. production). In addition, over 6 million tons were exported in the form of soybeans that would be processed overseas into soybean meal.

SOYBEAN OIL

As noted previously, soybean oil has become the major edible vegetable oil produced in the United States. Results of utilization research in deodorization, fat stabilization, and hydrogenation not only have made soybean oil more acceptable in the domestic products of margarine, shortening, and salad oils but also have improved the exportability of soybean oil which is exposed for long periods of time to air and storage temperature variability. Because of these recent technological improvements, edible fats and oils have a fairly high degree of substitutability. Therefore, changes in available export supplies of other edible fats and oils will affect the foreign market for U.S. soybean oil.

Table VI-8 presents a summary of world production of fats and oils as well as the oil equivalent obtainable from processing oil seeds that are exported. One will note from Table VI-8 that world soybean oil production has had the largest tonnage increase in the past decade. Exhibit VI-5 gives a graphic presentation

EXHIBIT VI-5

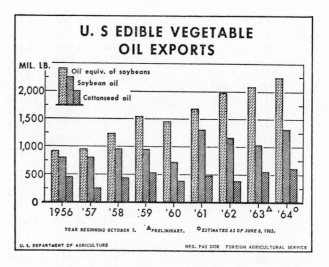

of U.S. soybean oil export increases. In 1966 the United States was the leading supplier and trader in oilseeds, oils, and fats, accounting for 28% of the world output and 37% of world exports of soybean oil.

The pattern of world trade in fats and oils has changed considerably since the 1930s. In the 1930s 60% of the world exports were from 38 of the developing countries. The principal sources of edible oils in these countries are coconut, palm and peanuts. Currently (1966) less than 47% of the oil and oil seeds are shipped from these developing countries. In addition three-fourths of the imports of oil and oil seeds are purchased by the developed countries. Western Europe is by far the largest importer of fats and oils, followed by Japan and Southern Europe. The elasticity of demand for fats and oils is relatively low as income reaches a high level and most of the growth in demand in the developed countries has come about from increasing population. Income elasticity is relatively high (1.0 or more) in low income countries but these countries have a small per capita consumption and

TABLE VI-8. World Production of Fats, Oils, and Oilseeds: Average 1955–1959, Annual 1960–1966, and Forecast 1967[a]

(In 1,000 short tons)

	Average 1955–59	1960	1961	1962	1963	1964	1965	1966[b]	Forecast 1967
Edible vegetable oils[e]									
Cottonseed	2,081	2,280	2,305	2,430	2,490	2,610	2,715	2,695	2,550
Peanut	2,605	2,560	2,725	2,855	2,985	3,100	3,285	3,115	3,155
Soybean	3,024	3,815	3,660	4,020	4,195	4,270	4,500	4,960	5,380
Sunflowerseed	1,422	1,575	1,990	2,190	2,545	2,285	2,910	2,795	3,100
Rapeseed	1,209	1,280	1,320	1,300	1,190	1,230	1,665	1,490	1,585
Sesameseed	590	590	530	585	590	600	605	565	615
Safflowerseed	89	125	140	155	220	235	205	220	290
Olive oil	1,091[d]	1,300	1,480	1,475	1,020	1,875	1,080	1,330	1,420
Corn oil	170	195	210	225	240	255	270	265	275
Total	12,281	13,720	14,360	15,235	15,475	16,460	17,235	17,435	18,370
Palm oils[e]									
Coconut	2,286	2,240	2,395	2,325	2,420	2,435	2,360	2,475	2,400
Palm kernel	464	455	440	405	410	420	405	415	425
Palm	1,394	1,455	1,410	1,365	1,390	1,400	1,405	1,410	1,420
Babassu kernel[f]	51	64	57	66	50	66	70	85	85
Total	4,195	4,214	4,302	4,161	4,270	4,321	4,240	4,385	4,330
Industrial oils[e]									
Linseed	1,138	1,075	1,110	1,080	1,150	1,190	1,150	1,210	1,060
Castorbean	235	295	265	295	320	390	320	295	330
Oiticica	9	22	18	28	6	19	22	24	25
Tung	128	136	120	108	103	123	130	109	147
Total	1,510	1,528	1,513	1,511	1,579	1,722	1,622	1,638	1,562
Animal fats									
Butter (fat content)	4,014	4,250	4,295	4,375	4,375	4,455	4,615	4,660	4,780
Lard[g]	3,727	4,000	4,045	4,085	4,065	3,845	3,940	4,000	4,020
Tallow and grease	3,243	3,440	3,640	3,745	4,085	4,405	4,285	4,285	4,350
Total	10,984	11,690	11,980	12,205	12,525	12,705	12,840	12,945	13,150
Marine oils									
Whale	427	418	428	390	295	249	218	175	155
Sperm whale	119	122	120	130	149	165	170	170	175
Fish (including liver)	427	512	662	734	684	836	875	935	940
Total	973	1,052	1,210	1,254	1,128	1,250	1,263	1,280	1,270
Estimated world total	29,943	32,204	33,365	34,366	34,977	36,458	37,200	37,683	38,682

[a] Years indicated are those in which the predominant share of the given oil or fat was produced from its related raw material.

[b] Preliminary.

[e] Estimates of U.S. oil production include actual oil produced plus the oil equivalent of exported oilseeds; estimates for other countries are based on the production of various oilseeds times the estimated normal proportions crushed for oil.

[d] 1955–1958 average.

[e] Estimated on the basis of exports and information available on consumption in the various producing areas.

[f] Figures for 1960–1967 represent mill production only.

[g] Rendered lard only in most countries. Foreign Agricultural Service. Prepared or estimated on the basis of official statistics of foreign governments, other foreign source materials, reports of U.S. agricultural attachés and foreign service officers, results of office research, and related information.

SOURCE: *Soybean Blue Book*, March 1967.

limited funds for the purchase of edible oils. Therefore, most imports of the developing countries have received some type of financial aid.

Because soybean oil and soybean meal are joint products of the soybean crushing process, there is always the problem of uneven growth in value and in market outlet. Soybean meal has had a domestic utilization growth of 7% per year since 1947, whereas domestic soybean oil consumption has barely kept pace with domestic population growth. This uneven growth resulted in the build up of soybean oil stocks which reached a peak of 1,024 million pounds as of December 31, 1963. The dollar export market to the developed countries remained fairly constant at about 500 million pounds. The Department of Agriculture through its use of P.L. 480 funds was able to increase soybean oil shipments to the developing countries to 825 million pounds in the 1964 crop year which has resulted in a reduction of domestic soybean oil stocks to 400 million pounds (the lowest level since 1960). Table VI-9 summarizes the dollar and P.L. 480 export of soybean oils during the four crop years 1962–1965.

Table VI-9 indicates that in recent years over half

TABLE VI-9. Dollar and P.L. 480 Exports of Soybean Oil: Crop Years 1962–1965
(In millions of pounds)

Export financing	1962[a]	1963[a]	1964[a]	1965[a]
Dollars[b] (in millions)	$515	$504	$463	$215
P.L. 480				
Title I[c]	531	409	472	286
Title II[d]	43	28	45	30
Title III[e]	68	59	284	350
Title IV[f]	15	111	54	42
Total P.L. 480 exports	657	607	877	708
Total U.S. soybean exports	1,162	1,105	1,340	923

[a] Partly estimated.
[b] Includes some AID.
[c] Sales for local currency.
[d] Grants for disaster relief and for economic development.
[e] Donations and barter.
[f] Dollar credit sales at low interest rates.
SOURCE: *Fats and Oils Situation*, May 1964, p. 11, and November 1965, p. 18. Figures for 1965 from USDA, ERS.

and as much as three quarters of U.S. soybean oil exports have been sold under government-financed (soft currency and donation) programs. Dr. George W. Kromer stated that "P.L. 480 shipments will play an even more important role in U.S. exports of edible oils over the next few years." [3]

CHANGES IN PRODUCTION

Soybean acreage planted for all purposes in the United States rose sharply after World War II from around 12 million acres in 1947–1949 to over 36 million acres in 1966. Soybean production increased during this same time from approximately 216 million bushels to an estimated 931 million bushels for the 1966 crop year. Yields per acre harvested for soybeans rose from 17 bushels per acre in 1947 to approximately 25 bushels per acre in 1966 although yields remained fairly constant for the past five or six years.

Soybeans are now considered the second most important cash crop in the United States, surpassed only by corn. (Soybeans outranked wheat in value in 1966 if one does not include the wheat certificate payments au-

[3] Correspondence dated February 27, 1967.

thorized under the 1966 wheat program.) The value of the crop was $500,000 in 1947 and $2.7 billion in 1966.

The domestic and export consumption requirements for the end food products of the soybean have been outlined above, including the increased consumption of livestock and poultry products and the substitution of vegetable fat for animal fat. The production responses to these demand requirements were affected by the existence of relatively high government price supports, the acreage restrictions on alternative price supported crops such as corn and cotton and the substitution of mechanical power for animal power, which reduced the need for a crop such as oats. During the postwar period over 20 million acres have been shifted to soybeans from other crops (mainly oats, corn and cotton).

The Corn Belt (Illinois, Iowa, Indiana, Ohio, and Missouri) historically has been the main production area for soybeans because of the similar growing conditions required by both corn and soybeans and similar planting equipment. However, new varieties better suited to new production areas with improved oil content and yields have been developed widening the production area. In 1947–1949, 70% of the soybean acreage was located in the five states comprising the Corn Belt. In 1965 this percentage had been reduced to 55% even though acreage in these five states had risen from 9 to 19 million acres. The Delta States (Arkansas, Mississippi, and Louisiana), the Lake States (Minnesota, Wisconsin, and Michigan) and the Atlantic States (North and South Carolina, Virginia, Maryland, and Delaware) have all increased soybean acreage significantly.

The expansion of the soybean production area is important as a determinant in locational strategy for the domestic crushing industry and as a source of supply for the soybean, meal, and oil export markets. The development of a southern livestock and poultry industry and the expansion of New Orleans as an export port are but two examples of the production and market interaction that exist in the soybean industry complex.

The U.S. production of soybeans is expected to double again in the next decade as the world shortage of protein and fat becomes more acute with the anticipated increase in population and income levels. Researchers are developing new varieties and better weed, pest, and disease control; they hope to increase yields of soybeans in all production areas. In addition, although soybeans are not currently permitted to be grown on diverted wheat and feed grain acreage, current cotton legislation would permit their production on diverted cotton acres which would encourage considerable soybean production in the Delta States.

CHANGES IN PROCESSING AND MARKETING

By far the most important outlet for U.S. soybeans has been the domestic soybean processor (crusher). Exhibit VI-6 shows that domestic crushing utilized over 80% of the crop in 1953 and approximately two-thirds of the crop in 1966. (Of course part of the domestic crush is exported in the form of meal and oil.)

EXHIBIT VI-6

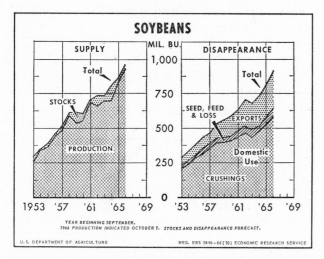

From 1947 to 1965 the number of soybean processing plants decreased from around 200 to 120 while the crop was quadrupling. Average processing plant size and crushing capacity expanded greatly as newer, more efficient hexane solvent extraction processes replaced older hydraulic and screw press methods. The larger, more efficient plants also were made possible by the rapid increase in soybean production, improved harvesting techniques, improved transportation from the farm to larger, more efficient country subterminals and improved transportation to the processor's plant.

The processing plants not only processed soybeans more efficiently; the oil yield from a 60-pound bushel of soybeans was increased from 9.5 pounds in 1947 to 10.8 pounds in 1964 and the meal yield was increased from 47.5 pounds to 47.7 pounds. Waste products were reduced from 3 pounds to 1.5 pounds in the same period.

Not only were yields improved but both oil and meal products were upgraded. Soybean meal went from 41% to 44% protein content as a standard product. In addition, many crushers have specialized in high protein content meals as standard products with an average protein content of 50%. The oil quality also has been constantly improved with most processors going beyond the crude oil product to satisfy their various customers better.

Advances in technology also have permitted the development of methods to stabilize refined soybean oil products, and this stabilization has been a factor in the increased consumption of margarine, shortening, and salad dressing. It has also increased product and price competition in the end products of the soybean. There has been a substantial increase in private labels among margarine, salad oil, and shortening products. The inauguration of the P.L. 480 program encouraged the development of mass handling of soybean oil for the concessional export markets.

Research and development in protein technology has encouraged the use of soybean meal in structural foods (foods that can simulate meat, fish, poultry, eggs, and vegetables) and as a cheap source of protein in the developing countries' diets. In fact, research and development is evident in every phase of the soybean system, from production, processing, and distribution to consumption.

SUMMARY

In summary, this general description of the soybean economy suggests strongly that changes and innovations are occurring at each stage of the vertical soybean system. As in the case of the wheat economy, these changes can be classified as: (a) changes that have developed in the diverse and expanding needs of domestic and foreign consumers (external demand), (b) changes in marketing and processing activities responding to these needs (internal response to demand), and (c) changes in the way the raw product is presented to the marketing system.

VII

The Structure of the Soybean System

THE CHANGES in production, processing, and marketing summarized in Chapter VI have had an impact on the total soybean system in terms of (1) marketing channels utilized, (2) number and size of units, (3) ownership patterns, (4) development of coordinating institutions, (5) and the increase in all forms of integration. The current soybean industry is portrayed in this multidimensional manner in Exhibits VII-1, VII-3, and VII-4. These three exhibits will serve as a broad framework for describing and analyzing the structure[1] of the soybean industry, including numbers and types of firms, marketing channels, and integrating devices.

CHANNELS

The movement of 665 million bushels of soybeans from producer to consumer is shown in Exhibit VII-1. As explained in the notes accompanying this exhibit, some 96% of total farm production moves from the farm into various marketing channels. One note of caution; the soybean industry, like the wheat industry, exists as a separately defined entity only in a conceptual sense. In actual practice a soybean producer raises many other crops and engages in other farm practices in addition to soybean production. Similarly, country and terminal elevator operators and exporters handle all grains grown in their product and market territories. In addition, many soybean processors are equipped to process cottonseed and flaxseed as well as soybeans and are integrated into many other related

[1] The word "structure" as used throughout this study refers to the broad dimensions of an industry system at a given moment of time. These dimensions include the description and number of firms and entities at different functional stages of a commodity system, the measurements of size and concentration, the descriptions of products and product definitions, and the inclusion of all parts of a market environment that are used to implement the movement of goods and services from producer-supplier to ultimate consumer.

agribusiness activities such as mixed feed operations and grain merchandising. Food wholesalers and retailers obviously distribute thousands of other food products in addition to those made from soybean products. In spite of the diversity of operations that exist at every stage of the vertical structure of the soybean industry, it is possible to present an overall picture of the soybean complex at a given moment of time and determine the participants and arrangements that comprise the system.

Exhibit VII-1 indicates that the primary purchasers of the farmer's soybeans are country elevator operators who obtained 587 million bushels or almost 90% of total farm soybean sales in the 1963 crop year. These country elevator operators, together with the larger country subterminals, act as buying agents for the soybean processor. Because soybean processing plants are usually built in areas that have both a large supply of soybeans and an excellent market for soybean meal, soybean processors attempt to purchase soybeans from local country elevators and country subterminals in the adjacent farming area rather than from a terminal location. The shortened harvest season, improved highway system, and increased soybean production on larger farms have encouraged the construction of larger country elevator and country subterminals to serve the farms' requirements. On the other hand, the construction of larger scale soybean processing plants in close proximity to the soybean production area requires these elevators to expand their facilities to satisfy the increasing demands of large-scale soybean processors.

Although Exhibit VII-1 indicates that terminal elevators are being by-passed, it understates the movement through terminals because the figures of the volume handled do not include export terminal facilities. Realistically, terminal elevator operators not only handled 55 million bushels of soybeans from

EXHIBIT VII-1

Marketing Channels for U.S. Soybeans: Crop Year 1963
(In millions of bushels)

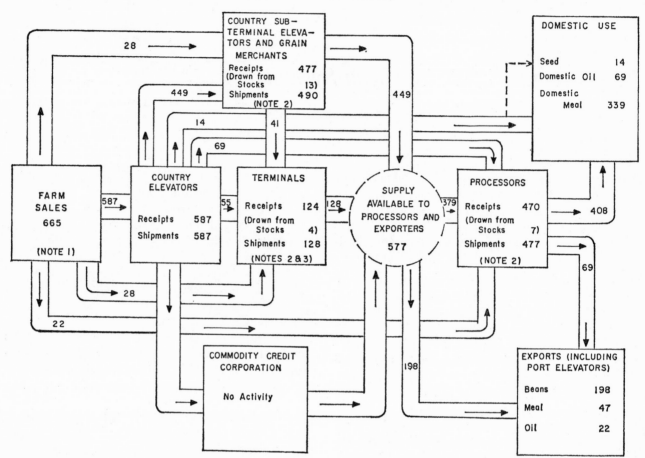

NOTES TO EXHIBIT VII-1

1. Total supply during the 1963 crop year was 689 million bushels. Off-farm sales totaled 665 million bushels, or 96% of the total supply. Reduction of off-farm whole bean carryover totaled 17 million bushels, or 3% of the total supply, and entered the marketing channels from the terminal and subterminal elevators. Reduction of off-farm carryover of oil (342 million pounds) and meal (37 thousand tons) equaled 1% of the total supply, and entered the marketing channels from processing plants.

2. The difference between shipments and receipts is accounted for by the reduction of 17 million bushels of soybean oil carryover, 342 million pounds of oil, and 37 thousand tons of meal. It was assumed that 13 million bushels of the

soybean carryover (78%) entered the market through subterminal elevators, while 4 million bushels (22%) entered through terminal elevators. These projections reflect the percentage of supply originating in off-farm sales which was ultimately handled through each of these two market outlets. The reduction of soybean oil and soybean meal stocks equal to 7 million bushels of soybeans was assumed to be obtained from processing stocks.

3. Terminal receipts are based on volume of inspected receipts. Fourteen terminal markets include Chicago, Duluth, Hutchinson, Indianapolis, Kansas City, Milwaukee, Minneapolis, Omaha, Peoria, Sioux City, St. Joseph, St. Louis, Toledo and Wichita.

country elevators, 41 million from country subterminals, and 28 million directly from farms, they also handled some 198 million bushels for export through port facilities. The expanding export market for soybeans should maintain the importance of terminal elevators for the soybean industry in the future.

The box entitled "Supply" in Exhibit VII-1 is used to indicate the convergence of soybean supplies from interior terminals, country subterminals, country ele-

vators, and farms. The soybean movement from these combined sources is split into two major flows — one stream of 379 million bushels shipped to soybean processors and the other of 198 million bushels transferred to soybean exporters. Part of the 379 million bushel processing supply becomes part of the export market in the form of soybean meal (47 million bushels by weight) and soybean oil (22 million bushels by weight).

The boxes in Exhibit VII-1 entitled "Domestic Use" and "Exports" represent the final physical disposition of the soybean crop in the form of 14 million bushels of soybean seed; 69 million bushels of soybean oil (4,140 million pounds) and 339 million bushels of soybean meal (10,170 thousand tons) to the domestic market; and 198 million bushels of soybeans, 47 million bushels of soybean meal (1,410 thousand tons), and 22 million bushels of soybean oil (1,232 million pounds) to the various export markets.

Exhibit VII-1 represents the physical movement of soybeans and soybean products measured in millions of bushels. Over the years the major impacts on the utilization of marketing channels for soybeans have been (1) the technological revolution on the farm encouraging the development of subterminal markets that were virtually nonexistent in the immediate postwar period (1947–1949), (2) the expansion of the livestock-poultry-feed complex and the resultant increase in domestic and export meal marketings, and (3) the dominance of the United States in world soybean trade in recent years which resulted in a marketing channel that also was not present some 18 years ago.

In addition to the quantity changes in the production and movement of soybeans and soybean products and the resultant development of new marketing channels, there have been significant changes in the monetary relationship between the two major products of the soybean, meal and oil. Volumewise, the current ratio in 1964 of soybean meal to soybean oil in the processing process was 4.4 to 1. During the war and immediate postwar period the monetary ratio of soybean oil to meal exceeded the quantity ratio of soybean meal to oil, a circumstance indicating the dollar-and-cents importance of soybean oil to the processor and producer of soybeans. In recent years, the monetary ratio of soybean oil to meal has fallen substantially below the quantity ratio of soybean meal to oil; thus soybean oil in 1966 was not the most valuable product of the soybean in either a monetary or a physical sense. The historical price ratio of soybean oil to meal was as follows:

1942	5.5	1957	4.0
1947	5.8	1962	2.5
1949	3.8	1963	2.4

The drop in the price of soybean oil after World War II reflected (1) the postwar availability and production expansion of all edible oils (cottonseed oil, coconut oil, olive oil, and palm oil as well as soybean oil), (2) the lack of funds for oil purchases by the developing countries, and (3) the strong demand for protein meal which relegated soybean oil to a by-product relationship. In spite of the expanding domestic and world markets for margarine, shortening, and salad oil, and the increased technological improvement in soybean oil, soybean oil prices have remained low. The pressure of growing world edible oil supplies coupled with the limitations in the buying power of those countries that have the greatest population increases will mean continued low prices for soybean oil and/or continued use of P.L. 480 funds to export soybean oil. If the potential world demand for fats and oils becomes effective through additional P.L. 480 funds or stronger foreign economies, and if technology continues to enlarge the uses of soybean oil, then soybean oil will not be relegated to its secondary position as a product of the soybean.

The utilization of soybeans and products measured in dollar value terms for two time periods, 1947–1949 and 1962–1964, is presented in Exhibit VII-2. This exhibit highlights the changes in utilization measured in dollar values as discussed above. The exhibit

EXHIBIT VII-2

Farm Level Value and Utilization of Soybeans
and Soybean Products: 1947–1949 and 1962–1964
(In millions of dollars)

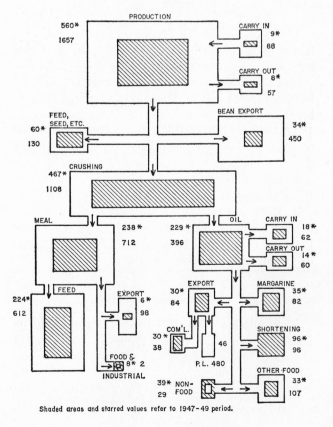

Shaded areas and starred values refer to 1947–49 period.

EXHIBIT VII-3

Firms and Entities in the Soybean Economy: Crop Year 1963

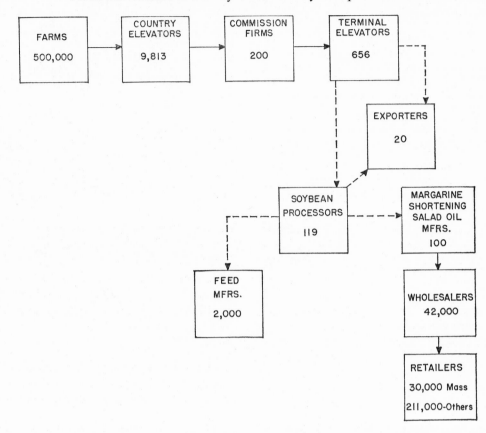

is a snapshot of the industry superimposed on a picture of the industry as it was 15 years ago. In this exhibit the values of all sectors have been converted to "farm level" values.[2] Because farm prices for soybeans in 1962–1964 were almost the same as in 1947–1949, Exhibit VII-2 gives an overall view of soybean product and channel dollar value changes during a three-fold expansion of the crop. Exhibit VII-2 substantiates (1) the growing dollar importance of soybean meal in the domestic feed industry and export feed market, (2) the increase in the value of soybean oil utilized in margarine and salad oil markets, and (3) the great dependence of the soybean oil export market on P.L. 480 funds.

FIRMS AND ENTITIES

The explosion of the soybean industry not only affected the physical and dollar volume flows through expanded and new channels, but it also resulted in a change in the number, size, and type of enterprises that make up the soybean economy. The soybean

[2] See *Agriculture Handbook,* No. 91, 1955, pp. 14 and 25.

economy in crop year 1963, as described in Exhibit VII-3, consisted of 500,000 soybean producers, 9,813 country and terminal elevators (concentrated in a few hundred cooperatives or other business-type enterprises), 200 commission and/or brokerage firms, 119 soybean processing plants involving some 60 firms, 100 major margarine, shortening, and salad oil manufacturers, 2,000 mixed feed manufacturers (concentrated in 100 cooperative or other business-type enterprises), 42,000 wholesalers, 241,000 retail firms (including 30,000 mass retailers), and 20 export firms (with most of the volume handled by four major companies).

In practically every decision-making center in Exhibit VII-3 the number of firms is decreasing and each firm was handling larger volumes of soybeans, soybean oil, and soybean meal. This trend is substantiated by Table VII-1 which is an overall summary of the changes in the number of firms, dollar value of shipments, and percentage of dollar value of shipments by the larger firms between the census years 1947 and 1958 for the major sectors of the soybean economy.

TABLE VII-1. Number of Firms, Dollar Volume of Shipments, and Percentage of Dollar Shipments by Largest Companies in the Major Sectors of the Soybean Economy: 1947 and 1958

A. THE FARMER[a]

Year	Number of farms	Value of shipments (thousands)	Over 100 acres	50–99 acres	25–49 acres	Under 10 acres
			Number of soybean farms			
1949	369,780	$ 451,129	11,116	41,366	89,066	81,145
1959	499,710	1,017,902	45,825	94,476	135,673	73,613

[a] Because the U.S. Census of Agriculture has a different census year, soybean farm data had to be on a 1949 and 1959 basis.

B. SOYBEAN OIL MILLS

Year	Number of firms	Value of shipments (thousands)	4 largest	8 largest	20 largest	Coverage index
			% of value of shipments by largest firms			
1947	105	$585,709	44%	63%	81%	.80
1958	66	999,202	40	63	86	.94

C. PREPARED ANIMAL FEEDS

Year	Number of firms	Value of shipments (thousands)	4 largest	8 largest	20 largest	Coverage index
			% of value of shipments by largest firms			
1947	2,372	$2,122,241	19%	27%	40%	.89
1958	2,016	2,942,008	22	30	43	.91

D. MARGARINE

Year	Number of firms	Value of shipments (thousands)	4 largest	8 largest	20 largest	Coverage index
			% of value of shipments by largest firms			
1947	17	$214,598	64%	90%	100%	.73
1958	22	214,379	62	86	—	.61

E. SHORTENING AND COOKING OILS

Year	Number of firms	Value of shipments (thousands)	4 largest	8 largest	20 largest	Coverage index
			% of value of shipments by largest firms			
1947	68	$884,713	59%	81%	99%	.96
1958	66	938,216	49	75	97	.88

SOURCE: U.S. Census of Agriculture.

Table VII-1 shows that increases in the number of firms occurred in two sectors of the soybean economy: farming and margarine. In the farming sector, however, there was only a 35% increase in the number of farms compared to a 226% expansion in the value of shipments from 1949 to 1959. A more detailed examination of the farming sector indicates that the most rapid increase in the number of soybean farms occurred in the larger farm categories (over 100 acres). There was an actual decrease in the number of farms growing under 10 acres of soybeans. In the case of margarine firms and operations, there was a decided increase in the number of principal margarine manufacturers from 1947 to 1958 and an even larger increase in the number in recent years, totaling 65 firms in 1964. Although the dollar value appears to be constant for the shipments of margarine in 1947 and 1958, the decline in margarine prices masks the increase in total tonnage shipped. The actual tonnage increased from 552 million pounds in 1947 to over 1 billion pounds in 1958 and to 1.8 million pounds in 1964.

Table VII-2 summarizes the other changes that oc-

TABLE VII-2. Number of Firms or Entities Operating as Country Elevators, Commission Firms, Terminal Elevators, Exporters, Wholesalers, and Retailers in the Soybean Economy: 1947 and 1958

	1947	1958
Country elevators	11,200	9,813
Commission firms	300	200
Terminal elevators	350	656[a]
Exporters	15	20
Wholesalers	39,329	42,555
Retailers	378,320	259,796

[a] In 1958 terminal elevators included country subterminals.
SOURCE: U.S. Bureau of the Census, *U.S. Census of Manufactures, 1958.*

curred in the number of entities in the remaining major sectors of the soybean economy. With the exception of the increase in the number of wholesalers and soybean exporting firms responding to an expansion of soybean and soybean product exports, the domestic expansion of the crop and its products was handled by fewer and larger elevator, commission, and retailing firms. The increase in mass retail markets and the ease of transfer of processing technology have enabled standardized margarine products to be produced. In many cases this has led to private label contracts between manufacturer and retailers of margarine and other soybean oil based products. Wholesalers with cooperative retail outlets have also developed private label brands of margarine to serve their mass distribution centers.

COORDINATING PATTERNS

Even though the economic, technological, and governmental environment was conducive to an expansion of the soybean economy in the United States, it was entrepreneurship which was the catalyst needed to develop, coordinate, and expand this industry. The early leaders of the soybean industry utilized third parties such as railroad agricultural agents, county agents, federal extension marketing specialists from the U.S. Department of Agriculture, and bankers to encourage the simultaneous production of soybeans and the construction of soybean processing plants. Farmers were not anxious to produce a new crop without an available market nor were oil crushers anxious to build crushing facilities without a source of soybeans. One of the major soybean processing firms, the A. E. Staley Manufacturing Company, built its first plant in 1922 at the *request* of a large number of farmers in the Decatur, Illinois, area. Other areas in the midwest expanded both soybean production and processing operations through meetings held over a wide area of the Corn Belt. Some of these meetings were sponsored by the railroads to encourage the development of new industries in their geographical areas, other meetings were held by various farm organizations, such as the Farm Bureau Federation and the Farmers Union. At these meetings the agrono-

plantings. (One of the earliest contracts was that offered by W. T. Culpepper of Elizabeth City, North Carolina, in 1915.) As the rapid expansion of the crop and processing facilities took place, and as changes in technology on and off the farm occurred, together with changes in domestic and foreign consumption, a need was created for greater coordination among the various major decision-making centers. One of the most important coordinating developments has been the increase in vertical integration (common ownership) of the many segments of the soybean complex.

COMMON OWNERSHIP IN THE SOYBEAN INDUSTRY

Exhibit VII-4 summarizes the ownership patterns in the soybean economy as measured by quantity flows

EXHIBIT VII-4

Ownership Patterns in the Soybean Economy as Measured by Quantity Flows: Crop Year 1963

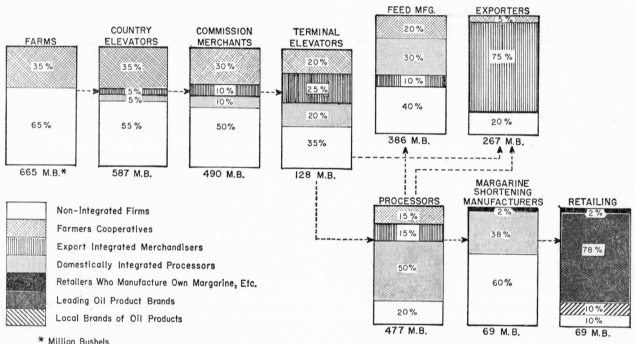

mists, the extension agents, the farm leaders, and the potential builder of a soybean plant discussed their problems and the opportunities that might be mutually advantageous.

Many forms of coordination have been developed for the soybean industry since the development of the early educational programs described briefly above. In addition to farmer-processor "gentlemen's agreements" formal contracts were established in the early periods of the industry with the processor offering growers production contracts in advance of soybean

at each stage in the vertical movement from farm to end user.

Farm Cooperatives. One of the more important forms of forward integration in the soybean industry is that of farmer cooperatives. In 1964 some 35% of all soybeans were purchased by country elevator operators from their farmer members, a major portion of which were in turn sold by cooperative commission agents. The cooperative terminal elevator handled 20% of all terminal soybean shipments and some 5%

of direct export sales. Cooperatives in 1952 accounted for over 14% [3] of the total number of processing plants but they were small local crushing plants of either the screw-press type or the now outlawed tri-

EXHIBIT VII-5

Advertisement by Cargill Taken from a Local Arkansas Newspaper: November 5, 1961

TO ARKANSAS FARMERS:

Independent Country Elevators Are Competitive

The independent country grain elevator has always been the backbone of America's free grain marketing system. Their business is tough and highly competitive, and profit margins are low.

THEY GIVE YOU BEST PRICES

This very competition forces the independent country elevator to search out the best possible market for grain, whether it be for export or domestic processing. Then it must find the highest bidder in that market. In this way you, the Arkansas Farmer, get the highest possible prices for your grain.

THEY GIVE YOU FREE CHOICE

In addition, you decide when to sell your grain. For example, last year soybean prices skyrocketed to $3.00 per bushel and many of you took advantage of this price at your independent country elevator, either storing your soybeans on the farm or in your local elevator.

THEY PAY TOP PRICES FOR SOYBEANS

Another example exists today when country elevators are paying $2.25 per bushel (or more) for soybeans and in the face of the largest soybean surplus in history. (Conservative estimates put the 1961 surplus of soybeans at 70 million bushels.)

COMPARE DIFFERENT MARKET SYSTEMS

We ask you to compare this with what you got last year and what you can expect to get this year from pool-type marketing before marketing your soybeans.

CARGILL, INCORPORATED

Source: *The Brinkley Argus,* November 5, 1961.

chlorethylene solvent type, and they accounted for less than 5% of the total crushing volume. By 1964 cooperatives had made major inroads in the soybean processing industry, accounting for 15% of the soy-

[3] Goldberg, *The Soybean Industry*, p. 72.

bean processing volume. Most of this increase occurred through acquisitions of major soybean firms such as Honeymead Products of Mankato, Minnesota (the world's largest soybean plant) and Dannen Mills of St. Louis, Missouri. Through these acquisitions the cooperatives gained not only facilities but experienced management as well.

Cooperatives are also active in feed manufacturing although the same cooperatives that process soybeans into meal and oil are not necessarily the same cooperatives that manufacture mixed feeds. In recent years cooperatives have built new processing facilities as well as purchasing existing ones. The most prominent example of this type of cooperative integration is that of the Arkansas Valley Grain Cooperative. It met severe opposition by existing crushers who felt that "pool" buying of soybeans by the cooperative from their members would be uneconomical for the soybean economy of that area. Once the cooperative was established, however, competition offered the farmer similar arrangements as outlined below.

Exhibit VII-5, taken from a local Arkansas paper dated November 5, 1961, indicates the type of advertisement that appeared during the first season of the cooperative soybean activity in Arkansas.

Exhibit VII-6 is a newspaper account dated April 14, 1963, indicating the change in market competition brought about by the entrance of the cooperative one and a half years later.

Appendix Exhibit VII-1 is a copy of the Contract of Purchase given by the local elevator in Arkansas to soybean farmers on behalf of Cargill, Incorporated, during the 1963 soybean crop movement. The provisions of this contract provided for a cash advancement a few days after the soybeans were delivered to the country elevator and other periodic advances. Final settlement was made 10 days *after* the final settlement of the Arkansas Valley Grain Cooperative pool. The producer was guaranteed a price *greater* than the *cash* settlement of the Arkansas cooperative pool plan.

Appendix Exhibit VII-2 is a copy of the Cargill Elevator Handling Agreement whereby Cargill sets forth the duties and responsibilities of the elevator in processing soybeans for its crushing activities and the compensation Cargill will pay to the elevator during the 1963 soybean crop movement. In essence this contract enables the elevator that signs up with the "Cargill program" to buy, assemble, and clean soybeans for Cargill on a "toll-charge" basis.

The appendix exhibits are but one example of the effects on the market structure that the cooperatives are having in the soybean industry as they participate at various decision making points.

EXHIBIT VII-6

Newspaper Account of New Soybean Marketing Program

**LOCAL FIRM REPORTS
NEW SOYBEAN MARKET
PLAN STARTED HERE**

A new, broad-range market program for soybean producers in this area has been announced here by J. W. Rascoe, manager, Brinkley Dryer and Storage Co.

"We are among a number of selected grain elevators in eastern Arkansas that are signing agreements for the coming crop year with Cargill, Inc., large soybean processor in Memphis," Mr. Rascoe said.

"The program, basically, provides improved free market opportunities for soybean farmers. It offers farmers several distinct advantages, including a newly-formed plan similar to a marketing pool but paying higher cash prices, and should help strengthen a competitive market overall," he said.

Mr. Rascoe said his agreement with Cargill will enable him to give farmers a unique choice of three options:

1. To sell his soybeans outright at time of harvest and receive that day's established market price;

2. To store his soybeans, take his government loan or not, and sell them whenever he thinks the price seems best;

3. To put his soybeans in a new Cargill marketing plan and receive periodic payments guaranteed to total more in cash than is paid by the competing cooperative pool.

"In addition," Mr. Rascoe said, "the participating farmer will not have to join any organization, pay any dues or make any investment." Earlier pool arrangements have required farmers to invest up to $7.50 per acre harvested, he explained.

"Cargill has marketed farm products for 98 years and operates nearly 200 plants in the United States and abroad. It has become one of the world's largest in the grain, oilseed and feed business by relying on the strengths and efficiency of a free competitive market. By working with Cargill, we aim to maintain that kind of market in this area," Mr. Rascoe said, "and farmers can find no stronger or more reliable marketing organization with which to do business."

SOURCE: Mason W. Clifton, "Across the Editor's Desk," *The Brinkley Argus,* Brinkley, Arkansas, April 4, 1963.

Exhibit VII-7 summarizes the vertically integrated functions performed by farmer cooperatives. The reader will note that the forward integration by the producer-cooperative stops short of the manufacture and distribution of edible oil products such as margarine, shortening, and salad cooking oils. The technology of this type of manufacturing and the marketing channels and type of direct consumer advertising needed for edible oil products are a great deal different from the marketing channels for meal and the use of soybean meal by the mixed feed industry. This is not to say that leading farm cooperatives, such as the Farmers Union's Honeymead Products Co., do not utilize new soybean oil processing technology. They do, and Honeymead's expansion in April 1965 in refining capacity from crude oil, to refined oil, to hydrogenated oil is but one example of cooperative processing technology. Yet Honeymead does stop short of the manufacture and distribution of final consumer edible oil products. Basically, the farmer cooperatives are anxious to control the marketing and processing channels as far up the vertical chain to the consumer as possible so long as the product is marketed on a commodity basis. Once product differentiation takes place, they do not feel adequately prepared for the consumer marketing processes they face.

Export Firm Ownership Patterns. Exhibit VII-8 summarizes vertically integrated functions performed by export firms in the soybean economy. The leading export integrated firm in the soybean economy, as in the wheat economy, is Cargill, Incorporated. It has country, terminal, and port elevator facilities as well as its own commission firm. Its feed division, Nutrena, is the third largest feed company in the United States, and its soybean crushing facilities rank as one of the four largest in the country. Another prominent exporter, Continental Grain in August 1965 purchased a controlling interest in Allied Mills, Inc., which is the sixth largest feed company in the United States as well as being a firm that is a leading soybean processor.

The advantage for the exporter to be integrated in the soybean industry can be summarized under one heading, namely, flexibility. By being integrated, the exporter can have a direct source of soybean supplies that may have both storage and transportation advantages. The exporter has alternative markets for the soybeans, soybean oil, and soybean meal he handles. He can use high oil content beans for processing and he can sell low oil-yielding beans for export. The mixed feed industry provides a market for not only the exporter's soybean meal but other grains the exporter may handle such as corn, barley, oats, and feed wheat. With the exception of the Dreyfus Company, the remaining exporters all play integrated roles in the soybean industry. In addition to Cargill and Conti-

EXHIBIT VII-7

Integrated Functions Performed by Farmer Cooperatives in the U.S. Soybean Economy as Measured by Quantity Flows: Crop Year 1963

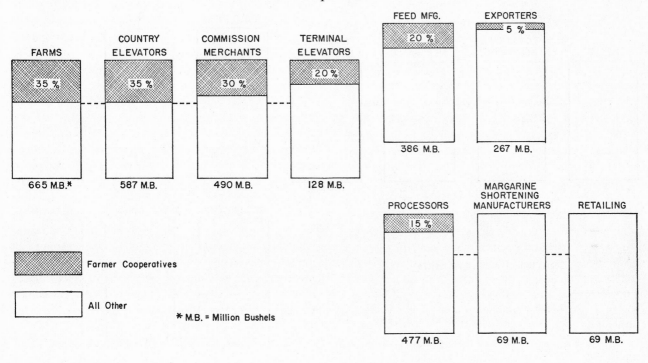

EXHIBIT VII-8

Integrated Functions Performed by Exporter-Owned Firms in the U.S. Soybean Economy as Measured by Quantity Flows: Crop Year 1963

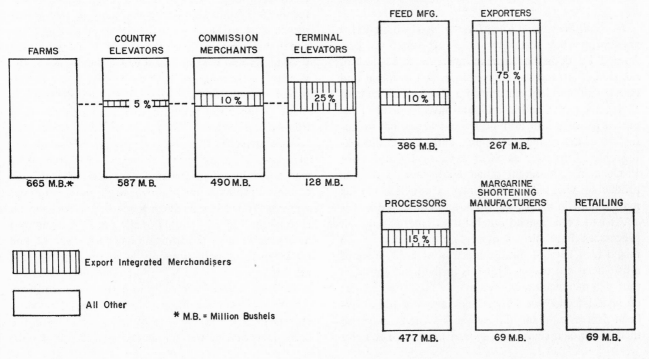

EXHIBIT VII-9

Integrated Functions Performed by Soybean Processors in the U.S. Economy as Measured by Quantity Flows: Crop Year 1963

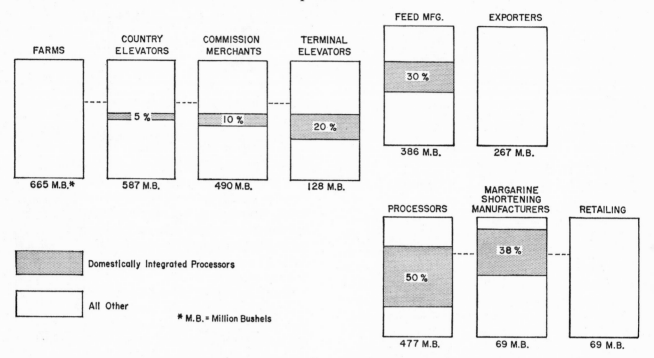

nental, the other prominent integrated export firms are Bunge and Archer-Daniels-Midland.

In addition to handling their own soybeans, soybean oil, and soybean meal, the four prominent exporters (Cargill, Bunge, Continental, and Dreyfus) also handle the soybeans, oil, and meal for many other firms.

Soybean Processing Firm Integration. Exhibit VII-9 summarizes the vertically integrated functions performed by domestic soybean processors. Several of the domestic processors have their own terminal and country subterminal elevators for the procurement of soybean supplies and in addition have vertically integrated forward into oil refining and the actual manufacture of margarine, shortening, and salad and cooking oils. Firms such as Swift & Company and Corn Products are important oil-seed crushers as well as producing well-known consumer products such as margarine, shortening, salad oil, and cooking oil.

As had been pointed out before, domestic soybean processors have strong ownership positions in the mixed feed manufacturing industry. At least 50% of all soybean processing volume is in the hands of firms that also manufacture approximately 50% of all types of mixed feed. Many feed manufacturers built soybean processing plants during World War II to assure themselves of a source of soybean meal. The scarcity

of soybean meal during the Korean War was also a factor in the integration of soybean processing and feed manufacturing. Since the 1950s the dollar value of meal in relation to oil has increased thus affecting the location of soybean processing plants. Usually an increase in meal dollar values (soybean meal accounts for 80% of the product of the soybean by weight) means that soybean processing operations are better situated if they are located adjacent to both soybean production and soybean meal consumption areas. Obviously soybean plants built adjacent to feed mixing plants with direct bulk shipments of meal from one plant to the other provides an important transportation saving.

During World War II the supply of soybean oil was also inadequate to meet the demand. Therefore there was some incentive for manufacturers of consumer edible oil products and/or soybean oil refiners to integrate backward into soybean processing in order to insure themselves of a supply of oil. After World War II and more recently the situation has been reversed, and oil is in overabundant supply in relation to the U.S. market.

One example of a change in strategy by a firm in response to the changing supply and demand relationship is that of the Buckeye Cellulose Corporation, a subsidiary of the Procter & Gamble Co. Procter &

Gamble sold its three soybean crushing plants and one cottonseed crushing mill to Ralston Purina Company (the largest feed manufacturer in the United States) in 1958. At the time the sale was made, Walter L. Lingle, Jr., President of the Division, said:

Buckeye entered the soybean crushing business primarily to supply Procter & Gamble with soybean oil for food products. Recently, however, the increasing importance of soybean meal for animal feed has made it desirable for soybean crushers to enter the mixed feed business. That's not Procter & Gamble's or Buckeye's kind of business, so it became sound business policy for us to buy soybean oil on the open market and to dispose of these facilities for crushing soybeans.[4]

Another example of a firm that is exiting from backward integration in the soybean industry is that of Textron Company. After Textron purchased the Spencer Kellogg Company in 1960, management decided that in view of an abundant supply of soybean oil and the major investment required to operate a soybean crushing plant, the firm would be better off to divest itself of its crushing plants and retain the oil refineries. These soybean plants were sold to other soybean crushers such as Central Soya Company, Inc., and the operating results justified management's strategy with an excellent improvement in return on investment.

On the other hand, firms such as Anderson Clayton that are in the soybean oil refining business and crushing operations also are integrating forward into branded and private label margarine, salad oil, shortening and cooking oil products on both a regional and a national basis.

When one summarizes the simultaneous integration and withdrawal of soybean oil crushers and/or refiners into the manufacture of margarine and other edible oil products, as shown in Exhibit VII-9, one notes that approximately 38% of the volume of all margarine, shortening, and cooking oil is handled by manufacturers who are also soybean oil refiners and/or crushers.

Edible Oil Product Manufacturers' Ownership Patterns. Minor vertical integration exists between margarine manufacturers and retailers. The writer was able to discover only one prominent retail distributor that not only sold its own label of margarine but also manufactured it as well. Assuming that its percentage of margarine sales is equal to its percentage of all food sales to total U.S. food sales, the percentage of about 2% was estimated as the amount of integration in this product. Exhibit VII-3 above also indicates that na-

tionally the leading branded items have a significant sales volume of margarine, shortening, cooking oil, and salad oil products through retailers, averaging approximately 78% in 1963. The remaining sales are almost equally divided between local retail private label brands and packer brands.

Nonintegrated Firms in the Soybean Industry. Exhibit VII-10 represents a composite picture of the residual firms in the soybean economy that do not have joint ownership with firms in other segments of the soybean complex. The weaker strength of farmer grain cooperatives in the Corn Belt led to a higher percentage of soybeans being grown by farmers who did not own their own local marketing facilities. Integration becomes more important as the crop moves into the terminal, processing and export markets. The strong interrelationships that exist among the soybean processing, feed manufacturing, and export markets have led to all types of vertical integration — both cooperative and corporate.

The independent, on the other hand, although a declining factor in volume handled in each functional area, has many important strengths and major alternative forms of coordination within the framework of the vertical market structure of the soybean industry. In the case of the farmer, he has had a relatively strong growth market for his production with or without cooperative marketing help. The independent country elevator operator has not been by-passed to any great extent in the soybean industry. He, too, has had an excellent market for the soybeans he handles. As economy of scale is important in soybean processing, the soybean processor has been unable to rely to any significant extent on obtaining very many soybean supplies directly from farmers. The volumes involved, tens of thousands of bushels a day, are impossible to get in important quantities from direct farm to processor truck shipments. Country subterminals, as in the wheat economy, are of growing importance in the soybean economy as they are built in response to the expanding requirements of the domestic and export markets.

Commission merchants are also more important in the soybean economy than in the wheat economy for three primary reasons: (1) less cooperative activity, (2) more "free" volume and therefore less competition with government storage programs, and (3) the expanding volume requirements of processors and exports that require them to use all varieties of procurement channels in obtaining their necessary supplies.

The independent soybean processor is perhaps in the most exposed position in the soybean economy.

[4] *Soybean Digest,* December 1958, p. 5.

EXHIBIT VII-10

Nonintegrated Functions Performed by Firms in the U.S. Soybean Economy as Measured by Quantity Flows: Crop Year 1963

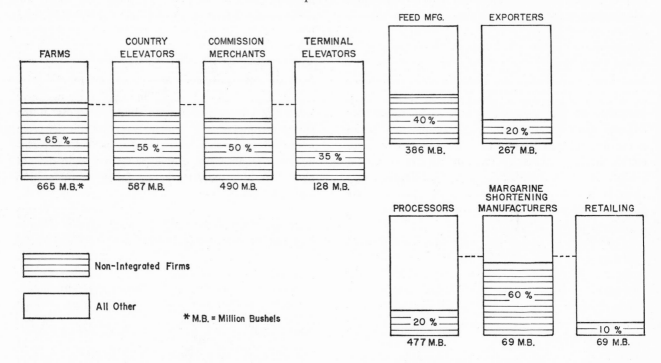

With no important integrated meal market, no direct export channels, and no direct ownership of procurement channels he is in a much less advantageous position than his competitors because he has less opportunity for transportation, storage, and selection advantages. On the other hand, he is in a more flexible position in that he has no prior procurement or market commitments as a result of common ownership policies.

The "independent" feed manufacturer in the soybean economy is less disadvantaged than his counterpart in the soybean processing operation because in most instances the feed manufacturer may be engaged in other operations such as egg and broiler production and marketing and grain merchandising. In addition, soybean meal, although an extremely important ingredient in feed manufacturing, is still only one input and independent feed manufacturers may have compensating locational advantages that more than offset vertical integration in the soybean economy.

The next major function that has a large volume handled by nonintegrated firms in the soybean economy is that of margarine, shortening, salad oil, and cooking oil manufacture. With a large volume of soybean oil readily available to the market in recent years, there has been little incentive for these manufacturers to integrate backward into refining oil or processing the soybean. At the same time, the major manufacturers of these products have built up important, desirable, and distinctive product features that have enabled them to appeal directly to the ultimate consumers and achieve a substantial balance of sales through retailers (approximately 78% of sales volume — See Exhibit VII-3). Some soybean processors and soybean oil refiners on the other hand have attempted to integrate forward into the manufacture of consumer edible oil products in order to improve their low margin commodity operations.

The independent retailers in the retail food business account for over 85% of the number of retail outlets but only 10% of the dollar volume. The mass retailers (chains and affiliated independents) have limited direct ownership of any segment of the soybean industry, but nonetheless they have important contractual relationships with the industry in the form of retail private label packaged products and long-term arrangements with soybean manufacturers that produce a local manufacturer's label.

In summary, nonintegrated firms in the soybean economy are most important if they are evaluated by the number of such firms in each functioning category (see Exhibit VII-2). However, nonintegrated firms are of declining quantitative significance *in each segment of the soybean economy* when measured by the volume of soybean and soybean products handled by these individual firms (see Exhibit VII-4). Many processors have integrated soybean operations because of procurement difficulties or lost market opportunities in feed manufacturing operations. With the exception of the nonaffiliated soybean producer and the nonintegrated edible oil product manufacturer, it would seem that in the past the nonintegrated soybean firms have been at a competitive disadvantage in the promotion and distribution of their finished products. On the other hand, the nonintegrated firm has one source of strength. A unique favorable factor is the flexibility of a one-function operation that can enable the firm to change direction rapidly — the development of independent country subterminal elevator firms and unique export terminal operations are but two examples of this adaptability to a changing market structure.

In addition to coordination of functions through common ownership both the nonintegrated and the integrated firm managements have developed countless numbers of important institutions and arrangements, other than spot markets, that are used for facilitating the movement of goods and services in the soybean economy.

COORDINATING INSTITUTIONS AND ARRANGEMENTS

As mentioned earlier in this chapter, the soybean complex during its rapid expansion has required various types of coordinating activities in order to provide for an efficient movement of soybeans from the producer to the domestic and export consumer of soybean-based products. In addition to vertical integration, firms in the soybean industry have found many ways to improve their operations by a better coordination of their procurement and marketing functions. Some of the earlier coordinating devices in the industry consisted of local meetings and educational programs and dealt primarily with only one link in the vertical soybean structure, namely, the relationship between the producer and the soybean crusher (see pp. 115–116). The more recent coordinating instruments tend to be broadly applied to the total soybean complex.

The Futures Markets. The soybean industry has made more use of the futures markets than any other commodity group in the United States, accounting for over 75% of the average annual value of all commodity futures contracts during the period from 1961 to 1966. (Corn and wheat futures have become more important in the 1966 crop year.) For the fiscal year ended June 30, 1966, out of a *total* estimated value of

commodity futures trading on all regulated contract markets of $71.8 billion, soybean futures accounted for $46.2 billion, soybean oil futures for $3.7 billion, and soybean meal futures for $2.6 billion. The quantities involved 16.3 billion bushels of soybeans, 34.2 billion pounds of soybean oil and 37.7 million tons of soybean meal. The soybean futures contract was begun in 1940, just prior to World War II. The soybean oil and meal contracts were established in 1950 and 1951 respectively to provide better hedging and price planning not only for soybeans but for the changing value relationships between soybean oil and soybean meal as related to the raw soybean. Table VII-3 summarizes the range of annual volume of trading on these three futures markets for the fiscal years 1962 through 1966.

TABLE VII-3. Volume Range of Futures Trading in Soybean and Soybean Products: Fiscal Years 1962–1966

Commodity futures market	Effective date of designation	Range of annual volume of trading
Soybeans	December 8, 1940	4.8 to 19.5 billions of bushels
Soybean oil	June 30, 1950	16.3 to 34.2 billions of pounds
Soybean meal	August 22, 1951	27.1 to 37.7 millions of tons

SOURCE: USDA, Commodity Exchange Authority.

The major uses of the soybean futures markets are similar to those of the wheat economy, namely, for hedging (offsetting a long or short position) and for pricing inventory or processed products on a spread between the cash and futures price of the commodity ("the basis"). In most commercial uses of the futures market by off-farm segments of the soybean complex it is the latter function, establishing the best arbitrage between the futures and cash price, which is the most important use of the futures market. On the whole, operators are less interested in vertical price movements than they are in the relationships between cash and futures prices.[5] The "basis" is a summary of the competitive and logistical advantages of a "cash" price for a particular quantity and quality of a commodity at a specific location in relation to a terminal "futures market quotation." In a sense it acts as a coordinating device which forces the businessman to assess the variety of economic factors that are affecting and will affect his ultimate procurement and marketing program.

The presence of a soybean oil and soybean meal

[5] One company's exception to this strategy was that of Mr. Tino De Angelis who allegedly attempted to forecast the needs of the P.L. 480 Soybean Oil Program and accumulated cash and futures contracts to cover anticipated needs which caused a potential run-up in the price level of soybean oil.

futures market as well as a soybean futures market broadens the basis concept and enables processors, feed manufacturers, oil refineries, edible oil manufacturers, and retailers as well as exporters and importers of meal, oil, and soybeans to participate fully in futures market operations. In addition the relationship between the values of soybean futures versus soybean oil and soybean meal futures acts as a check to unrealistic pricing practices. For example, if speculators push the price of soybeans above their product values, the soybean processor may end up buying meal and oil in the futures contracts and selling an equivalent amount of soybean futures. He may do this when the cash spread between the product and the soybeans is, to his knowledge, considerably less than the cost of conversion. As Dwayne Andreas, former Chairman of the Board of Honeymead Products Company, has stated, "This in fact, gives them [the processors] additional crushing capacity at less than it would cost to own a plant and operate it at capacity." [6]

The soybean farmer uses the soybean futures market in the same manner as a wheat futures market; namely, to:

(1) fix the price of a growing or not yet planted crop;
(2) fix the price of grain in storage for deferred delivery;
(3) fix the cost of soybeans to be purchased without taking immediate delivery; and
(4) speculate in the price of a crop that has been grown but for which storage is not available.[7]

The first two procedures involve being "short" (selling futures). In other words the farmer *sells* a futures contract in order to have a fixed price level for his unharvested crop or that portion of his crop that he is storing. The second two procedures involve being "long" futures. In these cases the farmer *buys* a futures contract in anticipation of a price rise if he plans to buy soybeans at a later date or if he wants to take advantage of a rising market even though he is unable to store his crop.

Other participants of the soybean complex use the futures markets in a variety of ways. Soybeans are harvested in late September to early November. Many processors acquire as much as 50% of their annual soybean requirements during this two-month harvest period.[8] Because it may be either impossible or unwise to sell soybean end products simultaneously with the purchase of soybeans, the futures market permits the

processors to sell soybean futures against cash bean purchases. Soybean processors also use the oil and meal futures markets in their operations. In the soybean processing business a high level of plant operation is desirable because of its impact on unit costs. At times processors may buy cash soybeans and sell meal and oil futures if there is a satisfactory margin involved. This procedure hedges the raw bean inventory, assures the firm of some kind of conversion profit, and provides a high level of operating capacity.

Product manufacturers such as margarine food companies use the soybean oil futures in their procurement operations and as a hedge against long-term contractual relationships with retail food distributors. Similarly, feed manufacturers use the soybean meal contracts as a hedge against long-term mixed feed contracts that they may have with feed-lot managers.

Although there is a price support program for soybeans (a form of alternative futures market), on the average the spot market price has been higher than the price support, thus indicating various price risks above the price support level which may be hedged in a futures market.

In essence, the futures market provides a pricing and procurement procedure over time that is an invaluable aid in coordinating functions in all segments of the soybean economy. It facilitates the movement of goods and services through the vertical structure of the soybean system over extended time periods.

Trade Associations. Just as the leaders of the soybean industry have been progressive in their development of several futures markets as coordinating devices in the soybean complex, so have they had the vision to develop imaginative and meaningful trade associations.

The *American Soybean Association* is a nonprofit organization devoted to the interests of soybean growers and handlers of the nation. It was organized in 1920, and incorporated in 1946. Organizational affairs are directed by a 19-man board chosen by vote from the leading soybean producing states. Board membership is limited to actual soybean farmers. Objectives of the association include (1) the bringing together of all soybean interests — producers, processors, handlers, manufacturers, exporters, etc.; (2) collecting and disseminating crop, processing, and marketing information; (3) encouraging the expansion of present and new markets; (4) developing an agreement with the U.S. Department of Agriculture in 1956 for a soybean market development project in Japan financed by P.L. 480 funds and soybean industry funds and founding the Japanese American Soybean Institute in Japan as the operating agency for this project; (5) maintain-

[6] Chicago Board of Trade Symposium, 1955.
[7] University of Illinois, Bulletin 696, *Use of Grain Futures Markets in the Farm Business*, p. 53.
[8] Speech by Robert P. Parrott, Executive Vice President, Central Soya Company, Inc., before mid-year conference of the National Independent Meat Packers Association, January 19, 1967, Scottsdale, Arizona (unpublished).

ing a Washington office and representing the industry on legislative matters and (6) publishing a monthly magazine — *Soybean Digest* — as well as the annual *Soybean Blue Book* and *Late Soybean Market News*. There are five state associations affiliated with the American Soybean Association: Minnesota, Arkansas, Illinois, Iowa, and Mississippi.

The *National Soybean Processors Association* is made up primarily of individuals, firms, and corporations regularly engaged in the actual processing of soybeans. This association has approximately 65 members who represent over 90% of the crushing capacity in the United States. Associate members who are refiners or mixed feed manufacturers also participate in the association's activities. These include: (1) the development of equitable trading rules for buyers and sellers of soybean products; (2) the formulation of a Soybean Research Council for improved effectiveness in all aspects of soybean production, processing, and marketing; (3) the establishment of a National Soybean Crop Improvement Council to improve yields of raw and finished products; and (4) the publication of *Soybean News, Soybean Farming,* and the *Year Book* and *Official Trading Rules*.

The *Soybean Council of America, Inc.* was organized in 1956 to further expand the markets for soybean and soybean products. In January 1960 the Council and the Foreign Agricultural Service of the U.S. Department of Agriculture signed a contract to use P.L. 480 funds to promote soybeans on a *global* basis. Some 60 countries are eligible for soybean promotional programs under the P.L. 480 program. The Council has many overseas offices to carry out its worldwide market programs. The Department of Agriculture has given a great deal of credit to the Council for the rapid growth of soybean, soybean meal and soybean oil exports.

In summary, the soybean industry, being a fairly new industry and a rapid growth industry, has formed unique and progressive associations that have stressed the mutuality of interests that exist among the many segments of the soybean industry. These associations have developed trade practices and consumer responsive production, processing, and marketing technologies, all of which have improved the coordination of the soybean complex in meeting the ultimate consumer needs. The soybean associations have been singled out by Secretary of Agriculture Orville Freeman as the best prototypes of industry-wide organizations.

Bargaining Associations. As in the case of the wheat economy, bargaining associations have had little impact on the marketing strategy of soybean producers. The *National Farmers Organization* has made some organized attempts to withhold soybeans from the market by encouraging farmers to store them. The result has been a slight increase in price for a short period of time followed by a price decline usually sharper and deeper than the increase.

The *Ontario Soya-Bean Growers Marketing Board of Canada* has 10,000 members, and its purpose is to control the marketing of soybeans in Ontario and to regulate their sale. It has the power actually to purchase and sell soybeans but has not done so. It was difficult for this writer to notice any success in improved soybean price levels or stability that could be directly attributable to the marketing board.

The wide geographical dispersion of soybean production, the important processing role that cooperatives play, and the rapid expansion of the cooperatives would suggest that bargaining associations without cooperative support will not be successful in maintaining or improving the price for soybeans over time.

Pool Arrangements. Typical of the pool arrangements for the marketing of soybeans by farmers was that of the Arkansas Valley Grain Cooperative described briefly on page 117. In essence a pool arrangement gives each farmer selling his grain to the cooperative the average market price *for the season* based on grade and quality. Soybeans are a crop with volatile prices occurring over a harvest season and from one crop year to the next. The advantage to the producer is that he will not receive the lowest price and may take advantage of a seasonal price increase once the harvest year has passed. At the same time the farmer who may be able to market his soybeans effectively will not maximize his market opportunities by participating in a pool. In addition, as one nonpool cooperative executive put it, "The pool concept makes our better cooperative members unhappy and subjects management to the temptation of holding soybeans or soybean products for speculation rather than trying to develop sound merchandising practices." In the 1963 crop year when soybean prices ranged from $2.25 to $3.00 a bushel, both weaknesses of the pool arrangement were apparent in some cooperative operations.

Vegetable Oil Export Company. The Vegetable Oil Export Company was organized under the Webb Pomerene Act to enable U.S. soybean oil processors to cooperate as a legal cartel for export oil operations. The assumption by those who participated in it was that a typical 50,000 ton soybean oil sale was too big for any single firm to risk covering. The disruption in the cash and futures oil markets might cause price fluctuations that would wipe out any profit potential. Therefore, the Vegetable Oil Export Company was created to make American soybean oil more competitive with that of other nations in the export oil market. The major firms in the export company are Archer-Daniels-Midland, A. E. Staley Manufacturing Company, and Honeymead Products (a division of the Farmers Union Grain Terminal Association). Others that belong but play a minor role are the Ralston Purina Company and the North Iowa Co-operative. One of the important provisions of the Webb Pomerene Act is that the export business must be conducted in such a way that it will not affect the price level of the domestic soybean oil market. Two large soybean processing firms are not in the export company (Cargill and Central Soya), and their absence encourages export price competition and permits domestic oil price levels to fluctuate without much fear of abnormal price impact from Vegetable Oil Export. If these firms and others were to join the export company, it would be difficult to assume lack of price impact on the *domestic* soybean oil market by the Vegetable Oil Export Company, unless total exports themselves were regulated by other authority, or unless the Department of Agriculture stabilized the domestic market by Commodity Credit Company activity.

Governmental Activities. The government, as has been mentioned previously, has in many respects replaced the "unseen hand" of Adam Smith: (1) by price programs to support certain price levels for the farmer who produces soybeans, and (2) by overseas and domestic "market" programs to act as a safety valve for storage programs that support the price of soybeans and to offset the imbalance of by-products resulting from price support programs and the different rates of growth of the soybean meal and soybean oil markets. Fortunately, the government's price support program on soybeans has been maintained at a reasonable price level, and for the most part price levels have been above the price support. However, there has been an imbalance in the rate of growth of the soybean meal and soybean oil markets. The rapid increase in livestock and poultry products resulted in a corresponding increase in the demand for soybean meal. Soybean oil domestic utilization has been less rapid. To offset this imbalance the Department of Agriculture has shipped large quantities of soybean oil under the P.L. 480 program for both "surplus removal" and market development. Elsewhere in this chapter it was noted that one-half of the dollar value

of soybean oil shipments are in the form of concessional soybean oil shipments. This program of P.L. 480 shipments has and will continue to be a major factor in the maintenance of soybean price levels. Even with a change in U.S. policy from "surplus disposal" to "self-help" the shortages of fats and oils in the developing countries, together with the U.S. by-product imbalances will probably result in large soybean oil shipments under P.L. 480 for several years ahead.

The government has also developed other programs to maintain the price level to producers, such as a tariff on beans, meal, and oil. On the other hand, during emergency periods the government has also stepped in and maintained ceiling prices on soybeans, meal, and oil. In addition, during periods such as World War II, crushing margin (processing margin) allowances and volume differentials for each type of processor (hydraulic, screw-press, solvent) were established. Other government programs that affect price include government storage payments for soybeans on and off the farm.

The government has also provided many services that facilitate the functioning and coordination of the many parts of the soybean system as it satisfies the ultimate consumer demand for soybean and soybean oil end products. Such services include market news information, crop and stock reports, the standardization of soybeans, soybean meal, and soybean oil grades and inspection services. The establishment of mechanical devices to give oil yields at country and terminal receiving points is another government service. The Department of Agriculture through its Farmer Cooperative Service also provides consulting services on feasibility studies for the construction and operation of soybean processing facilities and for the establishment of financial and management control systems for farmer cooperative firms. The government has also provided other services such as the lending of funds from the Area Redevelopment Administration for the construction of soybean processing facilities.

The government has been an important factor in improving the quality and yield of soybeans and soybean products. New high yielding soybean varieties have been developed by USDA agronomists. In addition, the USDA technicians have developed new hydrogenization and deodorization technologies to provide greater stability for soybean oil and related products.

In addition to price support and market operations, as well as a variety of services and research programs, the government has also developed various regulatory programs and agencies to improve the functioning of the component parts of the soybean system. These agencies include the Commodity Exchange Authority of the U.S. Department of Agriculture which supervises the futures markets of soybeans, meal, and oil. (These requirements were important in limiting the deleterious effects to the users of the exchanges during the De Angelis affair of 1963.[9]) Other regulations include sanitation and packaging, as well as general antitrust safeguards.

Specific examples and effects of the above government activities will be included in Section V of this study, but a few of the more important activities and their effects on coordination will be noted here so that the reader will have a clearer picture as to how the soybean structure developed and the effects of government actions on future structural changes.

The tariff rates on soybeans, soybean oil, and soybean meal encouraged the development of the domestic industry. The rates as of 1965 were as follows:

Soybeans	2 cents a pound
Soybean oil	45% ad valorem
Soybean meal	Free

Price supports for soybeans on the whole have been high enough to encourage a rapid growth in soybean production. On the other hand, over the 26-year period 1941–1966 the market price for soybeans was higher than the government price support with the exception of three years (1957, 1958, and 1961). Therefore, farmer soybean deliveries to the Commodity Credit Corporation for government storage occurred in sizable quantity only in these three years. Even in these years, the price support value for soybeans was only slightly more than the market price value. Table VII-4 summarizes soybean price support levels for selected crop years compared with average prices received by farmers for soybeans as well as soybean ceiling prices were applicable.

Reflected in Table VII-4 are some of the results of a government policy which has attempted, with fairly good success, to keep price supports high enough to encourage production and at the same time has reduced them when excess production seemed to be occurring.

Table VII-4 also indicates the narrow spreads allowed between ceiling prices and support prices during World War II and the wider spreads allowed in

TABLE VII-4. Price Supports, Price Ceilings, Average Prices Received by Farmers for Soybeans, and Deliveries to the Commodity Credit Corporation: Selected Crop Years, 1941–1966
(Price per bushel)

Crop year	Support price	Ceiling price	Average price received	1,000 bushel deliveries to CCC
1941	$1.60	$1.66	$1.61	953
1945	2.04	2.10	2.08	—
1946	2.04	—	2.57	—
1947	2.04	—	3.34	—
1949	2.11	—	2.16	29
1951	2.45	3.06[a]	3.08[b]	57
1956	2.15	—	2.18	27,286
1957	2.09	—	2.07	44,500
1958	2.09	—	2.00	83,000
1959	1.85	—	1.96	3,900
1960	1.85	—	2.13	—
1961	2.30	—	2.28	57,200
1962	2.25	—	2.34	1
1963	2.25	—	2.51	12
1964	2.25	—	2.62	N.A.
1965	2.25	—	2.37	N.A.
1966	2.50	—	N.A.	N.A.

N.A. = Not available.
[a] Legal minimum for ceiling prices in the country, February 15, 1951.
[b] Average, February 15, 1951.
SOURCE: Operating records of the USDA, Grain Division, Agricultural Commodity and Stabilization Service.

1951. However, in 1951 the shortage of beans was so acute that farmers were receiving higher than ceiling prices primarily by overgrading quality and/or ignoring dockage.[10] The government not only established ceiling prices for soybeans but also for meal and oil; and in World War II it established crushing margin differentials for types and sizes of plant (see Table VII-5).

During the Korean War the difficulty of establishing raw and processed product prices by government edict was made quite apparent. For example, the ceiling price relationships in Illinois were as follows: soybeans had a ceiling price of $3.23 a bushel, soybean oil a ceiling price of 20.5 cents a pound and meal a ceiling price of $74 a ton. In effect, this meant that if all three items were at ceiling prices, the processor would have a crushing margin of 56 cents a bushel which was more than adequate to cover costs and provide a profit. But in the early months of 1952 soybean meal remained at the ceiling price,[11] oil prices dropped to

---

[9] Mr. De Angelis was accused of issuing fraudulent warehouse receipts for oil and at the same time of taking a major position in soybean oil and cottonseed oil contracts in the New York and Chicago futures markets. At the time the case became public many of these contracts were closed out simultaneously, which put a heavy burden on the price of futures contracts. See Miller, *The Great Salad Oil Swindle*.

[10] Dockage includes foreign material in the soybeans, such as weeds, seeds, and chaff.

[11] Actually some meal was mixed with inferior products and called "mixed feed" in order to get above ceiling price values for it.

TABLE VII-5. Soybean Processing Margin by Size and Type of Plant: 1943–1944

Type and size	Cents per bushel
Hydraulic press	
Large	29
Medium	30
Small	31
Expeller or screw press	
Large	24
Medium	26
Small	28
Solvent extraction	
Large	29
Medium	30
Small	31

SOURCE: Office of Price Administration; see Goldberg, *The Soybean Industry*, p. 84.

50% of the ceiling price, and soybean prices remained high. The result was a crushing margin that was below many processors' variable cost. This pricing activity by the government encouraged vertical integration of feed manufacturers and soybean crushers and also lowered the quality of the "adulterated meal" that entered the market. The "encouragement" was caused

they would not be quite as accessible to markets as they would if the Commodity Credit Corporation took delivery at country or terminal elevator locations. This activity strengthened to a minor degree the holding activities of the NFO. However, in January 1965 the USDA called for the resealed soybeans six months before the normal due date of July 31. This occurred when NFO was still holding on to its members' beans hoping for a price rise. Spokesmen for the USDA said that there was no reason to pay reseal charges at a time when beans were selling above price supports. In 1967, however, the Secretary of Agriculture announced another reseal program for soybeans for the 1966 crop. This will allow producers to store the 1966 crop on their farms for another year at the government's expense. There has only been a soybean reseal program for crop years 1958, 1961, 1963, and 1966.

Although the government's price support activities for soybeans have provided very limited storage payments to the soybean industry, the existence of other storage programs such as wheat have enabled many integrated firms in the soybean industry to rely on storage of grain as an important part of their overall business operation, as Table VII-6 indicates.

TABLE VII-6. Storage Payments to Integrated Firms in the Grain, Soybean Oil Crushing, and Feed Industries: 1958–1963

	1958	1959	1960	1961	1962	1963	Total
Cargill, Incorporated	$13,226,341	$12,103,615	$ 9,808,744	$ 9,474,404	$ 6,335,499	$ 5,831,757	$ 56,780,360
Archer-Daniels-Midland Co.	6,240,199	6,076,898	5,919,132	5,134,987	2,779,579	4,875,545	31,026,340
F. H. Peavey & Company	5,623,702	5,528,810	5,398,505	4,169,304	4,064,223	4,690,655	29,466,199
Farmers Union Grain Terminal Association	3,328,488	4,781,426	4,089,595	3,945,877	2,390,665	3,700,543	22,236,594
Dannen Mills, Inc.[a]	1,761,138	2,477,522	2,605,322	2,166,612	1,605,453	831,172	11,447,219
Ralston-Purina Co.				788,097	656,519	561,452	2,006,068
Central Soya Co., Inc.	613,679	1,194,312	896,776	799,964			3,504,731
The Quaker Oats Co.		705,018	702,646	538,979			1,946,643
	$30,793,547	$32,867,601	$29,411,720	$27,018,224	$17,831,938	$20,491,124	$158,414,154

[a] Purchased by Farmers Cooperative Commission Company in 1963.

SOURCE: USDA, Commodity Credit Corporation, *Annual Reports of Storage and Handling Payments in Excess of $500,000 Under the Uniform Grain Storage Agreements*.

by the lack of availability of soybean meal that could be allocated by price. Therefore, many feed manufacturers purchased a source of soybean meal by buying a processing firm.

The government has also had a minor effect on price activities of the National Farmers Organization (NFO). For example, in June 1964 the government announced a farm "reseal program" which allowed farmers to keep their price-supported soybeans from previous crops on their farms and earn 14 cents a bushel per year storage on them. By being farm stored

The government has also affected the growth of the soybean industry by not having any acreage restrictions on soybean plantings in order to be eligible for soybean price supports. The 1965 Agricultural Act (passed October 12, 1965) also allows the Secretary of Agriculture to permit the planting of soybeans on feed grain acreage and still allow feed grain acreage restriction payments to be made to the producer if additional soybeans are needed. Once again, the government's actions are crucial to the rate and size of growth in production in the soybean industry.

The development of grading procedures and research in production, processing, and distribution, as well as market development programs by the government, have all been important aids in the growth of all segments of the soybean industry. The American Soybean Association and the Soybean Council of America are on record as applauding the government's activities, especially the use of the P.L. 480 program in market development. They point to an increase of 240% in soybean exports to Japan. In addition, Spain, once completely dependent on soybean oil P.L. 480 shipments, in 1963 purchased 234,000 metric tons of oil and 196,331 metric tons of meal for dollars. On the other hand some analysts like Dr. Eric R. Berg of the Department of Agriculture in his study of the soybean oil export market structure warns "that such programs will result in increased exports to these countries, and will maintain world prices above levels that would prevail if the fats and oils were sold for dollars. However, this encourages production of fats and oils in other foreign countries, increases their exports and tends to restrict consumption in the less developed countries not receiving such concessionally-priced exports." [12] Therefore, the success of the P.L. 480 program must constantly be reviewed as to its effects on other dollar markets for U.S. soybean product exports. Very little market structure research has been done on this program, which averages $1.5 billion a year. Such research would have to take into account the possible postponement of agricultural development in the recipient country as well as the impacts on the U.S. "commercial" grain exports.

Other government programs have encouraged price competition in the soybean industry through the encouragement of cooperative soybean processing activities and the construction of new soybean processing facilities through special loan arrangements.

Contractual Relationships. There are many contractual relationships existing in the soybean industry that vertically integrate many of the industry's operations in much the same way as that of actual ownership. In the case of cooperative purchasing pool arrangements, there are elevator and processor buying contracts similar to those outlined for Cargill (see p. 117). As an offset to cooperative payments of patronage dividends, many processing firms give "patronage dividends" of their own at the end of the year. To-arrive round lot sales to exporters and processors from country subterminal elevator operators

[12] University of Illinois, Bulletin 674, *Structure of the Soybean Oil Export Market Structure*, p. 88.

and terminal elevators are also quite common. Soybean meal sales to feed manufacturers covering as much as 50% of annual requirements also exist with prices established for the annual contract. These few price and product agreements suggest how difficult it is to draw conclusions about competition, costs, profitability, and so forth based on spot price, single quality, and national average data. The market structure and its many arrangements must be taken into consideration.

In the case of soybean oil sales from processors and refiners to edible oil manufacturers similar long-term sales agreements exist. One of the most recent developments in contractual relationships exists between the private label manufacturers of margarine and their voluntary and retail chain outlets. One major food store chain submits margarine specifications to five approved suppliers who in turn bid each week for the privilege of supplying that particular chain. In contrast, one major voluntary group buys its margarine on an annual bid basis. The daily price of the contract is based on the daily cash market for soybean oil at Decatur, Illinois (the basing point of the soybean industry; see Chapter VIII. Margarine is supplied to the retailer at various warehouses at so many cents a pound above or below the Decatur price.

The firm winning the contract also originated the idea of a one-year volume relationship. The strategy of the supplying margarine manufacturer was that he would operate his plants at 100% capacity by obtaining this retailer's volume and therefore he could afford to offer the retailer a margarine price based on covering just out-of-pocket manufacturing costs and make his profit on "full-costing" the remaining portion of his volume. The supplying firm felt that it was also in an advantageous position to supply the retailer by having several plants that could provide the retailer with excellent service for all the retailer's divisions as well as freight savings. The supplying firm also was a large one, and it could save by shipping in 60,000-pound rail cars rather than in smaller, higher cost cars or trucks. There were approximately nine central warehouses that were to be supplied. The retailer could specify the quantities he wished to purchase each day and the Decatur price would give the manufacturer a chance to cover his soybean oil requirements in either the cash or futures market. In return for these low-cost service arrangements, the retailer agreed to let the margarine manufacturer supply 100% of the retailer's business on an annual bid basis.

In general there has been a major increase in private label margarine-manufacturing contracts. Most of these contracts have taken the form of an arrangement whereby each major retailer has several qualities of margarine manufactured for him under several designated retailer private label brand names. The increase in the number of private label brands per retailer organization has complicated contractual arrangements and created inventory headaches for the manufacturer. Most of the contractual increase in retailers' private labels has come at the expense of the manufacturer's own second label and not his advertised brands, as may be deduced from the data in Table VII-7, which shows the dollar volume maintenance and/or increase of major brand sales of margarine, hydrogenated shortening, and cooking oils.

TABLE VII-7. Percentage of U.S. Dollar Sales Obtained by Major Advertised Brands of Margarine, Hydrogenated Shortening, and Salad Oils: 1961–1965

Year	Margarine	Hydrogenated shortening	Salad oil
1961	55.3%	62.9%	67.9%
1962	56.5	63.5	69.1
1963	54.7	67.3	69.7
1964	55.0	65.9	74.2
1965	55.7	64.3	76.2

SOURCE: Private firm.

In essence then, various forms of contractual relationships exist among all segments of the soybean complex from producer to ultimate retailer. On the whole these contracts have encouraged the development of cooperatives at the production and crushing operational levels and tended to favor the large national firms engaged in the refining, manufacturing, and retail functions.

SUMMARY

Thus far we have noted (1) the dramatic changes in the marketing channels utilized in the soybean industry — especially the development of the export markets for soybeans, meal, and oil; (2) the increase in the number of soybean farmers and the phenomenal increase in the production on each farm and the corresponding decrease in number and increase in size of all the operating units in every other segment of the soybean complex; (3) the rapid increase in vertical integration from producer to feed and edible oil products manufacturing and an impressive expansion in the number and variety of uses made of coordinating institutions such as futures markets, trade and bargaining associations, and governmental programs; and (4) the development of contractual and pool arrangements among all segments of the industry from producer to retailer. These changes in the structure of the soybean industry were triggered off by the technological breakthroughs in production, processing, and marketing described in Chapter VI. In order to complete our overall examination of the soybean complex, let us turn to an analysis of the behavioral and performance patterns of the changing market structure of the soybean complex. These patterns will be examined by (1) the profitability, (2) the price stability, (3) the competition, and (4) the adaptability that exists in the soybean industry as it adjusts its operations to meet the changing foreign and domestic consumption requirements.

VIII

Behavioral and Performance Patterns in the Soybean Economy

THE EMPHASIS on the structural and product flow analysis of the soybean industry in Chapter VII is intended to force the reader to recognize the complexity of the soybean market structure. Such an analysis suggests that the manager in an individual firm must be an effective and useful participant in the *total* soybean economy in order to function profitably and realistically within his own sphere of influence. Furthermore, the placing of company policy in such a broad environment enables management to re-evaluate its policies in the light of the changing total market structure of the soybean industry.

The purpose of Chapter VIII is to analyze, in a highly selective manner, the behavioral and performance patterns of the soybean economy. The interplays that occur between the physical and market constraints and the institutions of the soybean industry will be used to highlight the features of this organism. What types of behavior by firms and institutions characterize the overall behavioral patterns of the soybean complex? What performance results from the structural and behavioral patterns of the soybean complex as indicated by the profitability, price stability, competition, and adaptability of the parts and the whole soybean industry?

BEHAVIORAL PATTERNS

STORAGE

The behavioral patterns of the soybean industry are determined by a variety of interdependent demand, product, technological, institutional, and human factors. As in most agribusiness market structures, it is faced with the typical pattern of year-round consumption for the end products of the soybean (edible oil products and meat and poultry) and once-a-year harvest (in the fall — September, October, and November). Obviously storage of the crop in various forms takes place. Exhibit VIII-1 and Table VIII-1 represent two important time dimensions of storage activity in the soybean economy.

Exhibit VIII-1 indicates soybean stocks as of January 1, 1964: the first quarter after a soybean harvest. Approximately 45% of the crop still remains in the producers' hands. The overall capacity figures indicate ample storage with flexibility in handling all grains. The 55% of the crop that is in off-farm storage is stored primarily at interior mills or crushing plants, providing both flexibility of location in satisfying the crushing or export market and utilization of processing storage capacity during the harvest glut. The remaining major portion of soybean storage is located at the terminal market which may be a limited crushing supply location but an excellent export source of supply such as a river or port terminal. In addition to stocks of soybeans themselves, which are relatively nonperishable, the industry is also able to store soybean oil and soybean meal for limited lengths of time without impairing the quality of the product.

Stocks of soybean oil as of January 1, 1964, as noted in Exhibit VIII-1, were 988 million pounds representing about a two-month supply of oil for both the domestic and the export markets (a majority of it crude soybean oil stored at processing plants). Soybean meal stocks for the same date were approximately 172,000 tons or less than one week's supply of soybean meal for the export and domestic markets. Table VIII-1 presents the storage situation as of October 1, 1964, just prior to the harvest season compared with the January 1, 1964, stock levels. The reader will note that farm soybean stocks were reduced considerably and off-farm storage was reduced even more. In essence the crushers and exporters had only a few days' supply on hand and/or available to them at nearby locations.

Soybean oil and soybean meal stocks were also re-

EXHIBIT VIII-1

Soybean Stocks in the United States: January 1, 1964
(In thousands of bushels)

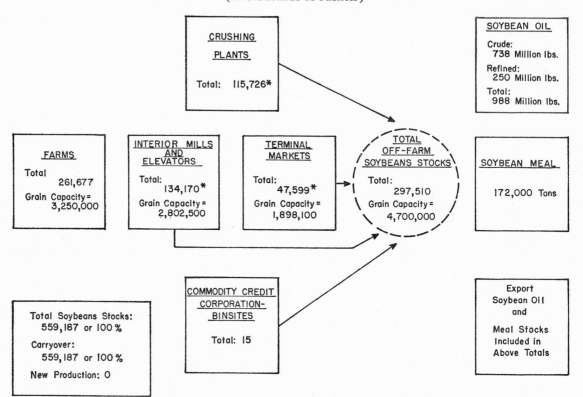

* The breakdown of off-farm soybean stocks among the separate holders has not been reported since the 1959 crop. The figures shown here are based on the proportions indicated for the 1958 and 1959 seasons combined.
SOURCE: USDA, *Stocks of Grain in All Positions,* October 23, 1964, p. 3.

duced from 988 million pounds and 172 thousand tons on January 1, 1964, to 578 million pounds and 121

TABLE VIII-1. Soybean Stocks in the United States at Selected Locations: January 1, 1964, and October 1, 1964
(In thousands of bushels)

Location	January 1, 1964	October 1, 1964
On farms	261,677	15,198
Interior mills and elevators[a]	134,170	10,968
Terminal markets[a]	47,599	2,700
Crushing plants[a]	115,726	3,103
CCC bin sites	15	22
Subtotal off-farm stocks	297,510	16,793
Total soybean stocks	559,197	31,991[b]

[a] The breakdown of off-farm soybean stocks among the separate holders has not been reported since the 1959 crop. The figures shown here are based on the proportions indicated for the 1958 and 1959 crop years combined.

[b] October 1, 1964, soybean stocks do not include the new soybean crop of 699,900 bushels ready for harvesting.

SOURCE: USDA, ERS, *Stocks of Grains in All Positions,* October 23, 1964, p. 3.

thousand tons on October 1 respectively. (Note the reduction in crushing plant crude oil inventories in Table VIII-1 which was due primarily to inverse carrying charges in the oil futures markets and normal low inventories at the end of the old crop year.)

These data have three main implications. In the first place they indicate a low carryover of supplies in the soybean economy. The forecast for a much larger crop for the 1965 crop year was looked upon with favor by the Department of Agriculture which felt that the carryover of soybeans was too low for such an important oil and protein supplying crop even in the face of previously large supplies of soybean oil.

The second implication of these data is the potential pressure that may be exerted on the processor by holding tactics of the producer or unusual exporter demands for soybeans. (These figures do not show the contracting for supplies that has occurred and that would alleviate some of this pressure.) As we shall note later on, there is excess processing capacity[1] in

[1] Excess processing capacity is defined here as the difference between total capacity and the soybeans actually processed.

the soybean industry and the processor has been quite anxious to obtain soybeans to maintain his processing operations and to make maximum use of his grain storage facilities that are usually built adjacent to the processing plant.

The third implication of storage patterns in the soybean economy stems from the location of stocks in relation to processing and export markets. The factors normally taken into consideration are as follows:

(1) the Decatur price basing system, which resulted from the historical development of the crop and processing industry around Decatur, Illinois;
(2) the national vs. the local market;
(3) the processing-in-transit privilege;
(4) the 5% weight loss in processing;
(5) the nonapplication of the through rate to soybean oil under transit;
(6) the relationship between rates on soybean and those on processed products.

Because of the Decatur pricing system, processors located in Illinois consider the total United States as their market. Processors in other states have concentrated on local markets of meal and local supplies of soybeans to minimize the nontransit inbound freight cost to the processor on that portion of the soybean that is used for oil and that portion that constitutes the 5% processing waste. As railroad rates increased, the transportation advantages of local markets and local supplies became more important to the development of the processing industry. The on-farm storage build-up and the increase in the interior and crushing plant storage levels are but one indication of the development of local crushing complexes. The large livestock population in the Corn Belt and the large poultry population in the South, together with the fact that soybean meal is the most important product of the soybean, leads one to the conclusion that soybean storage and processing capacity will continue to expand where the combination of soybean production and livestock and poultry population exists.

Recent new specialized nontransit rates on soybean meal and oil products may change the location of the processing industry but thus far this has not been the case.

The flat oil rate has resulted in the location of refineries and edible oil processors locating close to large consumption markets in the exact opposite fashion to the location of soybean oil crushers. The oil rate has also encouraged additional refining processes by soybean crushers who may ship edible or refined oils overseas through New Orleans or the Great Lakes and avoid the cost of transporting and refining the oil at port locations.

CONSUMPTION

Even though our previous analysis would indicate a continued expansion of the demand for soybeans and soybean products there are some indications on the horizon that might lead one to the conclusion that certain elements of this industry will cause it to mature. The maturing of the industry will bring on new responsibilities for the firms and institutions that make up the soybean complex.

One indication of maturing was presented in a recent statement of Professor T. A. Hieronymus before the annual meeting of the American Soybean Association in August 1965.

The trend increase in the consumption of domestic soybean meal per animal at a constant price and a constant price of livestock appears to have come to an end. Both 1963–1964 and 1964–1965 showed a decrease, meal and livestock numbers taken into account. There are two outstanding reasons why the trend may be turning down: (1) the deficit of protein in animal rations may have caught up, and (2) the use of urea is making rapid inroads in the meal market.

On the other hand, the export markets look to be stronger than ever. Soybean oil still remains one of the cheapest and most competitive oils in the world market. Oil stocks around the world continue at relatively low levels, and it would seem prudent to build some limited reserve amounts. Although P.L. 480 shipments will be needed to continue to move the excess oils, they have become more than just "surplus disposal" programs and have taken on an aspect of a continuing obligation on our part and as a committed source of procurement on the part of the recipient country.

Soybean meal exports (including the meal equivalent of soybeans) should also continue to expand as the poultry and livestock industries of the developing and developed nations continue to grow. Unlike the situation in the United States, soybean meal is more reasonably priced in relation to feed grains in the export markets because of the relative high price of feed grains in the consuming country's economy. (This may invite tariff protection on soybean meal in the future.) There is additional competition for the livestock mixed feed market from the increased world production of fish meal.

Although the protein market may be maturing domestically, the domestic soybean oil market seems to be improving through the reduction of soybean oil stocks under P.L. 480, the development of more stable flavor and hydrogenation of oil, and the general increase in the consumption of vegetable oil products.

EXHIBIT VIII-2

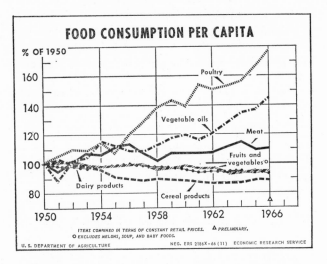

FOOD CONSUMPTION PER CAPITA

In Exhibit VIII-2, which indicates food consumption per capita of major food categories, the reader will note that the top three growth categories are all important soybean consuming end products: poultry, vegetable oils, and meat.

PRICING

Exhibit VIII-3 sets forth the allocation of the consumers' "margarine dollar" among the various segments

EXHIBIT VIII-3

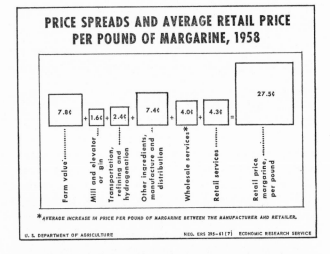

PRICE SPREADS AND AVERAGE RETAIL PRICE PER POUND OF MARGARINE, 1958

of the soybean economy as of 1958. As we shall note later in this chapter, the price levels and the price spreads vary not only from season to season and year to year, but between types of retail outlet (chain, voluntary, independent) and among geographical regions.

The Chicago cash terminal market and the Chicago futures market have been the central price indicators for soybean price quotations. Soybean processors throughout the country and for that matter throughout the world are dependent on these cash and futures markets to indicate the relative value of their soybeans, meal and oil. Obviously, the prices of soybeans vary from one location to another for the usual reasons of quality, transportation, and storage and the complex demand factors present in the soybean oil and soybean meal markets.

To the soybean producer, the country or subterminal elevator, the local processor, and the government price support program are all sources of price quotations. The Chicago Board of Trade and other terminal markets, through the cooperation of radio stations and government market news programs, broadcast hourly changes of price at Chicago. The soybean producer may also price his soybeans on a seasonal average pool basis with his local cooperative.

To the soybean processor, soybeans are raw materials to be converted into oil and meal. Prices paid by the processor are related to his present and anticipated returns from oil and meal and to the level of his soybean stocks (the low unit cost of operations act as an incentive for a processor to buy enough soybeans to keep his plant running at full capacity). To secure the necessary volume of soybeans in competition with other soybean buyers, the processor often must raise the price he pays for soybeans, in effect lowering his processing margin (the cost of his soybeans versus his sales price of meal and oil). One example of competitive price strategy was indicated in the soybean purchase contracts of Cargill in the Arkansas market (see page 117). Another example of processor pressure to obtain soybeans occurred during the time Honeymead merged with the Farmers Union. Because of some market antagonism to Honeymead's merger, Honeymead was finding it difficult to obtain soybeans. A 2-cent patronage dividend was announced to all suppliers of soybeans to the firm. In many cases the suppliers were grain commission firms whose managers were befuddled as to how to allocate this patronage dividend to their respective country elevator and farm shippers. They eventually settled on a volume rebate to all shippers.

There are daily fluctuations in the soybean market as crushers and exporters react to the changing relationships among soybeans, meal, and oil, and to the price strategies of each other. In addition, the time element, carrying charges in the futures markets, locational differentials, and quality and storability of products all add to the variability of prices of soybeans, meal and oil.

In the case of soybean oil, even with the new technology of hydrogenation and deodorization, it is difficult to differentiate the product. This lack of differentiation and, until recently, rather large supplies have meant continued price pressure on soybean oil. If the demand for protein meal is high, the processor will crush the soybean and the oil becomes a by-product or adjunct product to meal. As one processor stated: "A processor doesn't sell oil, but instead takes what someone will give him for it. The same is sometimes true for meal."

In the case of meal the Decatur price quotation reflects local competitive markets and transportation differentials. In general, processors have larger margins on meal sold locally. This was especially true when the basing-point system was in effect in the industry to a greater degree in the 1940s and 1950s. The most advantageous place to be was as far as possible from Decatur, Illinois, with a local supply of soybeans and a local market for meal. Part of the freight advantage could then be retained by the processor as additional revenue.

The Area Redevelopment Administration made a feasibility study on the construction of a soybean processing plant at the Delmarva Peninsula. This feasibility study outlined various freight and price data for soybean meal delivered to Delmarva. From Table VIII-2

TABLE VIII-2. Soybean Meal Prices[a] and Freight Rates to Delmarva Peninsula Area from Various Processing Locations: May 20, 1963

(In prices per ton)

Plant location	Mill price (f.o.b.)	Actual meal freight rate to Delmarva	Delmarva delivered price	Comparison with f.o.b. Decatur price
Decatur, Ill.	$74.00	$16.50	$90.50	$74.00
Decatur, Ind.	77.30	12.70	90.00	73.50
Marion, Ohio	76.30	11.20	87.50	71.00
Norfolk, Va.	83.70	3.30	87.00	70.50
Salisbury, Md.	85.00	1.50	86.50	70.00

[a] In this comparison 50% soybean meal was used as the quality of product rather than the "normal" 44%.

SOURCE: U.S. House, *ARA Loan for Construction of Soybean Processing Plant*, p. 37.

the reader will note that this study substantiates the advantageous position that a processor has if he has a relatively local market for his meal. For example, the mill at Salisbury, Maryland, can obtain $85 a ton for its product f.o.b. its plant compared with the Decatur, Illinois, plant price of $74. This $11 a ton advantage puts the Maryland plant in a position to gain a profitable local market with only a $4 a ton discount under the common Decatur price comparison. Part of this advantage may be reduced if local soybeans are

more costly to procure than in the Illinois location, or if soybean oil markets are more difficult to reach.

Throughout the soybean production, processing, mixed feed, and soybean oil complex, comparative advantages of local soybean supplies and local meal markets are constantly shifting in response to changes in competitive rail and truck rates on the soybeans versus meal and oil products, and in response to changing market developments in the end product uses of soybeans; e.g., the poultry, livestock, and dairy feed market and the margarine, salad oil, and cooking oil market. In addition, the expanding export market for soybeans, meal, and oil provides another important set of factors that management takes into account in deciding on plant location. Table VIII-3 summarizes the

TABLE VIII-3. Soybean Processing Margins[a] in Specified States: Crop Years 1956–1960

(In cents per bushel of soybeans processed)

State	1956	1957	1958	1959	1960	1956–60 average	1956–60 average, revised[b]
Illinois	23.4	28.8	26.8	16.9	17.9	22.8	22.8
Minnesota	47.0	53.7	47.0	34.7	34.6	43.4	43.5
Indiana	34.3	40.8	42.3	28.7	31.4	35.5	31.0
Iowa	35.4	47.6	49.4	35.9	31.3	39.9	40.3
Missouri	45.6	54.9	49.6	31.6	35.9	43.5	41.4
Ohio	45.5	50.7	52.5	37.1	38.1	44.6	41.2
Arkansas	26.6	32.9	38.3	21.7	22.8	28.5	25.7
Mississippi	38.3	44.0	40.9	28.7	37.3	37.8	41.5

[a] The computed margins use the farm price of soybeans and therefore include cost of moving soybeans through country elevators to processing plants.

[b] Revised to take account of relative inbound freight differences between states. This column is found on page 166 of the reference cited below.

SOURCE: Nakamura, *Structure of the Soybean Processing Industry in the United States: Economic, Institutional, and Technical Factors in Its Development*, p. 155.

various processing margins (difference between cost of soybeans and sale price of soybean meal and soybean oil) for selected states in the crop years 1956 to 1960. This table further substantiates the previous discussions of the relatively low processing margins in Illinois versus more distant and specialized local markets. This wide range of processing margins has encouraged soybean firms to have a "network" of soybean processing plants to take advantage of the changing logistics in the industry. Typical of the year to year changes in local crop production, markets, and transportation rates that affect crushing margins is the State of Missouri. As is shown in Table VIII-3, crushing margins in that state varied during these five years from a low of 31.6 cents a bushel to a high of 54.9 cents, or a

TABLE VIII-4. Yield, Price, and Value of Products Per Bushel of Soybeans Crushed, and Price Spread:
Crop Years 1947–1963

Crop year	Oil			Meal			Total value	No. 1 Yellow soybean price, Illinois points	Spread between value of products and soybean price
	Yield	Price[a]	Value	Yield	Price[a]	Value			
	Pounds	Cents	Dollars	Pounds	Cents	Dollars	Dollars	Dollars	Dollars
1947	9.5	23.7	2.25	46.4	4.04	1.87	4.12	3.66	.46
1948	9.8	13.1	1.28	46.1	3.30	1.52	2.80	2.36	.44
1949	9.9	12.3	1.22	47.0	3.22	1.51	2.73	2.52	.21
1950	9.7	17.8	1.73	46.8	3.22	1.51	3.24	2.97	.27
1951	10.0	11.3	1.13	46.7	4.17	1.95	3.08	2.97	.11
1952	10.8	12.1	1.31	47.4	3.38	1.60	2.91	2.78	.13
1953	11.0	13.5	1.48	47.4	3.93	1.86	3.34	3.26	.08
1954	10.9	11.9	1.30	45.8	3.04	1.39	2.69	2.56	.14
1955	11.1	12.5	1.39	46.2	2.63	1.21	2.60	2.51	.10
1956	10.9	12.7	1.38	47.5	2.37	1.13	2.51	2.33	.18
1957	10.7	10.8	1.16	46.8	2.67	1.25	2.41	2.19	.22
1958	10.6	9.5	1.01	47.3	2.79	1.32	2.33	2.11	.22
1959	11.0	8.3	.91	46.5	2.78	1.29	2.20	2.08	.12
1960	11.0	11.3	1.24	47.0	3.03	1.42	2.66	2.55	.11
1961	10.9	9.5	1.04	47.1	3.18	1.50	2.54	2.41	.13
1962	10.7	8.9	.95	46.9	3.56	1.67	2.62	2.53	.09
1963[b]	—	—	.92	—	—	1.80	2.72	2.68	.04

[a] Simple average price per pound using the following quotations: soybean oil, crude, tank cars, f.o.b., midwest mills; soybean meal, bulk, Decatur, quoted as 41% prior to July 1950, 44% beginning July 1950.

[b] October 1963–March 1964 average.

SOURCE: *Fats and Oils Situation*, November 1963, p. 21 for 1947–62; March 1964, p. 8 for 1963.

23.3-cent spread amounting to a 70% increase over the low crushing margin period.

Table VIII-4 summarizes the processing data for U.S. soybean processing firms. This table indicates the wide variations that exist between the soybean value and the joint products of the soybean. In general there has been a downward trend in the spread (crushing margin) reflecting improved processing technology and excess crushing capacity.

There seems to be no price leader in the soybean, oil, and meal markets. However, several large firms can influence the market during certain times of the year. For example, many processors buy over 50% of their processing requirements of soybeans during a two month harvest period. Part of the impact of large-scale buying and selling operations is lessened through the use of futures markets. Another time factor that may influence price levels is the opening of navigation on the Mississippi River once the ice has disappeared in the spring of each year. This leads to large export movements which appear in the form of temporary price bulges as the exporter competes with the domestic user of soybeans. Again, the futures markets help lessen wide price swings and are used rather extensively not only by domestic processors and exporters, but by importers and overseas processors as well.

In the finished products of margarine, salad oil, and hydrogenated fat there are brand price leaders, such as Wesson Oil and Crisco, that are used as price reference points by private label operations. In addition, private label, to-arrive contracts, and day-by-day shipments also have price patterns utilized by the trade. Although each firm is free to arrive at its own prices, A&P purchases of private label frequently are a guide to the day-to-day price pattern of the industry, e.g., 4 cents a pound over Decatur crude for private label margarine, whereas other firms set the patterns for long-term contractual relationships.

Price relationships and trends in the soybean system have evolved with the changing nature of the soybean system. Early price contracts gave way to sophisticated annual requirements for private label products based on formulas related to futures markets. Pool systems were developed by some cooperative processor firms. In the early stages of the system, advances in technology made product differentiation possible in the end products. Once technological imitation and mass distribution became commonplace, private labels became more important. Price discounts developed with as much as a 10-cent discount on a 29-cent pound of margarine. At the same time many processors developed new types of products such as soft margarine in a tub, liquid margarine in a squeeze bottle, whipped margarine, etc.

Of greater importance than the development of informal price leaders of products and commodities and private label price discounts has been the direct impact of large soybean oil shipments under P.L. 480 and the expansion of the mixed feed-livestock-poultry complex, both of which have been major factors in maintaining the price level of the two main products of the soybean: meal and oil. At the same time, the technological improvements in extracting soybean oil from the soybean, the improvement in soybean production and transportation, and the feeding efficiencies of livestock and poultry operations have tended to lessen the rise in stable retail food prices for poultry, fats and oils, and meat products even in the face of higher labor costs and added services, as indicated by Exhibit VIII-4.

EXHIBIT VIII-4

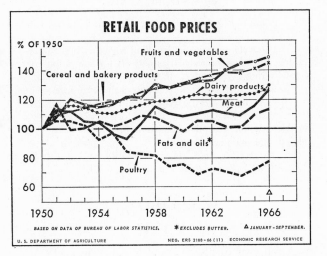

OUTPUT

As indicated previously, practically all parts of the soybean economy suffer from excess capacity with the exception of the producer who has been able to expand the acreage devoted to this crop without building up soybean supplies beyond what the government has been able to dispose of through its various programs. Soybean oil supplies, however, have been built up and the government has devised the P.L. 480 program, which has maintained the price of soybean oil, allowed soybean meal to remain at reasonable prices for the livestock and poultry feeders, and maintained satisfactory "market" price levels for soybean producers.

Excess capacity developed for the processing of soybeans. Over several time periods this resulted in excess supplies of soybean oil. Many manufacturers of both soybean oil and consumer products such as margarine were anxious to make use of idle capacity and therefore offered products to the market on a contribution-to-fixed-investment basis. As one processor stated: "We have a certain capacity and we must keep it

going full time. The only thing that will cause us to change output is the inability to cover variable costs. Then we close down." Before closing down, his competitors' strategy is also taken into consideration. "When margins are thin, if we think by closing down we will allow others to keep crushing, then we will probably keep crushing also." Table VIII-5 summa-

TABLE VIII-5. Estimated Number of Soybean Oil Mills and Processing Capacity in the United States: Crop Years 1951–1965

Crop year	No. of processing mills[a]	Total processing capacity[b]	Utilized[c]	Excess[d]	Ratio of utilized to total
		(millions of bushels)			
1951	193	310	244	66	79%
1952	174	315	234	81	74
1953	159	320	218	102	68
1954	162	340	241	99	71
1955	152	355	282	73	79
1956	144	370	314	56	85
1957	139	450	351	99	78
1958	130	450	399	51	89
1959	121	500	394	106	79
1960	123	525	406	119	77
1961	126	535	431	104	81
1962	128	550	473	77	86
1963	127	575	437	138	76
1964	123	585	479	106	82
1965	124	600	537	63	89

[a] Estimates developed from Census data and trade directories. Includes cottonseed and other oilseed mills that process significant quantities of soybeans.
[b] Trade estimates and USDA interpolations.
[c] Soybeans actually crushed.
[d] Difference between total capacity and soybeans utilized (crushed).
SOURCE: *Soybean Blue Book*, March 1967, p. 67.

rizes the excess processing capacity of the industry since 1951 and its persistence in spite of the phenomenal growth of the industry.

Riley describes the output strategy of the soybean industry as follows:

The answers to the questions concerning choice of output level indicates that the industry as a whole and its individual members essentially follow an independent policy of determining output and letting price take care of itself, rather than announcing a selling price and then supplying the quantity of output buyers wish to take at that price. As Bain points out, this policy is usually found only in industries of relatively atomistic structure in which each seller faces a well publicized going market price. This well known price in turn results from the operation of the futures markets, to which the price of soybeans and soybean products is so closely tied.[2]

[2] Riley, *Marketing Structure in the Soybean Industry*, p. 114.

PERFORMANCE PATTERNS

PROFITABILITY

Soybeans have been one of the most profitable crops for farmers to produce. As in the case of wheat, it is difficult to isolate soybean operations on a farm from all other crop and livestock production. Using the same 1958 input-output data described on page 66 of the Wheat Section, however one notes that soybean production at the farm level was $1.437 billion. The cost of producing the crop was approximately $1,063 million, leaving farm projected income at $374.4 million. If one adds depreciation of $223.2 million to the income of $374.4 million, then soybean farmers had a cash flow of $596.6 million on a crop of 580.2 million bushels, or over $1 a bushel without the aid of government price supports.

Soybean processing profits have declined in recent years as evidenced by the small crushing margins. Part of the reason for these small margins is due to the fact that the soybean processing industry has over-anticipated the growth of the soybean crop. The resultant excess processing capacity has placed increased pressure on crushing margins. The increase in vertical integration and the size of the crop, however, have enabled vertically integrated processors to make profits on the storage, handling, and transportation of soybeans, meal, and oil as well as on the processing of them. Smaller processors have been especially hard hit because of their high per unit production costs (see Table VIII-6).[3] Cooperative studies by the Farmer Cooperative Service in 1964 and 1965 [4] also substantiate the unit cost saving of larger processing mills with costs ranging from 29.61 cents per bushel for small-scale plants to 13.97 cents per bushel for large-scale plants. Profits varied in the cooperative study from a loss of $281,000 on sales of $10.5 million and a $2.5 million investment to a profit of $321,000 on sales of $10 million in 1964 and a $3 million investment by two cooperatives separated by only a few hundred miles.

The following selected quotations from various leading soybean crushers' annual reports indicate the types of competitive environment that existed in the processing segment of the industry. Please note the *exit* from soybean crushing operations by diversified firms such as General Mills, Procter & Gamble, and Textron.

[3] Table VIII-6 also indicates that soybean acquisition costs by the small firm are much cheaper because of direct farm to processor purchasing—but such savings do not offset increased operating costs.

[4] Private studies made by the USDA, Farmer Cooperative Service, for selected cooperatives in the soybean industry.

TABLE VIII-6. Estimated Processing Cost per Bushel of Soybeans, Solvent Mills, by Size of Mill: Crop Year 1952

Size of mill (Tons/day)	Soybeans processed annually[a] (1,000 bu.)	Soybean acquisition[b] (Cents)	Plant[c] (Cents)	Operating expenses[d] (Cents)	Total (Cents)
25	275	1.90	20.76	40.84	63.50
50	550	3.40	12.76	27.76	43.92
100	1,100	6.90	9.05	24.03	39.98
150	1,650	9.20	8.27	22.95	40.42
200	2,200	9.20	7.63	22.15	38.98
300	3,300	10.30	6.50	21.17	37.97
400	4,400	10.30	5.81	20.77	36.88
500	5,500	11.10	5.75	20.62	37.47
600	6,600	11.10	6.26	20.33	37.69
800	8,800	11.10	5.57	19.70	36.37
1,000	11,000	11.10	5.06	19.95	35.11

[a] Assumes a 12-month season or 330 working days, with no unutilized capacity.

[b] Includes (1) charges for handling soybeans by country elevators and other intermediaries and (2) transportation charges for delivering soybeans to mill.

[c] Includes depreciation, interest, taxes and insurance.

[d] Includes labor, electric power, fuel oil, water, solvent, meal bags, maintenance and repairs, laboratory services, insurance on stocks, salaries, general administration, welfare risks, working capital, and selling expense.

SOURCE: USDA, Marketing Research Report No. 121, *Size of Soybean Oil Mills and Return to Growers*, p. 24.

ALLIED MILLS, INC.

1961

A full year of processing at the plant opened early in 1960 at Guntersville, Alabama, contributed to increased sales of soybean meal and soybean oil. In addition, improved efficiency of the soybean operations of your company at Guntersville, as well as at Taylorville, Illinois, contributed to a slightly improved return over a year ago, despite constant fluctuations in the market prices of soybeans throughout the year. It is predicted that the 1961 soybean crop will be as much as 20% over last year. If this record-breaking crop is harvested, it should help stabilize the soybean market during the coming year. If the heavy demand for soybean meal and oil for domestic and export use continues, soybean processing profits should be more satisfactory in the year ahead.

1962

Our soybean operation during the year was improved over last year. . . . We anticipated a larger soybean crop for the new year which we may expect will produce a larger tonnage of soybean meal and soybean oil. Soybean meal is readily absorbed in markets, however, the movement of soybean oil is difficult, and the market price of oil from the new crop will have a substantial effect on the profits of this Division.

1963

Our Soybean and Alfalfa Processing Divisions operated profitably, with volume in each at an all-time high. New low cost production records were established, and we feel we are in an excellent position to enjoy continued successful operations in the current year. We are hopeful for adequate crops of both soybeans and alfalfa, so that conversion into finished products can be accomplished price-wise to the benefit of our farmer customers.

1964

Due to the pressure on soybean prices subsequent to harvest time last year and to the adverse effects upon the industry by reason of the "salad oil scandal" which resulted in sharply reduced soybean oil prices, the Soybean Processing Division operated on a less profitable basis than last year.

ARCHER-DANIELS-MIDLAND COMPANY
1960

The soybean industry was faced with many problems this past year. These included extremely low prices for soybean oil and reduced demand for soybean meal as the result of lower consumption of formula feeds.

Freight rates encouraged the export of soybeans rather than the end products, resulting in 24% of the crop being processed in foreign plants, a 4% increase over the prior year. As a result of these industry problems, ADM soybean operations were disappointing.

Prospects for the new year are dependent upon demand for soybean products, correction of domestic freight rates on soybeans and soybean products to reduce the economic advantage of foreign processors, and adjustment of freight rates so Illinois plants can serve larger markets.

1962

In the Soybean Division, we closed an inefficient mill in Ohio, entered into a long-term lease for a mill in Decatur, Illinois, and started construction of a new production unit in Kansas. These actions were prompted by the need for lower costs and more profitable market locations.

1964

For the Soybean Division, the year had some bright spots as well as dark. In addition to record volume further cost reductions were achieved in operations, and product markets were widened through intensive merchandising. The soybean market, however, was abnormally unsettled most of the year. The price of soybeans remained high in anticipation of increased demand for oil and meal. But demand did not materialize.

The soybean oil market was disrupted by disappointing exports and the failure of a large oil marketing firm. We did not have any direct credit losses in our dealings with the bankrupt firm. Its failure, however, did result

in contract termination losses of $322,000, the difference between the value of soybean oil that firm had agreed to buy from ADM and the price for which we eventually sold the oil to other buyers. The soybean meal market, both at home and abroad, was depressed by abnormally low prices for cattle and poultry. The overall result of these influences was a sharp reduction in soybean processing margins.

Toward the end of the 1964 fiscal year, a small gain in processing margins appeared, and we expect additional improvement in margins by mid-fall. If soybean prices remain at more normal levels, the hard-pressed cattle and poultry feeders, domestic and foreign, can be expected to increase consumption of soybean meal. Improvements at our soybean crushing plant and oil refinery at Decatur have increased efficiency and output there and will make ADM more competitive in that market.

CENTRAL SOYA COMPANY, INC.
1960

The Processing Division suffered from very unfavorable margins throughout the entire year of operation. Despite this, it made substantial contributions to the increased volume of soybean oil shipments made to foreign countries deficient in food fats and oils. Efforts are continually being made to further establish Central Soya in foreign soybean meal and oil markets.

1964

Barely adequate soybean supplies made for high priced soybeans and soybean meal. As a result, the industry priced itself out of the protein meal market at times.

GENERAL MILLS
1960

The past year was not a good one for the soybean oil processing industry. Profit margins between the costs of soybeans and finished products were less than one-half of what they were a year ago. This resulted partly from reduction in the demand for soybean oil meal in the feed industry and from lower exports of soybean oil. Government price supports kept the cost of soybeans high despite the weak market.

1962

In August, 1961, General Mills closed its soybean processing plant at Rossford, Ohio, and consolidated all soybean processing operations at the company's plant at Belmond, Iowa. Sewall D. Andrews, Jr., Vice President and General Manager of the Specialty Products Division which is responsible for soybean processing, said that unsatisfactory margins made it impractical to continue operations in the Rossford area. He emphasized that the Belmond plant was capable of handling production needs and that an effort would be made to increase this plant's output of specialty, upgraded soy protein products.

1964

Effective June 1, 1964, General Mills leased its soybean processing plant at Belmond, Iowa, to the Central Soya Company, Inc., headquartered at Fort Wayne, Indiana. The lease, covering three years, includes an option to buy the property. Discontinuance of basic soybean processing represents another step in the company's planned concentration on convenience foods, flour and specialty chemicals. It does not preclude the continued development and production of specialty products, such as isolated soy proteins, based on raw materials from soybeans.

HUNT FOODS AND INDUSTRIES, INC.

1960

Wesson Division refineries operated at a record level of production and the Wesson crushing mills had one of the best periods in their history.

THE PROCTER & GAMBLE COMPANY

1960

In 1958–59 the Company completed a program of selling and closing certain oil seed crushing mills. Because of this program, our tonnage was down in 1959–60 in this division of our business. However, profit-wise we had one of the four or five best years we have ever had in the 58 years we have been in the crushing business.

1961

Our oil seed crushing operations in the United States have shown a modest increase in volume over the previous year. In addition over the past several years, there has been a continuing expansion in the market for soybean products consumed in Canada and, as a large soybean crusher in Canada, we have benefited from this trend.

RALSTON PURINA COMPANY

1960

Today we are the second-largest processor of soybeans in the world.

While the relatively high government support price coupled with a low world demand for soybean oil and meal have squeezed the profits in this division, we have faith in the future of this basic industry.

A. E. STALEY MANUFACTURING COMPANY

1960

Soybean Division results were the poorest the company has experienced since it pioneered soybean processing in 1922, with excess capacity intensifying competition throughout the year. The total industry crush was 392,250,000 bushels, compared with 401,233,000 the year before.

Demand during the past year was aided by rather substantial soybean meal exports, particularly during the first quarter, and by exports of soybean oil under Public Law 480.

The soybean crop was estimated at 561,932,000 bushels on October 1, up 4 percent from last year. With less carryover, however, the total supply for the coming year is estimated at 585,192,000 bushels, compared with 600,112,000 a year ago.

Some improvement in processing margins occurred at the close of the fiscal year, but the future trend of such margins will be determined by whether or not the industry continues to try to operate its plants at near capacity regardless of consumption or whether production is established at a level commensurate with demand.

SWIFT & COMPANY

1960

A record soybean volume was handled in the company's mills during 1960. However, because of narrower margins, earnings dropped below those in 1959.

Reduced processing margins were due, in part, to a record export of beans which reduced supplies available to the industry for domestic processing. Another unfavorable factor was the geographical dislocation of soybean supplies. The market for soybean oil averaged a cent a pound under 1959. This drop was not fully reflected in prices paid for soybeans. Profit prospects for 1961, however, are brighter.

1961

Earnings in soybean operations declined in 1961. Margins were under pressure all year, with futures trading in beans, oil and meal the largest in history. Temporary high prices developed from the prospect, rather than the actuality, of a scarcity of soybeans in late summer.

The 1961 soybean crop is the largest in history. With a 45-cent-a-bushel increase in the support price, farmers are expected to put more beans under government loan than ever before. This may once again result in a margin squeeze before the year's end.

1963

Swift's . . . soybean plants handled record production in 1963 . . . returns from soybean operations [were] slightly less than last year.

Another record soybean crop in 1963 and improved cotton yields indicate ample supplies to meet domestic and foreign demands next year.

Swift's Food Protein, a new concentrate from soybeans, is now being produced. . . . This new-type human food can be used as a low-cost supplement for such foods as meat loaves, dehydrated foods, baked goods, and casseroles.

1964

A plant to manufacture margarine, shortening, lard, salad and cooking oils will be built in the Chicago area. Plans now being developed provide for facilities to produce improved products at reduced costs. We plan to take bids on this new facility late this year.

TEXTRON'S SPENCER KELLOGG DIVISION
1961

In order to broaden further its earnings base and to enter the promising agrochemical field, Textron in July made one of its principal acquisitions of recent year. Spencer Kellogg and Sons, Inc., an old and established Buffalo company was acquired. . . .

Following the acquisition, Textron adopted a program to place greater emphasis on Spencer Kellogg's research and new product development. In furtherance of this program Textron withdrew from the soybean crushing business, which required too much capital for its demonstrated profit potential. The company's three soybean plants were sold as going concerns. . . .

In the case of margarine, salad oil, and hydrogenated fat products, severe competition exists in the production of private label products. Anderson Clayton's purchase of Cudahy's margarine operations is but one example of mergers taking place as old family companies divest themselves of margarine, etc. operations. Lehman Brothers acquired the assets of a major margarine and edible fat refining firm and have as of the summer of 1967 been unable to dispose of it.

At the brand levels most leading manufacturers are able to stay in business because of the profits developed from their unique and superior products. A study by the Department of Agriculture in August 1963 [5] indicated that in 1961, 95% of all advertising expenditures for margarine were spent on 11 major brands and the remaining hundreds of brands received only slight promotion activity. Advertising expenditures for the major soybean brands (primarily soybean formulated) averaged 1.8 cents a pound or 6% of the average retail price. Expenditures for the super brands (corn oil and butter formulated) averaged 5.6 cents per pound or 14% of the retail price. In the years 1957–1961 advertising expenditures on margarine were increasing at a faster rate for both super brands and lesser known private label brands. The so-called "major" margarine brands had a much smaller increase in advertising expenditures. Although this writer was unable to obtain individual profit product statements, interviews with various executives would lead one to the conclusion that the development of new margarine products making brand identification possible have improved the profit statements of these manufacturers compared with the rather poor showing of those manufacturers in primarily the private label business.

In explaining the profitability of soybean product retail operations, the writer used the same sample of six retail food chains described on page 87 of the Wheat Section. In the case of margarine, some 45% of the total margarine market was private label broken down as follows: 35% low price margarine, 7% intermediate type of margarine, and 3.5% premium price margarine. The particular sample of chain stores of this study were larger chains, and they had unit volume sales of approximately 70% private label and dollar volume sales of approximately 60% private label. Exhibit VIII-5 indicates

EXHIBIT VIII-5

Margarine Dollar Sales and Net Margin as a Percent of Sales for Private Label and Leading Manufacturers' Brands in Selected Chain Stores: 1960–1963
(Companywide averages annually)

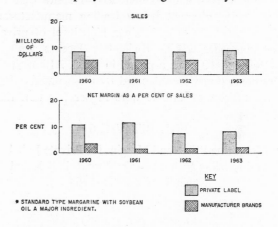

that for the years 1960–1963 approximately $9 million of margarine sales annually were private label and approximately $6 million were national brand sales. The same exhibit indicates the greater profitability of private label margarine in terms of net margin as a percentage of sales when compared with the net margins of manufacturers' brands. (Manufacturers' brands averaged 2% of sales and private label 9% of sales.) One word of caution: the net margin on private label is overstated because it is measured as a percentage of a much lower sales price per pound than manufacturers' brands. It is also overstated because of the unrealistic costs allocated by the retailer to manufacturers' brand margarine. A more realistic allocation would show about equal net margins for private label and manufacturers' brands.

---

[5] USDA, ERS, *Developments in Marketing Spreads for Agricultural Products in 1962*, p. 23.

TABLE VIII-7. Margarine[a] Prices and Margins for Private Label and Leading Manufacturers' Brands in Selected Chain Stores: 1960–1963
(Companywide averages annually in cents per pound)

Private label	1960	1961	1962	1963
Average cost per pound stocked in case	15.33	15.84	16.08	16.27
Average price of margarine sold	18.68	19.61	19.08	19.43
Shrinkage (0.5%)	.09	.10	.10	.10
Margin	3.26	3.67	2.90	3.06
Cost allocation to this item	1.32	1.40	1.45	1.48
Net margin	1.94	2.27	1.45	1.58
Manufacturers' brands				
Average cost per pound stocked in case	24.44	26.60	26.32	26.27
Average price of margarine sold	27.75	29.61	29.57	29.65
Shrinkage (0.5%)	.14	.15	.15	.15
Margin	3.17	2.86	3.10	3.23
Cost allocation to this item	2.16	2.41	2.53	2.62
Net margin	1.01	.45	.57	.61

[a] Standard type margarine with soybean oil a major ingredient.
Source: Six corporate food chains.

Table VIII-7 and Exhibit VIII-6 show that the selling price discount below leading manufacturers' brands necessary to maintain a high level of private label unit sales was approximately 9 cents a pound in 1960 and 10 cents a pound in 1963. Although the store costs that were allocated by these retailer firms to manufacturers' brands were higher per unit than

EXHIBIT VIII-6

Margarine Prices and Margins for Private Label and Leading Manufacturers' Brands in Selected Chain Stores: 1960–1963

(Companywide averages annually in cents per pound)

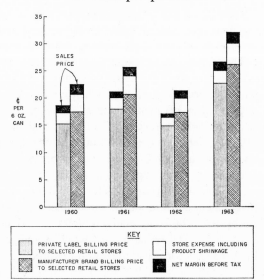

TABLE VIII-8. Margarine[a] Ranges of Prices of Private Label and Leading Manufacturers' Brands in Selected Chain Stores: 1960–1963
(In cents per pound)

Private label		1960	1961	1962	1963
Average cost per pound stocked in case	Low	14.24	15.23	13.62	14.02
	High	15.73	17.49	16.43	16.71
Average price of margarine sold	Low	16.95	18.31	16.95	18.50
	High	19.41	20.26	19.37	19.94
Shrinkage (0.5%)	Low	.08	.09	.08	.09
	High	.10	.10	.10	.10
Margin	Low	1.18	1.97	2.63	2.87
	High	5.07	4.20	3.97	5.06
Cost allocation to this item	Low	.91	.98	1.05	1.20
	High	3.21	3.21	3.26	3.26
Net margin	Low	(1.58)	(.65)	(.08)	(.08)
	High	2.36	2.95	2.25	1.93
Manufacturers' brands					
Average cost per pound stocked in case	Low	22.71	25.23	24.52	23.35
	High	26.26	28.03	27.98	27.35
Average price of margarine sold	Low	26.00	26.68	26.10	26.60
	High	29.50	30.18	32.87	31.68
Shrinkage (0.5%)	Low	.13	.13	.13	.13
	High	.15	.15	.16	.16
Margin	Low	2.85	1.12	1.45	1.46
	High	4.69	4.62	4.73	4.68
Cost allocation to this item	Low	.60	.63	.60	.60
	High	4.54	4.94	5.38	5.16
Net margin	Low	(.74)	(2.99)	(2.74)	(1.22)
	High	2.25	1.48	1.92	1.71

[a] Standard type margarine with soybean oil a major ingredient.
Source: Six corporate food chains.

for their private label, gross margins in cents per pound were about equal.

Table VIII-8 and Exhibit VIII-7 illustrate the striking difference in net margin and the costs that determine net margin among the individual chain stores using the retailer's method of allocating costs to the products. At least one food chain showed a net loss on either or both private label and manufacturers' brand margarine for the five-year period studied. Unlike bread, the widest differentials occurred among the leading manufacturers' brand margarine rather than the private label margarine. Perhaps this is due to the commodity orientation and lack of differentiation for many of the private label margarines. (On the other hand, many chains carry more than one quality of private label margarine under their store label.)

There are many quality differences that seem evident in margarine, such as taste, softness, unevenness of color, and consistency. However, advanced technology, quality control, rigid specification buying, and deep price cuts have resulted in a high percentage of the market being private label, and much of the private label margarine is bought by the retailer on

EXHIBIT VIII-7

Margarine Net (Before Tax) Margins Realized for Private Label and Leading Manufacturers' Brands in Selected Chain Stores: 1960–1963
(Range and weighted average of companywide annual net margins realized for each year)

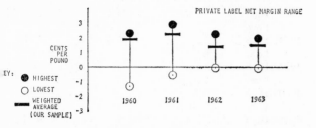

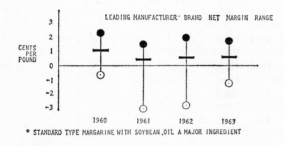

* STANDARD TYPE MARGARINE WITH SOYBEAN OIL A MAJOR INGREDIENT

a commodity basis — priced on a cash or futures soybean oil market. In spite of the commodity orientation, private label brands have had to be priced at an average of 10 cents a pound *under* the leading manufacturers' soybean oil margarine brand in order to move a large unit volume of private label margarine. This 10-cent discount on a 29-cent pound of margarine is a severe one. The "commodity" orientation of a large part of the market for margarine puts a premium on single line manufacturing runs, transportation savings, and a wide use of not only margarine markets but soybean oil and soybean oil futures markets — all of which may account for the fact that 70% of retail margarine chain store sales were able to be moved (largely on a price basis) under private labels, with a favorable net margin to retailers as compared with manufacturers' brands.

The example of margarine is fairly typical in the explanation of the life cycle of the differentiating attributes of a branded item. First, advances in technology made product differentiation possible and brands were developed. Once technological imitation and mass distribution became commonplace, margarine became more or less a standard commodity and private labels became important. The manufacturer of advertised brands had the choice of supplying private labels or of developing "new" types of margarine or margarines with different tastes and ingredient combinations of corn oil and safflower oil as

well as soybean oil. Many of the manufacturers followed the latter policy and generally expanded the total market for both the national branded and private label products without the normal erosion of profit levels.

PRICE STABILITY

Because of the worldwide importance of the U.S. soybean, soybean oil, and soybean meal market, the interrelationship among all oilseed crops around the world, and alternative sources of protein for the mixed feed industry, one would expect the price level of soybeans, soybean meal and soybean oil to be fairly volatile. Tables VIII-9 through VIII-13 in-

TABLE VIII-9. Average Cash Price of No. 1 Yellow Soybeans at Chicago: Crop Years 1951–1965
(In cents per bushel)

Crop year	Average	High	Low	Difference between high & low	Difference as % of seasonal low
1951	307	333	290	43	14.8%
1952	289	305	259	46	17.8
1953	334	383	266	117	44.0
1954	263	284	230	54	23.5
1955	259	319	229	90	39.3
1956	243	253	232	21	9.1
1957	228	230	221	9	4.1
1958	222	234	209	25	12.0
1959	217	223	214	9	4.2
1960	259	323	211	112	53.1
1961	249	256	239	17	7.1
1962	259	269	245	24	9.8
1963	260	279	252	27	10.7
1964	288	304	268	36	13.4
1965	298	373	249	24	9.6

SOURCE: *Commodity Year Book*, 1967, p. 318.

dicate the average annual price levels of soybeans, oil and meal from crop years 1951 to 1962 and the fluctuations that occurred within each crop year. The average annual price of soybeans over this 12-year period had a low of $2.17 a bushel in 1960 and a high of $3.34 in 1954. This difference of $1.17 over a 12-year period was the same as the yearly swing for 1954 from $2.66 to $3.83 a bushel, or $1.17. These fluctuations were the result of the continuing changes in the many variables that affected price levels throughout the year.

The spreads among soybean oil prices are also striking within a crop year such as the 4.7 cents a pound swing for oil in 1951 or a 51.6% change. Over the 12-year period the annual average price of soybean oil hit a low of 8.3 cents in 1959 and a high

TABLE VIII-10. Average Prices[a] of Crude Domestic Soybean Oil: Crop Years 1951–1964

(In cents per pound)

Crop year	Average	High	Low	Difference between high & low	Difference as % of seasonal low
1951	11.3	13.8	9.1	4.7	51.6%
1952	12.1	13.7	10.3	3.4	33.0
1953	13.5	14.8	12.1	2.7	22.3
1954	11.9	12.6	10.6	2.0	18.9
1955	12.6	15.3	10.9	4.4	40.4
1956	12.7	14.4	11.3	3.1	27.4
1957	10.8	11.6	9.8	1.8	18.4
1958	9.5	10.4	9.1	1.3	14.3
1959	8.3	9.5	7.6	1.9	25.0
1960	11.3	13.3	9.4	3.9	41.5
1961	9.5	10.7	8.0	2.7	33.8
1962	8.9	9.3	8.3	1.0	12.0
1963	8.5	9.7	7.9	1.8	22.8
1964	11.3	12.2	10.0	2.2	22.0

[a] F.O.B. Decatur, Illinois.

SOURCE: *Commodity Year Book*, 1965, p. 308.

of 13.5 cents in 1953, or a difference of 5.2 cents a pound.

The price of soybean meal also varied considerably within a crop year and between crop years. The spread of soybean meal prices within a crop year was as much as $29.60 a ton, occurring in 1951. Over the 12-year period examined in Table VIII-11, soybean meal had a 12-year high of $103.60 a ton and a low of $43.75 per ton.

TABLE VIII-11. U.S. Average Wholesale Prices of Soybean Meal, 44% Protein Bulk, Decatur, Illinois: Crop Years 1951–1965

(In dollars per ton)

Crop year	Average	High	Low	Difference between high & low	Difference as % of seasonal low
1951	$83.35	$103.60[a]	$74.00	$29.60	40.0%
1952	67.55	81.10	59.60	21.50	36.1
1953	78.65	95.95	57.25	38.70	67.6
1954	60.70	68.25	52.15	16.10	30.9
1955	52.55	60.75	46.90	13.85	29.5
1956	47.45	49.90	44.25	5.65	12.8
1957	53.40	68.60	43.75	24.85	56.8
1958	55.80	63.25	50.60	12.65	25.0
1959	55.55	61.50	50.75	10.75	21.2
1960	60.60	73.10	44.50	28.60	64.3
1961	63.60	76.70	55.80	20.90	37.5
1962	71.30	75.20	68.10	7.10	10.4
1963	71.00	77.50	63.50	14.00	22.0
1964	70.20	76.80	68.40	8.40	12.3
1965	81.50	97.90	75.50	22.40	29.7

[a] Soybean meal-grain mix.

SOURCE: USDA, Agricultural Marketing Service, *Feed Market News of the Grain Division*.

TABLE VIII-12. Highest and Lowest Prices of May Soybean Futures on the Chicago Board of Trade: 1957–1966

(In cents per bushel)

Year of delivery		Range	Difference between high & low	Difference as % of seasonal low
1957	High	269½	33¾	14.3%
	Low	235¾		
1958	High	254	31⅜	14.1
	Low	222⅝		
1959	High	236	18⅝	8.6
	Low	217⅜		
1960	High	215⅞	5¼	2.5
	Low	210⅝		
1961	High	314	93½	42.4
	Low	220½		
1962	High	265¼	22⅜	9.2
	Low	242⅞		
1963	High	281¼	42⅝	17.9
	Low	238⅝		
1964	High	302¾	57¼	23.3
	Low	245½		
1965	High	317¼	70½	28.6
	Low	246¾		
1966	High	308¾	56½	22.4
	Low	252¼		

SOURCE: *Commodity Year Book*, 1967, p. 315.

The May soybean futures contract reflects the cash swings itemized in Table VIII-9, but Table VIII-12 indicates that the futures prices were less volatile than the cash prices. The volume of trade in soybean futures has grown most rapidly during the periods of widest price swings (see Table VIII-13), but the

TABLE VIII-13. Volume of Trading in Soybean Futures at the Chicago Board of Trade: 1951–1966

(In millions of bushels)

Year	Total volume soybeans traded	Volume change from previous year	Percentage change from previous year	Index (1951 = 100)
1951	2,398	—	—	100
1952	3,090	+ 692	+ 28.8%	129
1953	3,552	+ 462	+ 15.0	148
1954	6,094	+2,542	+ 71.6	254
1955	4,246	−1,848	− 30.3	177
1956	5,720	+1,474	+ 34.7	238
1957	4,330.5	−1,389.5	− 24.3	180
1958	3,041.2	−1,289.3	− 29.8	127
1959	4,351.5	+1,310.3	+ 43.1	181
1960	5,837.9	+1,486.4	+ 34.2	243
1961	12,048.1	+6,210.2	+106.4	502
1962	4,731.3	−7,316.8	− 60.7	197
1963	14,231.0	+9,499.7	+200.8	593
1964	13,129.4	−1,101.6	− 7.7	548
1965	17,827.4	+4,698.0	+ 35.8	743
1966	15,760.0	−2,067.4	− 11.6	657

SOURCE: *Commodity Year Book*, 1967, p. 316.

presence of outside speculative interest in the futures market may have absorbed a portion of the cash price instability, thus providing more price stability to the soybean industry than would have occurred without the futures market, although we have no empirical proof of this.

The presence of (1) a government price support program on soybeans, (2) an export program on soybean oil, and (3) school lunch programs using margarine, etc. have all been influences that have tended to maintain a floor price for soybeans and soybean oil and thus may have prevented even greater price fluctuations than those that occurred with these government programs.

COMPETITION

Thus far the technological innovations, the profit levels, the responsiveness of prices, the development of unique and competitive contractual relationships, the expansion of processing capacity at a faster rate than that of domestic and export crushing needs, and the development of private label consumer products at sharply reduced retail price levels give some evidence of the general competitive environment of the many segments that make up the soybean system. At the same time, there are economies of scale present at each vertical stage of the soybean structure that may eventually eliminate small scale operators. In addition the one purpose nature of many of the soybean facilities increases the investment risk in various segments of this industry system.

Ease of Entry and Exit. The per unit investment in building, machinery, and equipment for a modern soybean processing plant decreases with the increase in the size of the operation because of economies of scale. Table VIII-14 indicates the average investment

TABLE VIII-14. Estimated Investment in Soybean Processing Plants at Varying Levels of Capacity: 1963

Capacity (tons per day)	Total investment (in millions)	Investment per ton on a 300-day operating year
1,000	$2.50	$8.33
1,200	2.75	7.64
1,500	3.20	7.11

SOURCE: USDA, Farmer Cooperative Service, 1965, unpublished.

involved for different sized plants. The processing plant investment estimates are based on plants capable of producing the following types of finished products: "50% protein" meal, soybean hulls, and *crude* soybean oil. Included in the plant investment are esti-

mates for soybean storage and handling equipment for a three-day supply of soybeans. The following costs do *not* include storage for large supplies of soybeans, land costs, roads, railroad sidings, and so on, which would increase the spread between the high and low plant investment per ton of capacity.

The operating costs for a 1,000-ton-per-day plant with a yearly throughput of 10 million bushels of soybeans are shown in Table VIII-15. Because there

TABLE VIII-15. Operating Costs for a 1,000-Ton-per-Day Soybean Processing Plant: 1963

Direct conversion costs	Cents per bushel
Wages and payroll taxes	3.50
Power and water	1.50
Fuel	1.50
Property taxes	.50
Depreciation	3.00
Insurance	.40
Repairs	1.35
Analysis	.15
Solvent	.30
Plant supplies	.25
Miscellaneous	.10
Salaries, etc.	1.10
Travel, directors' fees	.10
Advertising	.03
Dues, subscriptions	.12
Telephone and telegraph	.20
Office supplies	.15
Legal, audit	.05
Miscellaneous	.15
Financial expenses	5.00
Total	19.65

SOURCE: USDA, Farmer Cooperative Service, unpublished.

is no transit on crude oil and there is on refined oil, some cooperatives have added refineries at a cost of approximately $600,000. This cost is an added investment on top of the items listed in Table VIII-15.

The information outlined in Tables VIII-14 and VIII-15 indicates that a substantial investment is necessary for entering the soybean processing industry, and economies of scale in processing, storing, and transportation mean that maintaining and/or increasing that investment will be necessary. In addition, large-scale processing leads to large-scale procurement which further increases investment. The cost of equipment of this industry, together with the cost of building storage facilities and the financing of soybean storage at harvest time, all converge to make this the largest capital investment segment of the soybean industry. In spite of this heavy capital investment, several prominent processors place lower processing margins and excess capacity as greater obstacles to entering this industry than the additional

TABLE VIII-16. Extent of Concentration in the Soybean Processing Industry: Selected Crop Years, 1946–1961

Crop year	Industry daily processing capacity (tons)	% of processing capacity accounted for by:		
		4 largest companies	8 largest companies	20 largest companies
1946	15,564	43.8%	59.9%	78.0%
1953	24,829	33.3	58.1	75.9
1957	31,089	32.3	61.2	76.8[a]
1961	42,348	27.1[b]	60.0[c]	69.9[d]

[a] Percentage for 18 companies only. Two firms among the 20 largest in 1946 exited from the industry between 1953 and 1957.

[b] Percentage for 3 companies only. One firm among the 4 largest in 1946 exited from the industry between 1957 and 1961.

[c] Percentage for 6 companies only. Two firms among the 8 largest in 1946 exited from the industry between 1957 and 1961.

[d] Percentage for 14 companies only. Six companies among the 20 largest in 1946 had exited from the industry by 1961.

SOURCE: Riley "Marketing Structure of the Soybean Industry," p. 46a, Table D-7.

capital required for new plants. This is because of the transportation advantages of having local soybean supplies and meal markets. For example, in Table VIII-3 above, the average processing margin from 1956 to 1960 was 22.8 cents a bushel in Illinois and 41.5 cents in Mississippi.[6] This difference of 18.7 cents a bushel in processing margins between the two locations is considerably more important than the $1.22 a ton (approximately 4 cents a bushel) ad-

significant when compared with the low crushing margins noted in Table VIII-4. Furthermore, some of the more prominent new entrants into the industry are farmer cooperatives that have not been deterred by the heavy capital investments or excess capacity because of their unique cash flow advantages described elsewhere in the study. (Parenthetically one might add that on the average the cooperative processing plants are running at higher capacity rates than noncooperative plants.)

As the last footnote in Table VIII-16 points out, much exiting from the soybean industry has occurred in that 6 of the 20 largest companies in 1946 had left the industry by 1961. However, because this is a one purpose type of facility (with the exception of crushing flax seed and/or cottonseed) resources are trapped and facilities are sold at large discounts, resulting in increased competition because new owners come into the industry with a below book investment in plant and equipment.

Concentration. As Table VIII-16 suggests, the soybean processing industry is not very concentrated and the major firms in the industry in 1946 had a smaller percentage of total processing capacity in the industry and/or had left it by 1961. When compared with other segments of the soybean structure (Table VIII-17), the processing industry is less concentrated than the margarine and cooking oil industries. Furthermore, when one examines the principal market for soybean

TABLE VIII-17. Proportion of Shipments Accounted for by the Largest Companies in Selected Food and Kindred Products Industries: 1947, 1954, and 1958

Industry	% of value of shipments accounted for by:								
	4 largest companies			8 largest companies			20 largest companies		
	1947	1954	1958	1947	1954	1958	1947	1954	1958
Linseed oil mills	75%	85%	81%	97%	100%	100%	100%	—	—
Margarine	64	48	62	90	78	86	100	100%	[a]
Other vegetable oil mills	41	63	84	67	81	96	91	96	99%
Shortening and cooking oils	59	55	49	81	80	75	99	99	97
Soybean oil mills	44	41	40	63	64	63	81	89	86
Cottonseed oil mills	43	47	42	55	57	54	68	72	71
Flour and meal	29	40	38	41	52	51	57	68	68
Prepared animal feeds	19	21	22	27	29	30	40	43	43

[a] Withheld to avoid disclosing figures for individual companies.

SOURCE: U.S. Bureau of the Census, *Concentration Ratios in Manufacturing Industry, 1958*, Table 2.

vantage of a 1,500-ton plant as compared with a 1,000-ton plant (see Table VIII-14). On the other hand, the 4 cents a bushel investment saving is also

[6] Part of the explanation for the wide variations in crushing margins is related to the crop restrictions on cotton in the southern states. With less cottonseed to process into oil, many cottonseed processing facilities became available for soybean processing, thus adding to the excess processing capacity of the soybean industry.

meal, the feed industry, the top 20 feed firms had 43% of the industry's capacity in 1958 and many of them owned and operated soybean processing facilities (see Table VIII-18).

Whatever the "concentration" in every segment of the soybean structure, there are no real barriers of entry but exiting from soybean processing operations may prove costly. It is true that personal relation-

TABLE VIII-18. Major U.S. Feed Manufacturing Firms Ranked by Capacity: December 31, 1962

Company rank	Company name	Maximum capacity (in tons)	Number of plants
1	Ralston Purina	5,430	46
2	Central Soya-McMillen	3,170	18
3	Cargill-Nutrena	2,040	17
4	Southern States Coop-Cooperative Mills	1,780	9
5	Allied Mills[a]	1,660	14
6	Carnation-Albers	1,545	15
7	Corn Products-Wirthmore	1,405	7
8	Quaker Oats	1,360	10
9	Spencer Kellogg Textron (Beacon)	1,195	11
10	J. W. Eshelman	1,150	6
11	Hales & Hunter	1,115	11
12	Moorman	1,035	5
13	Cooperative GLF Exchange[b]	1,030	4
14	Pillsbury	945	7
15	Eastern States Farmers Exchange[b]	830	2
16	Hubbard Milling Company	685	5
17	Western Farmers Association	630	6
18	Missouri Farmers Association	600	2
19	Kimbell Diamond	505	11
20	Walnut Grove Products, Inc.	465	5
	TOTAL of top 20 companies	28,575	211

[a] Purchased by Continental Grain as of 1965.
[b] Merged as of 1965.
SOURCE: USDA, ERS, "Feed Industry Concentration Study."

ships, integrity, and marketing and technical experience are all important variables in this industry. However, the mere fact that farmer cooperatives have expanded rapidly in the processing, refining, and feed formulation aspects of this business is ample evidence that no one firm or group of firms has any substantial market or unique technological advantage. In the manufacturing and distribution of consumer products the large percentage of private label soybean products sold by retailers at substantially reduced prices and profit is also indicative of the severe competition that exists throughout the food retailing and manufacturing segments of this industry.

ADAPTABILITY

The soybean industry — one of the fastest growing industries in the United States — has been extremely innovative in its development of (1) new processes to extract oil from the soybean, (2) new methods of oil hydrogenation, deodorization, and flavor stability, (3) new uses of soybean meal in feed formularization, and (4) new soybean varieties adapted to a wider growing area of soil and climatic conditions. The following tabulation indicates the

wide adoption of the solvent method between 1946 and 1966 by the soybean processing industry,[7] and it is but one example of the innovation of this industry:

Process	1946	1966
Solvent	31.4%	95.0%
Screw press	66.8	5.0
Hydraulic	1.8	0.0

Perhaps even more important than the technological changes that have occurred is the rapid and widespread use of a variety of coordinating institutions that help to move products and services in an efficient manner from producer to ultimate consumer. Seldom in American industrial history has an industry grown so rapidly and made so many changes and adjustments with so few hardships to the participants of that industry. In Section V of this study we will analyze this coordinating and adjustment effort in greater detail. One should not ignore the importance of these institutions and arrangements, however, when summarizing the adaptability of the soybean industry.

SUMMARY

This chapter has outlined the behavior patterns of the soybean industry in an attempt to underscore the interrelationships that exist between managers' competitive strategies and the various firms, entities and arrangements that help to form the soybean system. The rising standard of living in the United States and the rest of the world has increased the demand for meat and poultry products and fat and oil products. The soybean industry has benefited from this increased demand for its principal products of meal and oil. The historical evolution of the soybean system has demonstrated that various contractual agreements were necessary to facilitate the early growth of soybean production and processing. As the industry grew, so did the coordinating machinery which included vertical integration, farmer cooperatives, integrated transportation systems, price contracts, price pooling arrangements, futures markets, and private label contracts, as well as overall government balancing machinery consisting of price supports and P.L. 480 shipments of soybean oil. The coordinating machinery enabled the participants of the soybean system to adjust to change rapidly and to soften the impact of adjustment on any one segment of the system. At the same time, most of this coordinating machinery made use of the remaining quasi-free markets to provide bench marks for the coordinating machinery and to facilitate the necessary changes in short-run and long-run allocation of resources.

[7] Figures provided by Dr. Kromer, USDA, ERS.

Florida Oranges

THE FLORIDA orange industry is one of the most rapidly expanding and changing commodity systems in U.S. agribusiness. The growth of production of this crop is quite phenomenal, from 10 million boxes in the 1920s to over 140 million boxes in 1967. The new technological breakthroughs during World War II, making possible the development of a frozen orange concentrate that was storable for long periods of time and transportable, changed the nature of this industry and brought about new challenges and opportunities for its participants. Because increases in production and product development have come about in major spurts, this industry has had to make more rapid adjustments than most commodity systems. At the same time it has received a minimum amount of aid from the government in making these adjustments. In 1967 another 40% increase in the crop caused many participants in the industry to reappraise the long-run implications of this major change for their respective entities. This industry also has made and is making a variety of uses of different coordinating machinery such as cooperatives and futures markets. The development of coordinating devices, in turn, is having a major impact on the production and distribution patterns that are forming in the market structure for Florida oranges. The introduction of synthetics as competing products for orange-based food items also has intensified the search for new product innovations in the industry at a time when new tree plantings are adding to an already high production base.

IX

The Florida Orange Industry: Its Dynamics and Structure

THUS FAR in this study we have described and analyzed an established and relatively stable wheat-flour-bread industry that involves over one million producers of wheat located in practically every state in the union as well as an industry that is a major factor in the world's wheat economy. We have also outlined the structure and performance of one of the most rapidly expanding industries in the United States, namely, the soybean industry with its 500,000 producers and its dominance in world soybean trade. In both industry examples emphasis was placed on the coordinating institutions and arrangements that have been created to enable the participants in the industry to perform their functions of supplying ultimate consumer food products in a more efficient and profitable manner. The final industry selected to give us further insight into the subject of who or what coordinates the constantly changing functions and relationships of a commodity structure is the Florida orange industry.

This analysis was restricted to the domestic Florida orange industry because Florida oranges are especially well suited for the juice market in contrast to the California navel and valencia oranges. In addition, the export market was not included in any great detail as domestic production is primarily geared to the domestic markets.[1]

Although concentrated in one state with around 18,000 producers, the Florida orange industry has experienced many dynamic changes affecting the consumption, marketing, processing, and production patterns. This industry is an excellent example because of the number of complex and interrelated institutional and contractual relationships that have been developed by and for its participants.

[1] An excellent article summarizing the world citrus economy was published in September 1965 in the *Monthly Bulletin of Agricultural Economics and Statistics* entitled "The Citrus Economy and the Feasibility of International Market Arrangements" by Jurgen Wolf, pp. 1–15.

DYNAMICS OF CHANGE

PRODUCTION

The Florida orange industry is a growth industry with production averaging around 10 million boxes (90 pounds) of oranges in the 1920s, 30 million boxes in the late 1930s, 50 million boxes in the late 1940s, and from 58 million boxes in the early 1950s to a high of an estimated 142 million boxes in the 1966 season. Table VIII-1 shows the growth of the orange industry.

TABLE IX-1. Florida Orange Production: 1955 to 1966 Seasons

Season[a]	Millions of 90-lb. boxes
1955	91.0
1956	93.0
1957	82.5
1958	86.0
1959	91.5
1960	86.7
1961	113.4
1962	74.5
1963	58.3
1964	86.2
1965	100.4
1966 (estimated)	142.4

[a] The season begins with the bloom about October 1 and ends in early summer.

SOURCE: USDA, ERS, as quoted in *Florida Citrus Mutual, Annual Statistical Report*, 1963–1964, p. 1.

The production of this crop is concentrated in a few major producing counties in Florida and is highly susceptible to weather conditions, such as the freeze of late 1962. In spite of these hazards, Florida has become the major orange producing state in the United States (see Exhibit IX-1) and produces over one-quarter of the world's oranges.

EXHIBIT IX-1

Orange Production by Total United States and Major Producing States: 1935 through 1966 Seasons

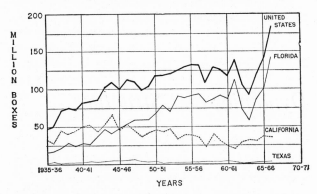

SOURCE: Compiled by author from *Florida Citrus Mutual, Annual Statistical Report*, 1963–1964, pp. 3 and 5, updated with statistics obtained from USDA.

Unlike wheat and soybeans, Florida orange production has to be planned years ahead. Many groves are productive for sixty to seventy years, but it takes four years before a young nursery tree bears its first fruit in any great quantity. Therefore, planting new trees during times of high prices may be out of phase with "normal" consumption expansion of fresh and processed orange food products. Even after the freeze of 1962, many nonbearing trees may eventually lead to a production flood.

As of September 1965 it was estimated [2] that there was a total of 30.4 million orange trees bearing fruit in the State of Florida of which 14.2 million, or 46.7%, were early and mid-season types. Of the total production in the 1962 season 61.1% was accounted for by early and mid-season type oranges. Late type orange trees were estimated at 16.2 million, or 53.3% of the orange tree total in September 1965. Late type trees accounted for 38.9% of the total orange production in the same season. It is also estimated that there are 21.5 million nonbearing orange trees in Florida, of which 8.3 million trees are late types and 13.2 million trees are early and mid-season types. These nonbearing trees will add a potential increase to the crop of 71% of current production in excess of retirement. Most estimates conclude that by 1970 production of the orange crop may exceed 190 million boxes for the State of Florida.

In the past the rapid expansion of Florida orange production has not resulted in prolonged periods of depressed price levels for several reasons: (1) the susceptibility of the Florida orange crop to changing

[2] Florida Department of Agriculture, *Florida Citrus 1965 Sample Tree Survey*.

weather conditions (mostly hurricanes and freezes); (2) the technological breakthrough of the development of frozen orange concentrate; and (3) the increased demand for frozen orange concentrate after World War II. Table IX-2 indicates the relatively profitable, if erratic, price levels for the Florida orange producers.

TABLE IX-2. Season Average On-Tree Prices per Box of Florida Oranges by Utilization of Sales: Selected Years, 1935 through 1963
(In dollars per 90-lb. box)

Season	Fresh use[a]	Processing	All sales
1935	$1.19	$0.71	$1.18
1939	0.62	0.03	0.52
1941	1.15	0.79	1.10
1945	2.35	2.41	2.37
1947	0.76	0.52	0.63
1949	2.19	2.12	2.14
1951	0.86	0.76	0.80
1952	1.31	1.27	1.28
1960	3.15	2.94	2.98
1961	2.05	1.56	1.66
1962	3.41	1.80	2.05
1963	4.61	4.51	4.53

[a] Based on fraction shipped fresh to interstate markets.
SOURCE: USDA, ERS, as quoted in *Florida Citrus Mutual, Annual Statistical Report*.

The Florida orange industry has encouraged improved production technology through its close cooperation with the University of Florida, Florida Citrus Mutual (a grower cooperative association representing over 13,000 Florida orange producers), Florida Citrus Commission (a state commission to improve Florida's production and marketing of citrus), and market order institutions.[3] Furthermore, the development of mechanical harvesting devices, improved fertilizer application, and improved grove technology mean that production adjustment problems may occur. In addition, the structural changes in the industry, such as the ownership of important and expanding grove acreage by many orange processors, have also added to potential overproduction problems. Other adjunct organizations, such as insurance companies and other financial institutions, have encouraged existing orange grove owners to expand their operations by using their present grove as collateral to form a syndicate, and on a highly leveraged basis greatly expand grove acreage. Most of this expansion takes place during high prices for fruit, and the pro forma financial statements use this current inflated price value rather than a potentially declining value in estimating grove values for the future.[4] The technological and structural changes in pro-

[3] See page 160 for a detailed description of these organizations.
[4] Interview with executives in Florida orange industry.

duction have received excellent stimulation from the equally dynamic changes that have occurred in the processing, marketing and consumption of orange products. However, new products, new markets, and new freezes cannot be counted on to avoid the potentially enormous build-up of orange production in Florida.

CONSUMPTION

Total citrus consumption in the United States has had a phenomenal growth over the last fifty years, expanding from 20 pounds to 83 pounds per capita, as Table IX-3 shows. Since 1955 per capita citrus con-

TABLE IX-3. U.S. Per Capita Citrus Consumption: 10-Year Averages, 1910–1959

10-year average	*Pounds per capita*
1910–1919	20.4
1920–1929	31.2
1930–1939	47.1
1940–1949	82.6
1950–1959	83.8

SOURCE: USDA, ERS, *Agricultural Statistics, 1957*, and *Handbook of Agricultural Charts, 1966*.

sumption has leveled off with uneven declines and the form of the consumption has changed with a decrease in fresh consumption and an increase in frozen consumption (see Exhibit IX-2). This change is especially notable in the U.S. per capita consumption of oranges

EXHIBIT IX-2

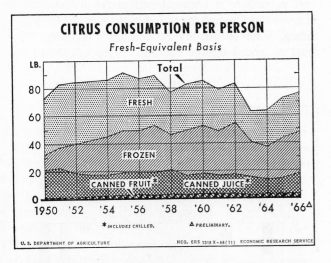

CITRUS CONSUMPTION PER PERSON
Fresh-Equivalent Basis

U. S. DEPARTMENT OF AGRICULTURE   NEG. ERS 1318 X–66(11) ECONOMIC RESEARCH SERVICE

which totalled 58.3 pounds fresh weight equivalent in the 1946 season, of which 0.2 pounds were consumed in frozen concentrate form, 16.6 pounds in canned form, and 41.5 pounds in fresh form. By the 1961 season the relationship was completely reversed: 33.4

pounds in frozen orange concentrate form, 3.9 pounds in chilled juice form, 5.7 pounds in canned form, and only 15.7 pounds in fresh form.

The relationship of processed to unprocessed orange consumption expressed in terms of the *Florida* orange crop is even more dramatic. About 80% of the Florida orange crop is currently processed in one form or another. Approximately 62% to 65% of the crop is utilized in the form of frozen orange concentrate, about 8% to 10% is canned or used in salad sections, and the remaining 7% to 10% is used for chilled orange juice.

The Florida Citrus Commission, the Florida Agricultural Department, Florida Citrus Mutual, the University of Florida, the U.S. Department of Agriculture, various consumer advertising agencies, and the Bureau of Labor Statistics have all made countless detailed consumption studies[5] of frozen orange concentrate — the major consumer product of the Florida orange industry. Several of these studies are cited in the bibliography at the end of this study. Briefly stated, the conclusions are as follows:

(1) The 6-ounce can of frozen orange concentrate is a convenience food that is especially economical for the consumer to buy because she does not pay for the transportation of water and waste. In 1963 the Department of Agriculture estimated that a 23-cent 6-ounce can of frozen orange concentrate made one and a half pints of orange juice (if the recommended amount of water is added). The same amount of juice from *fresh oranges* costs about 47 cents.[6]

(2) In spite of the above value to the consumer less than one-third of all the families in the United States buy frozen orange concentrate on a regular basis, although over 85% of all families have tried frozen orange concentrate and buy it from time to time. Fifty percent of all frozen orange concentrate purchases are made by 10% of the families in the United States.[7] The income elasticity of this product is especially evident in Table IX-4. The responsiveness to price is summarized in Exhibit IX-3 which indicates the monthly *average* number of 6-ounce cans bought per family by seasons in relation to the average price for the 6-ounce can of juice.

(3) The U.S. per capita consumption of orange concentrate has tended to level off at 16.5 to 17.5 pounds per capita (single orange juice strength basis). The expansion of the orange concentrate industry was

[5] These studies have been supported by per box fees assessed to growers and processors.
[6] USDA, ERS, *Comparative Costs to Consumers of Convenience Foods and Home Prepared Foods*, p. 75.
[7] Booz, Allen & Hamilton, *Long-Range Planning, Florida Citrus Commission*, 1964.

TABLE IX-4. Dollar Weekly Expenditures for Frozen Orange Concentrate by Level of Family Income: 1960

Family income	Average weekly expenditure
All families	$0.16
Under $3,000	0.04
$3,000–$5,000	0.09
$5,000–$7,500	0.18
$7,500–$10,000	0.22
$10,000–$15,000	0.32
$15,000 and over	0.35

SOURCE: National Industrial Conference Board release, 1965.

rapid in the late 1940s and early 1950s, and has approximated population growth in the United States during the last decade. The industry in the fall of 1966 was in the process of improving the citrus product by (a) adding an extra orange per 6-ounce can in the concentrate, (b) experimenting with "sugar added" concentrate, (c) the development of a new 8-ounce convenience package, and (d) experimenting with orange blends such as orange-lemon. New products were also being developed as, for instance, orange crystals

EXHIBIT IX-3

U.S. Monthly Average Number of 6-Ounce Cans of Frozen Orange Concentrate Purchased per Family in Relation to Average Price of 6-Ounce Can for the Same Period: 1953 to 1965 Seasons

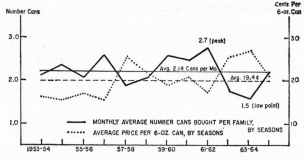

SOURCE: *Florida Citrus Mutual Triangle,* October 7, 1965.

that require no refrigeration. Thus far, however, these have proved to be too costly to market on any large scale volume. (The armed services have used the product because of its nonperishability.)

(4) Not only has per capita consumption of frozen orange concentrate begun to level off but the increases that have occurred in per capita consumption of Florida orange concentrate have been at the expense of fresh Florida oranges. Table XIX-5 demonstrates this point. Note the drop in fresh juice equivalent from 1.5 to 1.0 gallons per person and the uneven expan-

sion of other orange juice consumption from 2.3 to 2.6 gallons per person. The fluctuations in per capita consumption of total oranges are related to production and price variations described above (see Table IX-5).

TABLE IX-5. U.S. Civilian Per Capita Consumption of Frozen Orange Concentrate and Fresh Oranges (Juice Equivalent) Compared with Total Beverage Per Capita Consumption: 1957–1962 (In gallons)

Type of consumption	1957	1958	1959	1960	1961	1962
Total beverage consumption	125.1	125.6	126.9	126.2	125.6	127.7
Concentrated orange juice consumption	2.3	2.0	2.2	2.4	2.2	2.6
Fresh orange consumption (juice equivalent)	1.5	1.2	1.3	1.3	1.1	1.0
Total orange (juice equivalent) consumption	3.8	3.2	3.5	3.7	3.3	3.6

SOURCE: Booz, Allen & Hamilton, Inc., *Long-Range Plan, Florida Citrus Commission,* 1964, p. I-16a, Exhibit VIII.

Note the high consumption in 1957 and 1962 when plentiful supplies and low prices existed. Table IX-5 also indicates the ability of the industry to re-establish consumption patterns once the instability of supply becomes corrected.

(5) Although the development of the frozen concentrate process in 1945 made orange marketing less of a perishable operation, there still exists a seasonal pattern of frozen concentrated orange juice consumption as well as a seasonal pattern for the shipment of fresh Florida oranges as Exhibits IX-4 and IX-5 indicate. Such seasonality of consumption affects the level of frozen orange concentrate stocks as well as

EXHIBIT IX-4

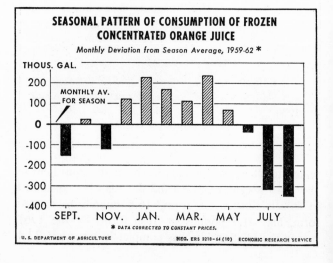

the volume contract relationships between the processor and the retailer.

EXHIBIT IX-5

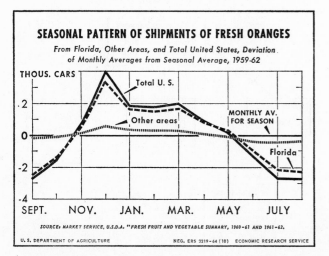

(6) Not only does the Florida orange industry have to be aware of consumption changes of frozen and fresh orange food products but it also must be aware of the growing competition of synthetic orange drinks, such as Awake and Tang. Table IX-6 presents a pic-

TABLE IX-6. Consumer Purchases of Frozen Concentrated and Synthetic Orange Drinks as a Percentage of Total Sales of Frozen Orange Juice Concentrate: April 1964–August 1965

Month	Concentrated orange drinks	Concentrated synthetic
April 1964	19.6%	3.6%
May	19.5	5.2
June	17.9	6.0
July	21.9	8.4
August	16.5	12.0
September	14.2	12.8
October	13.2	12.4
November	12.2	11.7
December	8.5	13.5
January 1965	8.0	10.9
February	6.9	10.8
March	6.8	13.3
April	6.6	10.9
May	8.2	11.0
June	7.1	9.4
July	7.2	10.3
August	6.3	8.8

SOURCE: Marketing Research Corporation of America.

ture of the importance of synthetic concentrated orange drinks and frozen orange drink mixtures as a percentage of the total sales of frozen orange concentrate. The synthetic concentrate product obtained a high of

EXHIBIT IX-6

Consumer Purchases of Frozen Concentrated and Synthetic Drinks: April 1964–August 1965

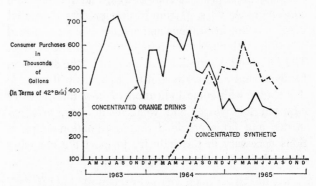

SOURCE: Marketing Research Corporation of America.

13.5% of frozen orange concentrate sales in December 1964. Exhibit IX-6 gives the same picture in thousands of gallons.

(7) Consumption of Florida orange products has another dimension that may become more important in future marketing programs — namely, purchase of frozen orange concentrate for the school lunch program by the U.S. Department of Agriculture. (Such purchases were made in great quantity during the volume build-up in 1962, but were returned to the processors after the freeze in 1962 since the government did not want to be in the position of profiting on its purchases of frozen orange juice. Again in December 1966 Secretary Freeman indicated that the Department of Agriculture planned to purchase from 10 to 15 million gallons of concentrate for the school lunch program to support prices in the Florida orange industry.)

(8) Export shipments of Florida oranges and Florida orange concentrate have not proved to be an important market outlet, although in the 1961–1962 bumper crop year 317,000 boxes of fresh oranges were exported (0.3% of the crop) along with 972,000 gallons of processed orange concentrate or 0.6% of the crop.

(9) Although frozen orange concentrate has many differentiable qualities, only about 25% of total retail sales are sold as recognized manufacturer brands, 35% of the volume is sold under retail food chain labels, and the remaining 40% of sales are a mixture of local or packer brands[8] of one kind or another.

SUMMARY

In summary, the shift from fresh orange consumption to processed orange product consumption has had pro-

[8] "Packer brands" as used throughout this study refer to brands developed by the processor but not promoted on a national scale.

found effects not only upon the producers, packers, handlers, and processors within the State of Florida, but also on their relationships with the food distributors, the juice product competitors, and the ultimate consumers. As the shift from fresh to processed product occurred, new institutions and arrangements developed allowing the industry to adjust to this dramatic change. The following description and analysis of the structure, behavior and performance of the industry will *provide* the reader with some indication of how this industry adjusted to change, and what institutions, arrangements, and firms provided the coordination of functions necessary in this industry to meet the changing demands for Florida orange products.

THE STRUCTURE

The many changes in production, processing, and consumption described above had an impact on the total Florida orange economy in terms of (1) the marketing channels utilized, (2) the number and size of units, (3) the ownership patterns, (4) the development of coordinating institutions, and (5) the increase in all forms of integration. The current Florida orange economy is portrayed in this multidimensional manner in Exhibits IX-7, IX-9, and IX-10. These three exhibits which will be discussed in turn, will serve as a broad framework for describing and analyzing the behavior and performance of the Florida orange economy.

CHANNELS

The movement of 113.4 million boxes of Florida oranges from producer to consumer is shown in Exhibit IX-7. Unlike the soybean and wheat producers who are commonly diversified into other crops or livestock operations, the Florida orange producers are not so diversified (with the exception of other citrus production, such as grapefruit, tangerines, and lemons). Nor are these producers in a position to store their perishable crop. They may delay harvesting a crop from an orchard or attempt an early harvest, but they cannot store the finished product in the raw orange state. Some 19% of the crop moves in fresh form; the remaining 81% is divided among various types of processing, the major one now being frozen orange concentrate.

The 19% of the crop that moves through fresh citrus packing houses (approximately 21.5 million boxes) has the following end uses: (1) 16.4 million boxes are exported from Florida to U.S. retail outlets, (2) 4.8 million boxes remain in Florida for home use, and (3) the remaining 0.3 million boxes are moved through the export market. The packing houses are

EXHIBIT IX-7

Marketing Channels for the Florida Orange Industry: 1961 Season
(In millions of boxes)

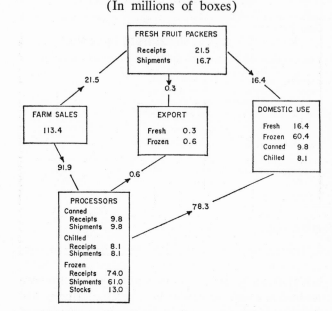

an integral part of the Florida orange industry. They also handle other fresh Florida citrus products such as grapefruit and tangerines. In addition they are integrated into processing operations which provide them with important outlets for some of their fruit.

The remaining 81% of the crop, approximately 91.9 million boxes, is divided among the processing operations as follows: (1) 9.8 million boxes for canned juice and salad sections; (2) 74.0 million boxes for frozen orange concentrate; and (3) 8.1 million boxes for chilled juice. Many processors may combine all three operations. Although the processing plants in Florida are all primarily citrus-crop oriented, their ownership (as will be noted later) in many cases is by large integrated food and beverage firms, such as The Coca-Cola Company, National Dairy Products, General Foods, Libby, McNeil & Libby, H. P. Hood & Sons, and Salada. In the year used as an example of the volume flow of the product (the 1961 season), not all the frozen orange concentrate produced was sold through retail outlets. Approximately 48.1 million boxes in the form of frozen concentrate were sold through retailers while 12.9 million boxes were sold to institutions, and the remaining 13 million boxes[9] were added to the processors' inventories as indicated by the stock build-up shown in Exhibit IX-8.

[9] The average yield (gallons of 42° brix) per 90-pound box of Florida oranges used for frozen concentrate in the 1961 season was 1.57. *Florida Citrus Mutual, Annual Statistical Report,* 1962–1963, p. 34.

EXHIBIT IX-8

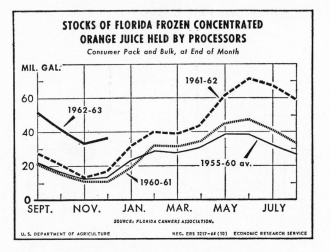

STOCKS OF FLORIDA FROZEN CONCENTRATED
ORANGE JUICE HELD BY PROCESSORS
Consumer Pack and Bulk, at End of Month

SOURCE: FLORIDA CANNERS ASSOCIATION.

U. S. DEPARTMENT OF AGRICULTURE   NEG. ERS 3217-64 (10)   ECONOMIC RESEARCH SERVICE

FIRMS AND ENTITIES

The technological development of the frozen concentrate process not only changed the marketing channel relationships of the Florida orange industry but also resulted in a new industry structure in the number, size and type of enterprise that make up the Florida orange industry (see Exhibit IX-9). By 1962 the number of orange farms in Florida were estimated to be approximately 18,000. The average size grove has increased in size by the number of orange trees per farm and by the number of field boxes harvested by farms as shown in Table IX-7. In addition, the uncertainty of orange production and the profitability of growing them have

TABLE IX-7. Average Number of Trees and Average Number of Boxes of Oranges Harvested per Florida Farm, by Type and Variety: Four Census Years 1940–1959

Type and variety	1940	1950	1954	1959
Number of orange trees of all ages, per farm:				
Valencia oranges	539	841	835	1,202
Temple oranges	n.a.	232	279	308
Other oranges	n.a.	554	691	1,035
Number of field boxes harvested, per farm:				
Valencia oranges	n.a.	2,759	3,268	3,522
Temple oranges	n.a.	682	1,007	1,011
Other oranges	n.a.	2,080	3,006	3,200
Number of farms reporting fruit harvested:				
Valencia oranges	n.a.	7,498	11,664	10,123
Temple oranges	n.a.	1,765	3,477	3,215
Other oranges	n.a.	11,736	14,935	12,693

n.a. = not available.
SOURCE: Farmer Cooperative Service, U.S. Census of Agriculture, 1959, Vol. I, Part 29, Florida Counties, pp. 18–19.

led several processors to own their own groves. For example, the Minute Maid Division of The Coca-Cola Company is probably the biggest orange farmer in Florida, controlling approximately 30,000 acres of citrus land in production, of which 22,000 acres is owned outright and the remainder is held through various leasing arrangements.

In the 1961 season approximately 155 firms operated fresh citrus packing houses (see Exhibit IX-9); this figure represents a reduction of 90 in a single decade. Actually, the number of packing house firms is declining slightly faster than the amount of Florida orange volume moved into the fresh market so that the volume per packing house is somewhat higher than it was a decade ago. In addition to the principal packing houses, approximately 700 gift or interstate shippers handled about one million boxes of oranges in 1961–1962. There is very little concentration among the fresh citrus packing houses, the ten largest accounting for only 31% of all fresh fruit shipments in 1960 as indicated below:

3 largest shippers	11.22%
10 largest shippers	30.83
25 largest shippers	52.41
50 largest shippers	74.95

There are approximately 48 firms (as shown in Exhibit IX-9) operating 58 orange processing plants in Florida. Several of them have multiple operations. The following tabulation gives the approximate number of processing firms and their products (several firms produce more than one product).

Concentrated orange juice	23
Single strength juices	23
Sections and salad	19
Chilled juices	10
Fruit beverages or ades	10

Of the 23 concentrated juice processors, 5 were cooperatives accounting for 25% of output, 7 were conglomerately integrated firms (involved in other food enterprises) accounting for 37% of Florida output, and 11 were specialized orange processors accounting for the remaining 38% of Florida's output.

Along with the development of the Florida processing industry came the intermediate orange procurement firms that supply independent processors with much of their oranges. They are called "bird dogs." They usually buy fruit on the tree, and they have their own harvesting crews to pick fruit and deliver it to the processing plants. They usually pay the growers a flat price and sell to the processors on the basis of pounds solids per box. Florida Citrus Mutual lists 131 intermediate handlers (bird dogs) in its citrus buyers' book

EXHIBIT IX-9

Firms and Entities in the Florida Orange Economy: 1961 Season

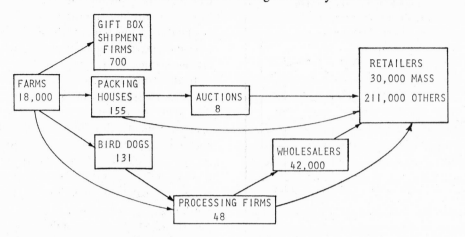

(see Exhibit IX-9). On the other hand, many independent processors also procure their fruit directly from the Florida orange farmer.

The terminal auction markets are handling a declining volume of fresh oranges. In 1960–1961 auctions handled 12% of the fresh orange sales from Florida compared with 40% in 1940–1941. Similarly wholesalers, including frozen food distributors, have declined in the percentage of all frozen concentrate sales they handle. By 1961, 38% of all fresh orange purchases by retailers were made by direct sale from packing houses to retailers. In that same year over 50% of all

frozen orange concentrate sales were made directly to retailers from processors.

The most "concentrated" part of the industry is the processing of frozen orange concentrate where one firm in 1966 accounted for 14% of total output; and the top eight firms accounted for 66.7% of total output in 1959. On the other hand, 57.5% of the dollar volume of frozen citrus products were purchased by the top ten food chains in the United States. The concentration of purchases leads to large scale retailing, processing, and production. Even with the growth of the Florida orange industry from 59 million boxes

EXHIBIT IX-10

Ownership Patterns in the Florida Orange Economy as Measured by Quantity Flows: 1961 Season

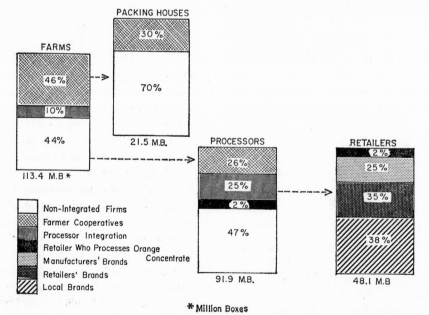

of oranges in 1950 to 113 in 1962 (and an estimated 142 in 1966) the number of entities in growing and processing oranges were up only slightly (farms from 14,400 to 18,000 and processors from 45 to 48); the number of fresh fruit handlers declined from 245 to 155.

COORDINATING PATTERNS

The development of the Florida processing industry created a new need for some type of coordinated production, processing, and marketing operations in order that the consumer could have a consistent quantity and quality of orange concentrate product despite the extremely volatile production and resultant price and quality variations of the raw product.

Common Ownership. Exhibit IX-10 summarizes the ownership patterns in the Florida orange industry as measured by quantity flows at each stage in the vertical movement from farmer to ultimate consumer. One of the most important forms of integration is that of farmer cooperatives. Some 46% of all sales from farmers to processors and fruit packers are through farmers' cooperative marketing organizations, in order to assure themselves of adequate supplies, Minute Maid helped to form Florida Orange Marketers, Inc., and sells the output of its own 22,000 acres and its 8,000 leased acres through the cooperative as well as purchasing from other "farmer" members of the cooperative,[10] and H.P. Hood helped form Quality Orange Growers. A typical type of farmer-cooperative marketing and cooperative-processor pooling contract is presented in Appendix Exhibit IX-1.

The main features of benefit to the farmer and the processor are summarized as follows:

Farmer Market Advantages	*Processor Procurement Advantages*
1. The farmer is guaranteed a market for a certain number of boxes of oranges.[11]	1. The processor is guaranteed a supply of a certain number of boxes of oranges.[11]
2. The farmer grower can average his qualities of oranges even if some lots are below minimum standards.	2. The processor gets fruit above minimum quality standards for sugar and solid content, and with "clear title."
3. The cooperative association makes advance pay-	3. The farmer delivers oranges to the processing
ments to farmer members but charges farmer's account for any interest expense. No final payment is made to the farmer until the cooperative and the processor make final settlement.	plant at his own expense and at a time that is designated by his cooperative association.
4. Cooperative association expense is limited to a maximum fee of 3 cents a box (90 lbs).	4. Liquidating damages of 25 cents a box are payable to the cooperative if the farmer does not deliver oranges. This money is available for cooperative-processor settlement.
5. The farmer is guaranteed a minimum price equal to the Florida Canners Association average price per pound solid.[12] The pool price is divided into two pools (one for early oranges, the other for late) so farmers who produce different varieties are paid an *average* price for their particular crop seasons.	5. The pool contract keeps average procurement costs in line with competitors' procurement costs (all are related to the Florida Canners Association price).

Some 26% of the actual processing capacity of frozen concentrate shown in Exhibit IX-10 is owned and operated by five cooperatives. In the movement of fresh fruit, the 30% of the fresh orange fruit shipments from the state are handled by 27 cooperative firms with a membership of approximately 3,000 farmers. They ship their fruit through a cooperative joint sales agency — the Florida Citrus Exchange.

The farmer cooperatives in Florida have thus far not gone beyond the processing stage although many of them have retail volume shipment contracts similar to the one set forth in Appendix Exhibit IX-2. They also have private label contracts with leading retail food chains.

The advantages of the retail volume shipment contracts to the processor and the retailer are as follows:

[10] In 1963 Florida Orange Marketers had 485 members and supplied approximately one-third of Minute Maid's raw material requirements exclusive of Minute Maid's own groves.

[11] Both the farmer and the processor are protected against the inability to deliver or to take delivery because of "Acts of God," such as "freeze" and "fire."

[12] Since this contract was written, many processors have changed the basis of the minimum guarantee price from FCA to other indices such as the non-ad card price put out by such firms as Adams, Pasco, and Wintergarden. ("Non-ad card price" means a weekly price card put out by processors who do not have a nationally advertised brand of frozen orange concentrate.)

Processor	*Retailer*
1. The processor is guaranteed a market for a certain volume of his orange concentrate with a tolerance for overdelivery and underdelivery of one-tenth of 1%.	1. The processor guarantees to deliver a specified quantity of frozen orange concentrate and to deliver the product in lithographed cans[13] specified by the retailer but supplied by the processor.
2. The processor receives storage payment from the retailer on invoiced merchandise that remains in the processors warehouse.	2. The retailer gets free storage on all concentrate invoiced until January 15 of the season.
3. The processor is guaranteed approximately equal monthly shipments of the product.	3. The retailer is guaranteed a quality product and USDA inspection.
4. The processor is guaranteed prompt payment of invoiced concentrate.	4. The retailer's cost is guaranteed to be no more than that of any other retailer on date of invoicing or shipment.
	5. The retailer gets coded samples of all finished products.

Processor Ownership. As indicated above, processors are quite anxious to assure themselves of a supply of oranges and in addition to encouraging the development of farm supply cooperatives, they have orange groves of their own. The Minute Maid Division of The Coca-Cola Company is cited as the most prominent example of backward integration. Approximately one-third of its raw orange supply comes from its own groves. Other processors, as well as farmer cooperatives, have also integrated backward into the ownership of their own groves. For example, Libby and Tree Sweet both own groves. The Tree Sweet operation is part of the Di Giorgio Fruit Co. There are also many processors who have not integrated backward, the most notable one being the Stokely-Bordo concentrate operation.

Retail Ownership. As is true of margarine, in the soybean industry, there is very little retail private label frozen orange concentrate actually manufactured by the retailer. This writer was only able to discover one retail food firm that processed its own orange concentrate, and this firm represents approximately 2% of total U.S. orange concentrate sales as shown in Exhibit IX-10.

---

[13] The lithographed can is being replaced by a foil-fiber can with an "easy opening" end.

OTHER COORDINATING INSTITUTIONS
AND ARRANGEMENTS

The Florida Citrus Commission. This commission was established in 1935 and is composed of 12 members appointed for a term of two years by the Governor of Florida. Each member must be either an outright grower, a grower-handler, or a grower-processor.

The commission is charged with the responsibility for administering the Florida Citrus Code (the citrus fruit laws of Florida). It also has the right to handle commodity advertising. In fact, the budget for 1967 (using special funds) is $18 million for the promotion of orange juice. This amount represents some 10% of the value of the crop on the farm.

In addition, the commission has a number of regulatory provisions for which it is responsible. The commission has the power to establish state grades and minimum maturity and quality standards. It also has the power to determine proper containers, tagging, and stamping of fresh and processed fruit (a current problem is whether to permit sugar to be added to orange juice and still call it "orange juice"), and it investigates transportation problems for the Florida citrus industry.

Research became one of the major functions of the commission in 1941 and is still being conducted both on the product and improvement in production and processing technology and on other economic aspects of the industry such as marketing and consumer orientation. One example of its research program was the basic frozen orange concentrate processing method that was aided by the commission's research program.

The commission has been especially effective in safeguarding the reputation of the quality of the Florida orange products. Sometimes it has had to resort to embargoes during "freeze" periods to avoid shipment of poor quality fruit.

The functions of the commission are financed through an excise tax levied on each box of fruit marketed either in fresh or in processed form. Exhibit IX-11 gives a breakdown of the orange advertising and research tax levied in the 1964 season. Because of the anticipated large crop for the 1966 season (142 million boxes), the tax per box has been increased to provide operating revenues to help support the $18 million promotional program.

Marketing Agreement of 1939. Before 1939 two earlier Federal Marketing Agreements failed because of volume controls that proved impossible to carry out. The 1939 agreement is now in effect and regulates grades and sizes of fruit to be shipped in interstate commerce. It has not incorporated provisions for a volume prorate which was an attempted feature

EXHIBIT IX-11

Utilization of Orange Advertising Tax: 1964 Season
(9 cents per box)

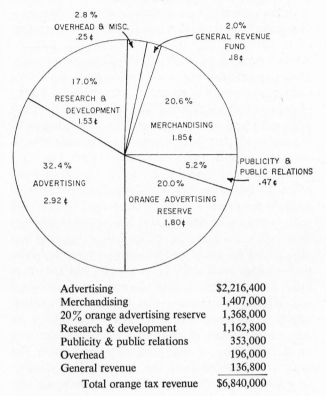

Advertising	$2,216,400	
Merchandising	1,407,000	
20% orange advertising reserve	1,368,000	
Research & development	1,162,800	
Publicity & public relations	353,000	
Overhead	196,000	
General revenue	136,800	
Total orange tax revenue	$6,840,000	

SOURCE: Florida Citrus Commission.

of earlier programs.[14] A proposal for a new marketing agreement was submitted by various industry leaders to Secretary of Agriculture Freeman on December 6, 1966. Because of the large Florida orange crop, these leaders would like to dispose of up to 15% of the crop in secondary markets (e.g., P.L. 480 and school lunch programs). The Secretary has already indicated that the government will purchase substantial quantities of frozen orange concentrate for the school lunch program (some estimates are for as much as 10 million gallons).

Growers' Administrative and Shippers' Advisory Committees. Two committees were formed under the Marketing Agreement of 1939: the growers' and shippers' committees. The shippers or handlers of fruit report to the growers' committee which in turn reports to the Secretary of Agriculture. These two committees are charged with making recommendations

[14] As of December 1965, the industry did have a modified prorate marketing agreement for fresh grapefruit, which means that grapefruit can be prorated as to volume for the whole state.

with respect to regulations authorized in the 1939 agreement, and order and submit these recommendations to the Secretary of Agriculture who may accept, modify, or reject them. These two committees have worked in harmony and have been extremely important in making the marketing agreement workable. They are responsible for regulating the grades and acceptable sizes that must meet state inspections for both domestic and export shipments.

Florida Citrus Mutual. Florida Citrus Mutual is a nonstock cooperative owned and controlled by growers producing citrus fruit. The association was begun in 1949 after 75% of the state's citrus production had been signed up. As of 1964, it had 13,200 members. It has unlimited activities: it sells and merchandises fruit, encourages better production methods, works to improve freight rates, conducts research in production, harvesting, and marketing fruit, secures state and federal legislation, and distributes price and market information. Under the active leadership of Robert Rutledge it has been in the forefront of improving product quality, advertising, and packaging and of demanding more research activity. It is constantly reviewing new ideas for the industry such as a reserve frozen orange concentrate supply pool and the use of a frozen orange concentrate futures market. It also has been extremely active in supporting a tariff on imported orange and orange concentrate products. The Florida Citrus Mutual was largely responsible for advocating and presenting the January 1967 proposal for a new market agreement order for the Florida orange industry.

A summary of the major provisions of the uniform marketing contract that the farmer signs when he becomes a member of Mutual (see Appendix Exhibit IX-3) provides further amplification of the important functions carried out by the Florida Citrus Mutual. They may be summarized as follows:

(1) The grower agrees to sell only through handlers that have contracts with Florida Citrus Mutual; this provision enables Florida Citrus Mutual to have a certified list of reputable handlers, bird dogs, and processors and to reinforce its data collecting and market research services.

(2) The grower agrees to an assessment per box to finance market and sales information and industry lobbying for or against tariff provisions, market orders, futures markets, and product and promotional activities.

(3) The grower provides current crop information that enables Florida Citrus Mutual to make crop estimates and market estimates that are considered by

some industry members to be more accurate than USDA sample activities.

(4) The grower pays a membership fee of $5.00 to help support activities under (2) above.

(5) The grower contacts Mutual as soon as any sales or contracts are made, thereby providing Mutual with rapid and current market information on price level, quantity, and quality of crop movement.

(6) The association in turn provides a list of bird dogs and processors to members to aid them in determining approved and alternative market outlets.

(7) If the grower does not sell his product through bird dogs or processors that have signed with Mutual, then the grower agrees to pay a penalty of 25 cents per box for such fruit marketed.

The Florida Citrus Mutual through all of its many activities and large membership is regarded as both an important economic coordinator of the producer and the processor of oranges in Florida, and as a major political factor and industry spokesman in the State of Florida and in Washington, D.C.

In 1957 the Federal Trade Commission examined some of Mutual's activities and "forbade resumption of the association's pre-1952 attempts to control the price or interstate shipment of fruit after grower-members had sold it to handlers and processors."[15]

Florida Canners Association. The Florida Canners Association was organized in 1931 and its membership today includes all processors of citrus products. The primary function of the association is to compile detailed statistical information on the weekly pack, inventories, and movement of the various processed citrus products as well as the weekly delivered-in prices, yields, and number of boxes utilized in the respective products. The association also is a body which can consider matters affecting processed product, quality, packaging and other industry regulations.

SUMMARY

In summary, the Florida orange industry in the development of its industry structure has been responsive to the agronomic conditions of the Florida orange crop. The long-time investment, the susceptibility to rapidly changing growing conditions, and the geographical compactness of the growing, processing, and marketing operations have all acted as catalysts to tie procurement, processing and marketing as tightly together as possible.

The tasks of coordinating all the functions performed in satisfying the ultimate consumers' demands for fresh and processed orange products have been accomplished by a great variety of associations, arrangements, contracts, laws, and market transactions.

In the case of the grower, many coordinating agencies have been devised. One device is the formation of a marketing cooperative to handle the farmers' sales of oranges to the fresh and processor markets. Most cooperatives work on a "price pool" basis. The cooperative keeps a record of the "solid content" of each grower's deliveries. The cooperative does not price each grower's oranges as they are delivered to the cooperative or to a processor, but rather pools all the sales over a time period that covers the early varieties for one period and the late varieties for another. In this way each member of the cooperative receives the *average* price of the pool for the pound solid quantities he delivered. It is no longer important to the grower whether or not he delivers his crop at a high priced or low priced period of the harvest. The pool enables each member to average out the enormous price swings that take place within a crop year. The farmers' cooperative that is integrated forward into processing not only provides average pricing but may permit more efficient and integrated procurement operations of the processing segment of the firm. (Cost statistics of the industry indicate that cooperatives, on the average, have lower processing costs than competitors — partly because of lower non-union labor costs and partly because of procurement-processing coordination.)

Many arrangements have also been devised by the processor to improve his coordination within the total Florida orange system. In order to improve procurement operations by maintaining a flow of raw material to the plant, some processors have resorted to backward integration in the form of actual ownership or lease of orange groves. Others have developed their own cooperatives which have benefited both the grower members who have a regular outlet for a branded product and the processor who has a "captive" supply.[16] The processor has also developed forward contractual relationships with food retailers through volume sales agreements and private label arrangements.

The retailer, too, has been pleased to have the protection of volume contracts and the merchandise alternative of developing his own private label.

In addition, the interest of the Florida Citrus Com-

---

[15] USDA, Farmer Cooperative Service, *Coordinated Marketing for Florida Fresh Citrus Shippers,* p. 20.

[16] Although ownership of a grove will not protect the integrated processor from frosts and hurricanes, it will provide him with "more" of a "guaranteed" supply than he would have if he were not integrated.

mission, Florida Citrus Mutual, and the U.S. Department of Agriculture in providing some price stability to the industry provides a certain investment protection to the farmer, the outside investor, and the integrated processor in the orange system. Also these agencies are working on product and market development and are providing a central intelligence system that enables the cash market and the various contractual arrangements to function more smoothly and efficiently. The development of an orange concentrate futures market in October 1966 is already proving to be a useful market and time extender in the planning of operations within the orange system as well as in providing outside investors with an opportunity to share a portion of the inventory risks involved. In addition, the development of an inventory pool, if provided with means of disposing of as well as adding to inventory, should also be a useful balancing device that will enable the participants of the system to address themselves to other functions than preoccupation with inventory management. The proposed market agreement should also provide *temporary* relief while the industry makes more realistic adjustments to the new higher production levels.

Fortunately, most of the long range programs are consumer-oriented and are aimed at the improvement of quality and the development of new products as well as providing a well-thought-out marketing mix of promotional activities to use in the growing battle for the consumer's dollar. In many ways, the orange industry system is the epitome of the maximum use of coordinating devices.

Thus far, the examination of this industry structure indicates a technological innovation that (1) added to the vertical integration of the industry and to the development of large-scale processors and producers and (2) fitted into an already highly coordinated commodity enterprise composed of state commissions, federal marketing orders, and grower and processor industrywide associations.

In order to complete our overall examination of the Florida orange industry, let us turn to an analysis of the behavioral and performance patterns of the market system of the Florida orange complex.

X

Behavioral and Performance Patterns of the Florida Orange Economy

THE PURPOSE of Chapter X is to describe, in a highly selective manner, the behavioral and performance patterns of the Florida orange system. What types of behavior by firms and institutions determine the overall behavioral patterns of the orange complex? What performance results from the structural and behavioral patterns of the orange complex as indicated by the profitability, price stability, competition, and adaptability of the parts and the whole orange industry?

BEHAVIORAL PATTERNS

STORAGE

The orange harvest does not take place in a brief period of time as does the harvesting of wheat and soybeans but is extended over a period of nine months, in the fall, winter, and spring, depending on the orange varieties. Because it is too costly and impractical to store fresh fruit, the processing industry in Florida must be geared to operate on a 24-hour basis during the major harvest periods. The build-up stocks of frozen orange concentrate either in bulk drums or in consumer 6-ounce and 12-ounce cans during peak processing periods are drawn down during periods of plant shut-down. California oranges consist of two crops (navel and valencia) which permit availability in fresh form throughout a large part of the year.

The build-up in inventories of frozen orange concentrate reached a peak in July 1962 of 69 million gallons. The inventories expanded most rapidly in bulk and institutional form (55 gallon drums and 32-ounce cans) in 1962 (see Exhibit X-1) which permitted maximum inventory flexibility and allowed processors to buy stocks from one another without

having them in retail-labeled 6-ounce and 12-ounce cans.

Exhibit X-1 shows the drawing down of inventories after the freeze in December 1962 and the maintenance of the new proportion of bulk and institutional inventories to retail-sized inventories. The maintenance

EXHIBIT X-1

Inventories of Frozen Orange Concentrate on or around September 1: 1960–1964

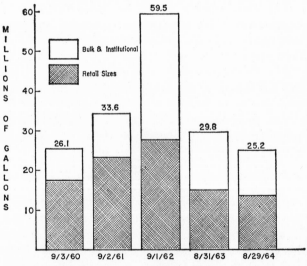

SOURCE: Florida Canners Association.

of bulk and institutional supplies of a significant quantity even in years immediately following a major freeze has led some industry leaders to look to two institutions as potential aids to inventory management of the frozen orange concentrate industry. One institutional suggestion is for a cooperative frozen orange concentrate inventory pool plan (outlined in Appendix Exhibit X-1) to help even out the wide production and price swings of the industry.

The inventory pool plan was outlined in June 1966 and its principal provisions called for the establishment of a cooperative organization composed of growers and processors of Florida orange products. The purpose was to acquire and store, if necessary, bulk concentrate in periods of "excessive" supplies and to sell in periods of shortage. In December 1966 the crop estimate of 142 million boxes of oranges for the State of Florida led to the temporary abandonment of this proposal. A marketing agreement for Florida orange concentrate was suggested in its place. A hearing was held on December 19, 1966, on the proposed agreement. The following provisions were suggested:

(1) The marketing agreement would cover only concentrate from the 1966–1967 crop year.

(2) No more than 15% of the total concentrate produced in 1966–1967 would be required to be disposed of in *secondary markets* (public and private schools, charitable institutions, underdeveloped markets, and other "non-normal" markets).

(3) At least one-half of the concentrate for secondary markets would have to be disposed of by December 1, 1967, and the remainder by December 1, 1968.

(4) The program would be administered by a Concentrate Marketing Board, composed of members representing the concentrate processors who sign the agreement.

(5) The Secretary of Agriculture approved it, but did not submit it for final approval by the concentrate processors because of lack of support.

(6) Processors of at least 80% of the concentrate produced in Florida in the 1965–1966 season would have to sign before the agreement became effective.

(7) The Florida Citrus Mutual reported that as of December 8, 1966, the agreement had the tentative support of the Mutual organization and the following processors: Pasco Packing Co.; Plymouth Citrus Products Cooperative; Golden Gem Growers, Inc.; Adams Packing Assoc. Inc.; B. & W. Canning Co., Inc.; Holly Hill Fruit Products Co. Inc.; Florida Fruit Products, Inc.; Treesweet Products Co.; and Cypress Gardens Citrus Products, Inc. Several of these processors changed their minds and the program was not instituted.

The mere suggestion of the marketing agreement together with Secretary of Agriculture Freeman's statement that the USDA will make "substantial" purchases of orange concentrate for the school lunch program has helped to keep the price levels of orange concentrate from declining to disaster levels. The inventory pool suggestion has not received as strong support from all segments of the industry because of a fear by many participants that the pool will serve as a price depressor rather than price stabilizer and/or that political pressure will be developed that will make it difficult for inventories in the pool to be reduced.

The other suggestion was the establishment of a futures market for frozen orange concentrate so that various participants in the Florida industry could hedge their inventory requirements and make a profitable analysis of the "basis" (relationship between cash and futures prices) for each particular firm's inventory position in the industry. Such a market was established on October 26, 1966. (See Section V for an analysis of the new futures market.) As of 1967 the orange concentrate market has been used effectively by many participants in the orange system. It has developed speculative interest. In addition deliveries have been made against contract in a satisfactory manner.

As noted in previous discussions, the processor holds most of the concentrate inventory for the retailer. A further analysis indicates that the in-store inventory of orange concentrate processors was less than that of those supplying competing products during the June–July 1964 period. For example, during that period chain stores had an inventory on hand of a 12.9-day supply of frozen orange concentrate, a 21.1-day supply of Awake, and a 25.7-day supply of all other frozen orange *drink* concentrates. The independent grocers had a similar pattern — a 15.9-day supply of frozen orange concentrate, a 19.4-day supply of Awake, and a 26.0-day supply of all other frozen orange *drink* concentrates.

One may say that the comparison is unfair because one is measuring a slower mover against a faster one and against a conglomerate of products. Nevertheless, it would appear that inventory management has been a strong element in the successful distribution of frozen orange concentrate.

PRICING

Exhibit X-2 sets forth the margins required to cover specific processing and transportation costs[1] of frozen orange concentrate and retail margins, assuming a standard percentage retail gross margin (22%) applied to various retail prices per 6-ounce can of frozen

---

[1] See Appendix Table X-1 for processing and warehousing costs.

EXHIBIT X-2

Returns to Orange Grower at Various Retail Prices
per 6-Ounce Can of Frozen Orange Concentrate:
1965

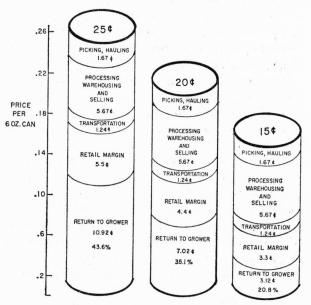

SOURCE: *Florida Citrus Mutual Triangle* May 21, 1965.

orange concentrate. The residual after these costs and margins are deducted would be the return available to the grower. At a 15-cent level, the grower would receive 3.12 cents per can, or $1.06 per box on-tree price which roughly approximates his cost of production. Exhibit X-3 indicates that in the ten years 1955–1964 a 15-cent price was reached only once for a brief period of time. However, in late January 1967

EXHIBIT X-3

Average Retail Price per 6-Ounce Can of Frozen
Orange Juice Concentrate and Cost to Consumer per
6-Ounce Serving: 1955 to 1964 Seasons

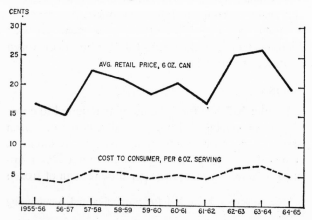

SOURCE: *Florida Citrus Mutual.*

the retail price was averaging approximately 13 cents per can.

Furthermore, Exhibit X-4 indicates that only during the market glut of late 1962, just before the freeze, did on-tree box prices dip below the $1.06 breakeven point. With the huge production of 142 million boxes forecast for the 1966 season, on-tree box prices dropped severely, and the cash on-tree box price reached 56 cents a box in late January 1967.

The spot pricing patterns for the grower not only fluctuate greatly because of great production shifts, but the average prices are also subject to a multitude of pool and purchase contract agreements discussed earlier in this chapter. These arrangements result in an overwhelming majority of Florida processed oranges purchased on a noncash price basis, overall settlements being made with the grower at the end of the season. Cash advances are made from time to time but do not necessarily bear a relationship to the cash market at that particular moment of payment. Many

EXHIBIT X-4

Average Price of Florida Oranges[a] and Equivalent
Returns per Box Received by Growers at Packing
House Door[b] and On-Tree Price: 1960–1964

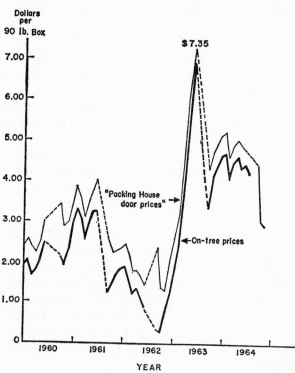

[a] Florida oranges include temples, other early and midseason, and valencias.
[b] Prices are a composite for all oranges, fresh and processed, available at the packing house door.
SOURCE: USDA, Statistical Reporting Service, *Agricultural Prices,* January 1960–January 1965.

advances under participation plans, however, provide for a payment on delivery which is related to the "Florida Canners' weekly or estimated season average for priced fruit." A common payment is 80% of the canners' average.

TABLE X-1. Price and "Nonprice" Statistics for Florida Processor Procurement of Oranges for Frozen Orange Concentrate by Type of Market: 1964 Season[a]

Market	Total no. of boxes (thousands)	Price per box	% of total market
Spot	4,765	$3.16	8.7%
Contract	9,406	3.40	17.3
Bulk	1,622	3.84	3.0
Subtotal Priced	15,793	$3.37	29.0%
Participation Agreements	11,100	—	20.4%
Cooperative Pools, etc.	27,575	—	50.6
Subtotal Nonpriced	38,675	—	71.0%
Grand Total Priced and nonpriced	54,468	—	100.0%

[a] Above prices and quantities include only those reported by Florida Canners Association members.
SOURCE: Florida Canners Association.

Table X-1 summarizes processed orange price and nonprice relationships for the 1964 season. From Table X-1 one can note that some 38.7 million boxes out of a total of 54.5 million processed into frozen orange concentrate (about 71%) were sold on a *deferred formula price basis*. Of the 29% of the fruit that was priced (some 15.8 million boxes) only 4.8 million boxes were priced on a spot basis. In other words, less than 9% of the fruit sold for use in frozen orange concentrate was on a spot cash basis. This spot cash price was an important factor in determining the ultimate price settlement of the total *unpriced* orange sales of 38.7 million boxes because many cooperative pooling and corporate participation plans use the Florida Canners Association season price per box figures or the non-ad card price of various firms as a major formula determinant in arriving at prices for those under the pooling and participation plan contracts.

Another characteristic of the pricing of frozen orange concentrate is the price leadership usually attributed in an unofficial manner to the Pasco and Winter Garden processing firms. At the retail level, Minute Maid is the leading, and for that matter the only, significant national manufacturers' brand accounting for 16% to 23% of the market, with Birds-Eye a far distant second at 3% to 4% of the market. Most private label processors price their orange concentrate in relation to Minute Maid's; however, this

changes with competitive situations as we shall note in the final section of this chapter.

PERFORMANCE PATTERNS

PROFITABILITY

As noted in the pricing section above, Florida orange producers' average cost of production is $1.06 per on-tree box of oranges. The average yield is 337

TABLE X-2. Per Acre and per Box Costs, Returns,[a] and Other Data by Seasons for Groves Averaging Over 10 Years of Age: 1960 and 1961 Seasons

	1960	1961
Number of grove records	140	142
Total acres of records	3,579	3,667
Average acres per grove	26	26
Average age	34	34
Number of trees per acre	67	67
Percent of trees grapefruit	15.3%	15.7%
Boxes harvested per acre	302	337
Costs per *acre*:		
Labor, power and equipment	$ 98.82	$103.90
Fertilizer materials	71.02	66.75
Spray and dust materials	34.83	36.53
State and county taxes	16.72	19.44
Miscellaneous	8.64	14.80
Total operating costs	230.03	241.42
Interest on grove valuation at 6%	87.53	94.51
Total cost without owner supervision	317.56	335.93
Returns per *acre*:		
Returns from fruit	$691.39	$546.12
Net returns	373.83	210.19
Returns above operating costs	461.36	304.70
Costs per *box*:		
Labor, power, and equipment	$ .33	$ .31
Fertilizer materials	.24	.20
Spray and dust materials	.11	.11
State and county taxes	.05	.06
Miscellaneous	.03	.04
Total operating costs	.76	.72
Interest on grove valuation at 6%	.29	.28
Total cost without owner supervision	1.05	1.00
Returns per *box*:		
Returns from fruit	$ 2.29	$ 1.62
Net returns	1.24	.62
Returns above operating costs	1.53	.90

[a] Note that 15% of trees on groves were grapefruit and were included in cost and return per box figures.
SOURCE: Florida Agricultural Experiment Station, *Movement of Citrus Trees from Florida Nurseries, July 1, 1928 to June 30, 1963.*

boxes per acre for groves averaging *over* 10 years (see Table X-2).[2] The cost of production includes an in-

[2] Note that 15% of trees on groves were grapefruit, and grapefruit were included in the cost of production and in the returns from fruit.

terest on grove valuation of 6% (grove valuation in 1961–1962 was approximately $1,500 per acre). The average return *above* production costs and grove valuation for 1960–1961 and 1961–1962 was approximately $1 a box ($1.24 for 1960–1961 and $0.62 for 1961–1962), or approximately $300 an acre on

TABLE X-3. Per Acre and per Box Costs, Returns,[a] and Other Data by Seasons for Groves Averaging 10 Years of Age and Under: 1960 and 1961 Seasons

	1960	1961
Number of grove records	63	64
Total acres of records	2,463	2,521
Average acres per grove	39	39
Average age	5	6
Number of trees per acre	74	75
Percent of trees grapefruit	1.3%	0.2%
Boxes harvested per acre	61	95
Costs per *acre*:		
Labor, power and equipment	$ 69.80	$ 72.87
Fertilizer materials	34.93	35.50
Spray and dust materials	10.98	13.01
State and county taxes	5.30	8.02
Miscellaneous	8.14	7.42
Total operating costs	129.15	136.82
Interest on grove valuation at 6%	47.22	57.81
Total cost without owner supervision	176.37	194.63
Returns per *acre*:		
Returns from fruit	$163.63	$180.58
Net returns	−12.74	−14.05
Returns above operating costs	34.48	43.76
Costs per *box*:		
Labor, power and equipment	$ 1.15	$ .77
Fertilizer materials	.57	.37
Spray and dust materials	.18	.14
State and county taxes	.09	.08
Miscellaneous	.13	.08
Total operating costs	2.12	1.44
Interest on grove valuation at 6%	.77	.61
Total cost without owner supervision	2.89	2.05
Returns per *box*:		
Returns from fruit	$ 2.68	$ 1.90
Net returns	−.21	−.15
Returns above operating costs	.56	.46

[a] Note that approximately 1% of trees on groves were grapefruit and were included in cost and return per box figures.
SOURCE: Florida Agricultural Experiment Station, *Movement of Citrus Trees from Florida Nurseries, July 1, 1928 to June 30, 1963.*

a $1,500 present market evaluation of the grove or a 20% return on investment over and above a 6% return on interest on the grove valuation. This return on investment is overstated since the cost of administration by neither the grower-owner nor the absentee-owner is included in the cost estimate.

On the other hand, on groves averaging *10 years of age and under,* the cost of production[3] (including a 6% interest charge on grove valuation of $900 per acre) is approximately $2.50 per box (see Table X-3). The yield per acre is only approximately 75 boxes. The operators of these younger groves had a loss of from 15 cents to 20 cents per box during the 1960–1961 and 1961–1962 crop periods, or a loss of 1.7% on their capital employed. Thus, though grower returns seem excellent, the original investment is fairly high with a waiting period of several years for a return on investment. (On the other hand, the availability of capital from insurance companies and other institutions seems to be sufficient to encourage grove expansion.)

Processing profitability has been adversely affected by the rapid fluctuations of the raw product and the extreme competition of retail private label operations. In some years, profits were abnormally high as the result of a freeze and the appreciation of inventory values; in other years irregular harvests or lack of raw materials adversely affected processing operations as noted in Table X-4, which gives processors' margins

TABLE X-4. Florida Frozen Orange Juice Concentrate F.O.B. Prices of Unadvertised Brands, Average Processing Cost, and Average Processor Margin, per 48/6-ounce Case: 1954–1963 Seasons

Season	Average f.o.b. price of unadvertised brands ($ per 48/6-oz. case)	Average total processing cost ($ per 48/6-oz. case)	Average processor margin ($ per 48/6-oz. case)	Processor margin as % of f.o.b. price
1954	$4.92	$4.4337	$0.4863	9.88%
1955	5.52	5.4540	0.0660	1.20
1956	4.68	4.6033	0.0767	1.64
1957	8.04	6.5814	1.4586	18.14
1958	7.40	7.2679	0.1321	1.79
1959	6.12	5.9705	0.1495	2.44
1960	7.12	7.3117	(0.1917)	(2.69)
1961	5.52	5.2067	0.3133	5.68
1962	9.52	8.3808	1.1392	11.97
1963	9.56	10.2506	(0.6906)	(7.22)

NOTE: Figures in parentheses denote losses.
SOURCE: Florida Agricultural Experiment Station, *Costs of Processing, Warehousing and Selling Florida Citrus Products* and *Futures Trading and the Florida Orange Industry;* Florida Canners Association, *Statistical Summary, Season of 1963-64* (mimeo.).

from 1954 to 1963. The profits fluctuated from a loss of 69 cents a case in 1963 to a profit of $1.46 in 1957. Table X-5 summarizes the financial data from Minute Maid's annual reports from 1950 through 1959 prior

[3] Note that 1% of trees on groves were grapefruit, and grapefruit were included in the cost of production and in the returns from fruit.

TABLE X-5. Selected Income and Balance Sheet Information for the Minute Maid Corporation: 1950–1959

Income statements (as of October 31)	1950	1951	1952	1953	1954
Net sales	$ 24,863,088	$ 28,634,222	$ 30,444,614	$36,373,743	$37,118,552
Cost of sales	20,305,355	21,198,185	22,897,036	28,395,222	29,874,604
Gross profit	$ 4,557,733	$ 7,436,037	$ 7,547,578	$ 7,978,521	$ 7,243,948
Selling, general and administrative expenses	4,187,660	4,739,917	4,684,650	5,208,974	5,127,320
Operating profit	$ 370,073	$ 2,696,120	$ 2,862,928	$ 2,769,547	$ 2,116,628
Interest expense	432,301	417,827	377,534	408,333	511,052
Income before provision for federal income taxes	($ 62,228)	$ 2,278,293	$ 2,485,394	$ 2,361,214	$ 1,605,576
Provision for federal income taxes	(5,114)	1,170,000	1,284,000	1,250,000	950,000
Net income or (loss)	($ 57,114)	$ 1,108,293	$ 1,201,394	$ 1,111,214	$ 655,576
Balance sheet information					
Inventories	$ 6,839,324	$ 6,246,147	$ 7,006,147	$ 6,203,452	$ 9,451,897
Fruit on trees	713,010	665,214	608,053	1,109,968	1,274,948
Total current assets	$ 20,321,231	$ 19,995,426	$ 19,795,970	$21,641,824	$24,716,288
Income statements (as of October 1)	1955	1956	1957	1958	1959
Net sales	$106,113,313	$114,225,131	$102,480,515	$99,024,474	$99,123,912
Cost of sales	77,198,976	85,490,297	83,026,603	72,568,750	69,553,563
Gross profit	$ 28,914,337	$ 28,734,834	$ 19,453,912	$26,455,724	$29,460,349
Selling, general, and administrative expenses	19,890,593	24,186,380	21,657,228	16,077,185	18,333,805
Operating profit	$ 9,023,744	$ 4,548,454	($ 2,203,316)	$10,378,539	$11,126,544
Interest expense	2,087,436	2,319,570	2,789,587	1,594,115	822,016
Income before provision for federal income taxes	$ 6,936,308	$ 2,228,884	($ 4,992,903)	$ 8,784,424	$10,304,528
Provision for federal income taxes	3,815,000	395,000	(2,450,000)	4,225,000	5,635,000
Net income or (loss)	$ 3,121,308	$ 1,333,884	($ 2,542,903)	$ 4,559,424	$ 4,669,528
Balance sheet information					
Inventories	$ 35,934,405	$ 49,058,776	$ 29,622,615	$14,752,098	$20,813,151
Fruit on trees	3,270,280	5,266,704	3,846,800	3,436,109	3,887,726
Total assets	$ 72,283,222	$ 90,611,872	$ 71,936,667	$62,027,843	$80,617,409

NOTE: Figures in parentheses denote losses.

to its merger with The Coca-Cola Company. These statements reflect both the growth of the industry and the widely fluctuating profit per unit of sales and per total investment. The reader will note Minute Maid's net loss figures in 1950 and 1957. Profits went from a loss of 2.5 million in 1957 to a profit of 4.7 million in 1959. In spite of the fluctuation in profits caused by the fluctuating price levels of orange raw materials and on-tree and in-process inventories, net profits averaged 3.23% return on total assets for the period from 1950 to 1959.

Typical of the problems of an orange concentrate processing firm are the following statements taken from Minute Maid's annual reports:

Last year's operations brought into sharp focus the problems of major concern to the management, and likewise the necessity for corrective action. Among these problems were:

1. An increasing share of the market was being taken over by unadvertised and captive or private labels.

2. Deliveries of raw fruit on a basis which would permit operation of our plants at maximum efficiency were becoming more difficult to obtain as a result of an industry trend on the part of growers to pre-season commitments of their fruit. During the processing season, it is essential to operate our plant on a 24-hour a day basis and inability to maintain a continuous flow of fruit results in costly shutdowns.

3. The company basically had but one product — an agricultural product — and thus its earnings could not be averaged out over a variety of items but were subject to unpredictable fluctuations arising from weather conditions or other factors over which we had no control.

Solution of the Problems

For some time your management has been convinced that two steps should be taken to alleviate these problems. One was to balance out fruit procurement between open market purchases, contract purchases, and our own production of fruit so that we could be reasonably sure of a steady supply of raw material. The other was to diversify the company's line. Diversification, we believed, would tend to stabilize earnings. Stabilized earnings would permit consistent advertising of the merits of our products, thus strengthening the demand for them.[4]

* * * * *

To accomplish the above two objectives, the company established a cooperative purchase program with growers in 1951 and began to diversify out of frozen concentrates in 1954.

The company entered into an agreement with Florida Orange Marketers, Inc., in 1957. FOM was a cooperative association of Florida citrus growers and agreed to supply Minute Maid with oranges for processing. The agreement was still in force by the end of 1966. In addition Minute Maid owned or leased 30,000 acres of groves of their own which supplied approximately one-third of their raw orange supplies. Another one-third is supplied by the cooperative and the remaining one-third from other suppliers.

The company acquired the Snow Crop Division of Clinton Foods, Inc. on December 1, 1954. This acquisition put the company into the businesses of frozen fruits and vegetables, Hi-C drinks, and institutional juices. Due to operating difficulties, however, the company on November 1, 1957 licensed Seabrook Farms, Inc. to manufacture and sell retail size frozen fruits and vegetables under the Snow Crop label. Thus, the company returned to a reliance on frozen concentrates under the Snow Crop and Minute Maid labels, with additional sales in the fruit juice line.

In September 1959 Minute Maid purchased all the outstanding capital stock of Tenco, Inc., one of the major producers of instant coffee in the United States.[5]

Profits at the retail level are difficult to put in proper perspective. The importance of private label operations, the varying strategies of corporate chains, and the different margin structures for the chains, independents, and voluntaries all complicate the analysis.

Utilizing the material [6] described on pages 88 and 141 of the wheat and soybean studies, one notes that the chain store material, as set forth in Exhibit IX-5, presents a picture of private label dollar volume dominance, and yet retailer net margin returns for leading manufacturers' brands on the average were higher than for private label.[7]

Exhibit X-5 also indicates that the net margin as a percent of sales for private label varied from a low of 3.5% in 1962 to a high of 7% in 1960. In contrast, manufacturers' brands provided the retailer with

[4] Minute Maid Corporation, *Ninth Annual Report,* 1954.
[5] *Fourteenth Annual Report,* 1959.
[6] The reader is cautioned to remember that this material represents only six retail food chain store operations in the U.S.
[7] In terms of *unit* sales, private label was even more important, ranging from a high of 78% of total unit sales in 1960 to a low of 73% in 1963 (the year of the freeze).

approximately 7% net margin on sales for the four-year period.

EXHIBIT X-5

Frozen Orange Juice Concentrate Dollar Sales and Net Margin as a Percent of Sales for Private Label and Leading Manufacturers' Brands in Selected Chain Stores: 1960–1963
(Companywide averages annually)

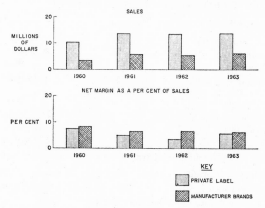

SOURCE: Six corporate food chains.

Exhibit X-6 and Table X-6 indicate a widening sales price discount by the private label operator in

TABLE X-6. Frozen Orange Juice Concentrate Prices and Margins for Private Label and Leading Manufacturers' Brands in Selected Chain Stores: 1960–1963 (Companywide averages annually in cents per 6-oz. can)

Private label	*1960*	*1961*	*1962*	*1963*
Average cost of 6-oz. can stocked in case	15.37	18.01	14.95	22.73
Average sales price	18.70	21.14	17.14	26.56
Shrinkage (0.5%)	.09	.11	.08	.13
Margin	3.24	3.02	2.11	3.70
Cost allocation to this item	1.86	1.97	1.52	2.20
Net margin	1.38	1.05	.59	1.50
Manufacturers' brands				
Average cost of 6-oz. can stocked in case	17.49	20.75	17.44	26.18
Average sales price	22.56	25.75	21.37	31.92
Shrinkage (0.5%)	.11	.13	.11	.16
Margin	4.96	4.87	3.82	5.58
Cost allocation to this item	3.11	3.22	2.45	3.66
Net margin	1.85	1.65	1.37	1.92

SOURCE: Six corporate food chains.

order to maintain his volume of sales. This discount increased from 3.5 cents per 6-ounce can under the leading manufacturers' brands in 1960 to approximately 5 cents under the leading manufacturers' brands in 1963. Although allocated store costs per unit were higher for the manufacturers' brands (on a margin percentage basis), the manufacturers' brands *on the average* still produced larger net margins per unit for the retailer than did private label brands.

EXHIBIT X-6

Frozen Orange Juice Concentrate Prices and Margins for Private Label and Leading Manufacturers' Brands in Selected Chain Stores: 1960–1963

(Companywide averages annually)

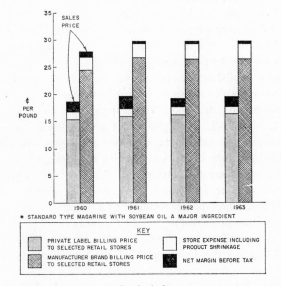

* STANDARD TYPE MARGARINE WITH SOYBEAN OIL A MAJOR INGREDIENT

KEY

PRIVATE LABEL BILLING PRICE TO SELECTED RETAIL STORES

STORE EXPENSE INCLUDING PRODUCT SHRINKAGE

MANUFACTURER BRAND BILLING PRICE TO SELECTED RETAIL STORES

NET MARGIN BEFORE TAX

SOURCE: Six corporate food chains.

As was found in the studies of bread and margarine, there are many individual company differences, as well as division and store differentials. Exhibit X-7 and Table X-7 indicate the wide differences in the ranges of the prices and margins of the individual chains in this study. One must note that some *individual* chains were able to provide better profit margins for their private labels than for the manufacturers' brands. Also in 1962 wise inventory purchases provided an excellent margin for private label retailers (such inventory profit was common to all segments of the orange concentrate industry from producer to retailer).

These examples, once again, seem to indicate that even with a product that appears to have unique properties — the consistency of the material, eye appeal, color, taste, appearance, and uniformity — nevertheless, specification buying and quality control enable the retailer to move large volumes of private label frozen orange concentrate. The retailer is motivated, as was true with bread and margarine, by his desire for a low price image, by his need to put competitive pressure on the manufacturer, and by his attempt to

TABLE X-7. Frozen Orange Concentrate Ranges of Prices and Margins for Private Label and Leading Manufacturers' Brands in Selected Chain Stores: 1960–1963

(In cents per 6-oz. can)

Private label		1960	1961	1962	1963
Average cost of 6-oz. can	Low	14.47	14.81	14.17	13.04
stocked in case	High	15.72	18.85	15.29	24.01
Average sales price	Low	18.00	19.89	16.41	20.04
	High	20.42	22.00	21.86	27.68
Shrinkage (0.5%)	Low	.09	.10	.08	.10
	High	.10	.11	.10	.14
Margin	Low	3.06	1.30	1.52	2.45
	High	5.32	5.26	7.05	6.90
Cost allocation to this	Low	1.41	1.07	.90	1.48
item	High	2.95	3.62	3.51	4.71
Net margin	Low	.52	.23	.17	.15
	High	2.37	1.92	3.54	3.63
Manufacturers' brands					
Average cost of 6-oz. can	Low	16.79	18.01	15.24	19.72
stocked in case	High	18.28	22.29	20.63	28.60
Average sales price	Low	21.33	21.46	20.07	24.32
	High	23.01	27.00	23.41	33.15
Shrinkage (0.5%)	Low	.10	.10	.10	.10
	High	.11	.14	.12	.17
Margin	Low	4.40	2.96	2.66	4.38
	High	6.04	6.65	5.68	6.88
Cost allocation to this	Low	1.41	1.35	1.08	1.48
item	High	4.35	4.80	3.70	5.76
Net margin	Low	.83	.05	.81	.53
	High	3.04	2.40	2.04	3.32

SOURCE: Six corporate food chains.

EXHIBIT X-7

Frozen Orange Juice Concentrate Net (before tax) Margins Realized for Private Label and Leading Manufacturers' Brands in Selected Chain Stores: 1960–1963

(Range and weighted average of companywide net margins realized for the year)

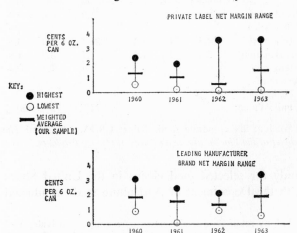

SOURCE: Six corporate food chains.

differentiate his food chain from others, either through quality, low price, or both,[8] generally at the expense of reduced overall margins for the product. On the other hand, many food chain operators have made excellent profits on private label usually because the buyer has been able to judge the volatile price swings of the market better than his competitors and makes his profit on procurement rather than merchandising.

These data also indicate that frozen orange concentrate manufacturer brands provide greater profit per 6-ounce can of frozen orange concentrate to the retailer than private label because of the ability of some manufacturers of brands to differentiate their products and maintain quality. Some retailers, however, through contractual relationships, have developed a private label product of similar quality. The premium that the manufacturers' brands earn is shared by the manufacturer with the retailer. There is no altruism here. The retailer puts pressure on the manufacturer of brands through the use of private label brands to encourage this "sharing" with all retail outlets. On the other hand, the retailer has had to cut his private label price by an average of 5 cents per can in order to move large volumes of private label orange concentrate.

Table X-8 compares the data developed in this

TABLE X-8. Orange Concentrate Prices and Margins for Private Label and Leading Manufacturers' Brands in Selected Food Chains: 1963, and U.S. Department of Agriculture's Selected Metropolitan East Coast Prices and Margins: 1962–1963

(In cents per 6-oz. can)

	USDA 1962–1963			Six food chains 1963		
	Manufacturers' brand	Private label	Difference	Manufacturers' brand	Private label	Difference
Retail price	30.1	25.0	5.1	31.9	26.6	5.3
Billing price to stores	24.5	21.3	3.2	26.2	22.7	3.5
Gross margin	5.6	3.7	1.8	5.7	3.9	1.8
Net margin	—	—	—	1.9	1.5	0.4
Percent of chain store unit volume:				27%	73%	100%

SOURCE: Six corporate food chains; USDA, ERS, and *The Impact of the Florida Freeze on Prices of Orange Products*.

study for selected food chains in the United States with the Department of Agriculture study conducted

in selected East Coast cities.[9] The data are not only comparable in general magnitude, but match closely with respect to both the leading manufacturers' brand and private label categories. One major discrepancy is in the item, "billing price to stores." This can be explained by the use of f.o.b. Florida processor prices for the USDA study, and the use of delivered store-door prices in the food chain study. The retail price differences can be accounted for by the more limited geographic sample of the USDA study and the slightly different time period.

This same USDA study[10] revealed that during the Florida freeze period (December 1962) the affiliated and unaffiliated independent retailers responded much less rapidly to processors' price changes than did the multi-establishments (chains). Individual establishments of both categories of independents followed diverse pricing strategies. These trends are summarized in Exhibit X-8. Also note that the advertised (manufacturers') brands through quality and promotion differentials were able to command a premium during most of the sample time period. Undoubtedly, during the December 1962 and January 1963 period when advertised brands were selling at a discount f.o.b. the plant, the processors probably increased their share of the retail or wholesale market or succeeded in building up the inventories of their concentrates in the hands of the wholesalers and retailers.

The difference in the price behavior of advertised (manufacturers') brands and unadvertised brands (private label) as shown in Exhibit X-8 was caused by two major factors. The most important was the fact that when the freeze occurred, Minute Maid tried to assess the effect of the freeze on supply before it raised its prices to the very high levels. The rest of the industry moved almost immediately and for a while there were periods when the unadvertised brands were actually higher than Minute Maid on an f.o.b. basis. The second factor was the annual Rose Bowl promotion of Minute Maid which meant that there was a promotional allowance in effect during the last part of December 1962 and the first two weeks of January 1963, a factor which lowered Minute Maid's price relative to private label offers.

An unpublished Ph.D. thesis "Demand and Substitution Relationships for Frozen Orange Concentrate"[11] indicated different price elasticities for different categories of brands. The results show that for nationally advertised brands the price elasticity was

---

[8] Many retail food chains have more than one private label orange juice concentrate appealing to price and quality motivations.

[9] USDA, ERS, *The Impact of the Florida Freeze on Prices of Orange Products*, p. 20.

[10] *Ibid.*, p. 21.

[11] Kenneth R. Henderson, University of Florida, June 1965.

2.3, for private label 2.6, and for packers' label 4.4. The tentative conclusions that the facts would indicate are that the brand loyalty for both an advertised and a private label brand is stronger than packers' label and sales increases or decreases of a given volume require more severe price changes for packers' and private label than for the manufacturers' advertised brands. As stated above, it seemed necessary for the retailers' brands of orange concentrate to be 5 cents a can below the price of the leading manufac-

EXHIBIT X-8

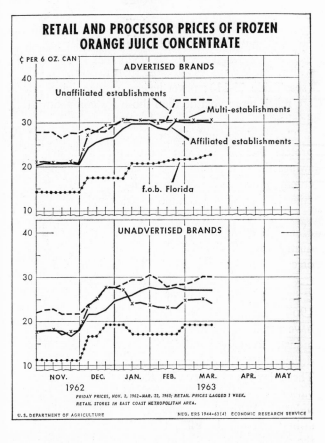

RETAIL AND PROCESSOR PRICES OF FROZEN ORANGE JUICE CONCENTRATE

¢ PER 6 OZ. CAN

ADVERTISED BRANDS

Unaffiliated establishments

Multi-establishments

Affiliated establishments

f.o.b. Florida

UNADVERTISED BRANDS

NOV. DEC. JAN. FEB. MAR. APR. MAY
1962 1963

FRIDAY PRICES, NOV. 2, 1962–MAR. 22, 1963; RETAIL PRICES LAGGED 1 WEEK. RETAIL STORES IN EAST COAST METROPOLITAN AREA.

U.S. DEPARTMENT OF AGRICULTURE   NEG. ERS 1944–63 (4) ECONOMIC RESEARCH SERVICE

turers' brands in order to move a large volume of private label.

Even though frozen orange concentrate is a highly competitive item for a food retailer to handle, it still is an excellent profit item in terms of returns per square foot of display space per week. Table X-9 indicates that frozen orange concentrate has the lowest gross margin for major product categories in the frozen food departments of eight New England stores. However, frozen orange concentrate averaged the highest dollars of sales per square foot of display space per week ($23.62), and accounted for 21.1% of the total sales volume of the frozen food department dur-

ing the time of this study.[12] The data indicate that rapid turnover of this product produces excellent profits for the retailer.

In summary, this mass of price and cost data indicates a wide range of competitive strategies among individual food chains, voluntary chains, and independent food store retailers. The data from the six

TABLE X-9. Sales, Margins, and Turnover by Product Group, Eight-Week Experimental Test, Eight Frozen Food Departments in Eight New England Chain Stores: 1961

Product group	Sales	Gross margins	Sales per square foot of display space per week
Drinks	27.6%	21.7%	19.64%
Orange juice	21.1	18.6	23.62
All others	6.5	31.7	6.73
Vegetables	15.4	24.4	7.28
Peas	2.7	22.9	7.79
All others	12.7	24.8	7.18
Dinners	9.9	26.6	12.43
Fish	8.0	28.9	8.16
Prepared foods	7.8	27.4	9.13
Potatoes	7.7	25.4	8.19
French fries	4.4	27.0	8.43
All others	3.3	23.2	7.88
Bakery	7.6	26.2	5.25
Meat pies	6.7	18.8	12.68
Meat and poultry	4.9	27.7	11.66
Fruits	4.4	27.1	9.54
Total department	100.0%	24.8%	9.72%

SOURCE: USDA, ERS, *Frozen Foods, Margins, Costs, and Returns in Relation to Display Space,* July 1965.

corporate food chains not only varied from one chain to another and among divisions of the same food chain but also among individual local store managements. The profitability aspects of the findings are interesting, primarily because of the wide disparity of results rather than because of significant differences from one set of stores to another. The disparity in these results may reflect differences in bookkeeping methods, special situations, innovation, or a combination of various differentiating elements in the conduct of business.

The diversity and the wide range in earnings that resulted is at the very heart of the ferment that keeps our economy resourceful and eager.

The accounting records to which we have had access were not refined or homogeneous enough to warrant more than tenuous and temporary conclusions about comparative profitability in individual situa-

[12] USDA, ERS, *Frozen Foods, Margins, Costs, and Returns in Relation to Display Space,* July 1965.

TABLE X-10. Florida Orange and Orange Concentrate Price Changes: 1960–1963

| | Oranges per 90-lb. box[a] | | | | | Orange concentrate per 6-oz. can[b] | | | | |
| | Average price | High | Low | Difference between high and low | | Average price | High | Low | Difference between high and low | |
Year				In dollars	As a %				In cents	As a %
1960	$2.74	$3.48	$2.29	$1.19	43.4%	22.5¢	23.3¢	21.9¢	1.4¢	6.2%
1961	3.27	4.11	2.27	1.84	56.3	24.6	25.9	23.3	2.6	10.6
1962	1.93	2.49	1.35	1.14	59.1	20.9	24.1	19.6	4.5	21.5
1963	4.46	7.35	2.06	5.29	118.6	30.4	32.8	24.7	8.1	26.6

[a] Equivalent returns per box received by growers at packing house door. Florida oranges include temples, other early and mid-season varieties, and valencias. Prices are a composite of all oranges, fresh and processed, available at packing house door.

[b] Average retail prices, selected U.S. cities.

SOURCE: USDA, Statistical Reporting Service, *Agricultural Prices*, January 1960–63; ERS, *Fruit Situation*, October 1964.

tions. The essential point is that change and adjustment are continuous, sensitive, and responsive.

PRICE STABILITY

As noted earlier in this chapter (1) the harvest season, (2) the geographical concentration of the crop, (3) the long-time investment in orange groves before they become productive, and (4) the hazards of a rapid change in climatic conditions all provide an environment conducive to volatile price movements.

The prices the grower is paid for his oranges are especially volatile because of quantity and quality changes. Table X-10 demonstrates the wide swings that occurred within each year for oranges delivered to the packing house door for the years 1960–1964. The changes between years are equally dramatic as indicated in Table X-11.

TABLE X-11. Florida Orange and Orange Concentrate Yearly Price Changes: 1960–1963

| | Oranges per 90-lb. box[a] | | | Orange concentrate per 6-oz. can[b] | | |
| | Average price | Yearly change | | Average price | Yearly change | |
Year		In dollars	As a %		In cents	As a %
1960	$2.74	—	—	22.5¢	—	—
1961	3.27	+$0.53	+ 19.3%	24.6	+2.1¢	+ 9.3%
1962	1.93	− 1.34	− 41.0	20.9	−3.7	−15.0
1963	4.46	+ 2.53	+131.1	30.4	+9.5	+45.4

[a] Equivalent returns per box received by growers at packing house door. Florida oranges include temples, other early and mid-season varieties, and valencias. Prices are a composite of all oranges, fresh and processed, available at packing house door.

[b] Average retail prices selected U.S. cities.

SOURCE: USDA, Statistical Reporting Service, *Agricultural Prices*, January 1960–63; ERS, *Fruit Situation*, October 1964.

Because of the regidities of processing and marketing costs and the desire on the part of the processor and the retailer to provide the consumer with some kind of stable price level throughout the year, the retail price changes for frozen orange concentrate throughout a year are less volatile (see Table X-10) than prices for the raw orange. Also, the price changes of frozen orange concentrate from year to year (even with a freeze) are less volatile than raw orange prices (see Table X-11); nevertheless, orange juice prices are much more volatile than those for competing fruit drinks.

The producer and the processor have attempted to protect themselves from seasonal and annual price swings through pooling, cooperative, contractual, and common ownership arrangements. Similarly, the retailer has developed volume contracts with the processor for private label, packers' label, and manufacturers' brands of orange concentrate. All segments of the industry are still dissatisfied, even with this whole host of contractual arrangements. The build-up before the freeze, the inventory declines in 1965, and the recently estimated bumper crop of 142 million boxes for the 1966 season, together with volatile price movements, have acted as a stimulus to the businessmen of this industry to analyze and develop new additional market devices; namely, futures markets and pool reserves. These devices may broaden the market alternatives at various times and narrow the price swings for the industry. With the possibility of less drastic price swings through the utilization of these devices comes the additional hope that management will have greater incentive to devote efforts to the development of new products and new ways of distributing present products and will have less preoccupation with inventory management. Obviously prices are supposed to fluctuate in order to equalize supply and demand. What the producer, processor, and retailer want is a buffer stock to help out as a balancing mechanism between years of glut and shortage and a futures market to allow inventories to be better hedged over time.

COMPETITION

Ease of Entry and Exit. The growth of the Florida orange grove industry has been stimulated by the availability of large quantities of outside capital from institutions such as insurance companies and other investment sources and by the backward integration of firms such as Minute Maid. In terms of producing oranges, there seems to be very little limitation on entering or exiting from the industry in spite of the high investment costs.

The Florida fresh citrus shippers had 182 independent and 4 cooperative entrants from 1951 to 1962; and 268 independent and 18 cooperative exits during the same period.[13] Again, no major restrictions seem to be evident.

In the processing industry there are also indications of a "free flowing" industry — 62 entries and 55 exits.[14] The increasing emphasis on the production of frozen orange concentrate and the decreasing emphasis on single strength and salad section processing caused the growth and decline in the number of firms in these two industries to take place. In recent years more stability seems to be evident in the processing industry. The overall *number* of *frozen orange concentrate plants* had only a minor increase from 27 in 1958 to 36 as of January 1965; however, the *capacity* of the Florida processing plants doubled during this period as Table X-12 shows. The 36 processing

TABLE X-12. Number of Processing Plants and Storage Capacity: 1958–1965

Date	Number of Florida concentrate processing plants	Capacity in pounds as measured by water vapor removal	Storage in cases of 48/6-oz. cans
Sept. 1958	27	965,255	26,148,000
June 1959	29	1,089,592	27,484,400
June 1960	29	1,162,955	30,210,400
Jan. 1961	30	1,226,200	30,675,400
Jan. 1962	31	1,219,900	32,099,400
Jan. 1963	34	1,456,700	35,384,391
Jan. 1964	36	1,584,700	39,088,594
Jan. 1965	36	2,001,400	39,404,594

SOURCE: Florida Canners Association.

firms were divided as follows: 5 cooperatives accounted for 25% of Florida's output; 7 conglomerately integrated firms accounted for 37% of the output; and 23 specialized orange firms accounted for 38% of the output.

Concentration. There is relatively little concentration in the production of oranges except for the 22,000

acres of groves[15] owned by the Minute Maid Division of The Coca-Cola Company. This ownership, together with its lease for 8,000 acres, represents only 7% of Florida's total orange bearing groves. Minute Maid obtains one-third of all its oranges for its processing operations from these 30,000 acres; another third is obtained from its associated cooperative; and the remaining third is obtained on the spot market.

In the handling of fresh oranges, concentration is also very slight with the three largest shippers accounting for 11% of all shipments, and the ten largest for 31%.

In the processing of frozen concentrate there is some concentration; one firm (Minute Maid's three plants), accounts for approximately 12% of the processing capacity. However, the presence of five cooperatives accounting for 25% of the processing output and the fact that 46% of the orange supplies for the processing industry are purchased from cooperatives are indicative of excellent competitive safeguards to the relatively strong market position of the Minute Maid Division of The Coca-Cola Company.

Despite the competition from the cooperatives, the Antitrust Division of the U.S. Department of Justice issued a complaint on September 7, 1955, concerning Minute Maid's acquisition of Snow Crop because it was felt that this acquisition might substantially lessen competition.[16] Prior to 1955 Minute Maid had 20% of the processing capacity and 15% of the sales of the national frozen orange concentrate market. With the purchase of Snow Crop, Minute Maid had 35% of the processing capacity and 25% of the sales volume. On the date the complaint was filed, Minute Maid signed a consent decree under which the company agreed to dispose of, as complete units, the frozen concentrate facilities located at Dunedin and Frostproof, Florida, which it acquired from Snow Crop. The decree also enjoined Minute Maid, for a period of five years, from acquiring, directly or indirectly, any stock or any other interest in any frozen concentrate facilities. Divestment of the facilities occurred in 1960. As of December 30, 1960, the Minute Maid Company merged into The Coca-Cola Company; the sales price was estimated to be $59 million.[17] For fiscal 1959 Minute Maid had a net profit of $4.7 million on net sales of $99 million or approximately an 8% return on investment.

---

[13] USDA, *The Florida Citrus Industry: Market Organization and Performance,* June 1963, p. 65.

[14] *Ibid.,* p. 68.

[15] Approximately 75% of the 30,000 acres controlled by Minute Maid is in oranges, the balance is grapefruit, tangerines, lemons, and other citrus fruits.

[16] USDA, Federal Trade Commission, *Economic Inquiry into Food Marketing, Part II The Frozen Fruit, Juice, and Vegetable Industry,* December 1962, p. 122.

[17] *Ibid.,* p. 123.

Minute Maid has not only been a strong market leader; it has supplied almost 100% of all advertising for frozen orange juice concentrate other than industry advertising by the Florida Citrus Commission. On October 5, 1965, Pepsi-Cola (The Coca-Cola Company's rival) announced its interest in entering the citrus field. The executives of Minute Maid have wanted other consumer-oriented firms to enter the industry because they feel that their present competitors have not improved their products or their packaging, and that they have treated their product as a commodity rather than as a specialized consumer beverage. Because so much of the Florida orange concentrate industry is in farmer-cooperative ownership, a normal tendency has been to be producer-oriented. Many such firms in the past have only desired to "move" their concentrate in as direct a manner as possible without anticipating new wants and needs of the consumer. Much of this producer orientation has led to volume contracts for private label — thus leaving the consumer orientation for the retailer to anticipate and manage. This attitude is changing. For example, Mr. Marvin Walker, General Manager of the Florida Citrus Consumers Cooperative in January 1967 stated: "No longer do the more progressive cooperatives limit themselves to marketing the farm products of their members. They are still farmer-oriented, but more and more they are becoming customer-oriented and profit-oriented." [18]

Retail private label buying power is especially strong in this industry and has added yet another dimension to the competitive strategies of the firms involved. The manufacturers' brands of frozen orange concentrate are sold in greater proportion to voluntary buying groups and independent retailers through frozen food distributors than are sold to retail food chains. This pattern of selling tends to increase the cost of distribution for the manufacturers of the branded product. (The disproportionate number of sales of white bread by national manufacturers to the smaller stores was evident in the wheat study.) The pattern of distribution of sales by seven diversified firms (primarily those that produce manufacturers' branded concentrate), by five cooperatives, and by eleven independent processors is summarized in Table X-13. The diversified food firms (manufacturers' brand) sold only 20% of their frozen orange concentrate to the ten largest chains and 16% to all other chains.

Table X-14 indicates that 80.6% of the sales of frozen orange concentrate from the diversified food firms was sold under their own manufacturers' brand.

[18] Statement before the Agricultural Policy Institute Conference, Raleigh, North Carolina, January 25, 1967.

TABLE X-13. Percentage Distribution of Sales of Frozen Orange Juice Concentrate for Three Classes of Florida Processors by Class of Customer: 1958–1959

Class of customer	Five cooperatives	Seven diversified food firms (manufacturers' brands)	Eleven others, mainly specialized citrus processors
Ten largest food chains	39.7%	20.2%	30.2%
All other food chains, 11 or more stores	17.5	16.0	9.9
Independent food stores and chains of 10 stores or less	4.1	4.4	4.2
Other retailers	.5	.3	4.2
Frozen food distributors	28.6	38.6	22.8
Mass feeding institutions	.8	4.2	.4
Manufacturers and processors	6.1	8.5	25.0
Used in further processing by same company	—	1.8	—
Exports	2.7	6.0	3.3

SOURCE: USDA, *Florida Citrus Industry: Market Organization and Performance*, June 1963, p. 70.

The sales of private label accounted for 12.4% of orange concentrate sales. The remaining orange concentrate sales from these diversified firms were in the form of bulk concentrate to other processors, institutions, or for export.

The eleven specialized concentrate processors relied on the ten largest chain stores for 30% of their frozen concentrate sales (Table X-13). These eleven firms also supplied the largest dollar volume of concentrate for private label sales by the top ten chains — some $24.7 million in 1958–1959 or 56% of the total sales of these eleven processors (see Table X-14). The other main outlets for these eleven processors were general frozen food distributors and other manufacturers and processors of concentrate that required additional production of orange concentrate.

The five cooperatives also had a distinctive market-

TABLE X-14. Percentage Distribution of Sales of Frozen Orange Juice Concentrate for Three Classes of Florida Processors under Manufacturers' Brands, Retailers' Brands, and as Bulk Concentrate: 1958–1959

Class of firm	Manufacturers' brands	Retailers' brands	Unbranded bulk
Five cooperatives	40.3%	55.1%	4.6%
Seven diversified food firms	80.6	12.4	7.1
Eleven mainly specialized citrus processors	28.8	56.0	15.2

SOURCE: USDA, *Florida Citrus Industry: Market Organization and Performance*, June 1963, p. 70.

TABLE X-15. Sales of Frozen Orange Concentrate from Florida Processors by Class of Customer and Form of Branding: 1958–1959

Class of customer	Value of sales (in thousands)	% of sales	% of total by form of branding Manufacturers' brands	Customers' brands	Unbranded
10 largest food chains	$ 76,281	27.5%	15.2%	53.8%	—
All other food chains (11 or more stores)	39,727	14.3	17.5	13.1	0.5%
Independent and small chains	11,839	4.3	5.3	3.6	0.50
Other retailers	4,442	1.6	1.5	2.1	0.22
Frozen food distributors	87,161	31.4	48.4	12.7	1.13
Mass feeding institutions	6,327	2.3	4.1	—	—
Manufacturers and processors	37,333	13.4	2.0	11.7	88.35
Used in other processes by same company	2,381	0.9	—	—	9.26
Exports	12,301	4.4	6.0	3.1	0.54
Other	41	—	0.3	—	—
Total	$277,833	100.0%	100.0%	100.0%	100.0%

SOURCE: USDA, *Florida Citrus Industry: Market Organization and Performance*, June 1963, p. 70.

ing pattern of their own. Some 57% of their total volume was purchased by food chains (see Table X-13), and 55.1% of their sales were in the form of private label sales (retailers' brand) to the chains (see Table X-14). On the other hand, 40.3% of the co-operatives' total volume sold was in the form of the cooperatives' own brands.

These buyer-seller relationships are further explained by the data in Table X-15. The reader will note that the ten largest food chains accounted for 53.8% of all customers' brand sales (private label) in the United States in 1958–1959. The next significant customers' brand volume was to "other food chains," followed closely by frozen food distributors selling to voluntary groups. Another interesting figure in this table is that $37.3 million of frozen orange concentrate out of total processor sales of $277.8 million (or over 13%) was sold to other manufacturers and processors. This latter volume could be orange concentrate used in chilled juices and soft drinks or it could be largely accounted for by the movement of concentrate from processor to processor as sales opportunities developed.

Another type of competition involved attempts by Panama and the Virgin Islands to allow development corporations to grow citrus, receive tax benefits, and import duty-free orange concentrate into the United States. Such an attempt was made on March 15, 1964, but was defeated when the Florida Citrus Mutual brought the situation to President Johnson's attention.[19] President Johnson would not approve the duty-free importation of this concentrate into the United States.

Adaptability. Thus far, the Florida orange industry could be considered a "lucky" innovator. Frozen

[19] See Appendix Exhibit X-2.

orange concentrate was developed by the combined research efforts of industry-government research teams at a time when orange production was rapidly increasing. This industry is most anxious to develop new products, processes, and packaging, and taxes itself to support its Citrus Commission, Florida Citrus Mutual, Canners Association, and private firm research. Sugar-sweetened orange concentrate, higher density concentrate, new packaging and promotion are evidence of the industry's product innovation. The rapid development of new and improved ways of processing orange concentrate to provide greater uniformity of product and better yields from the oranges has taken place under the urging of the progressive, far-sighted management policies of leading frozen concentrate firms as well as from the leadership of both private and public institutions.

SUMMARY

It would be redundant to list again the great variety of institutions and arrangements created by the managements of firms in the Florida orange system. Most of these institutions and arrangements were created out of the common desire to avoid production, procurement, market, inventory, and pricing problems and out of the common desire to plan for the market opportunities of the future. The volatile price movements, the uncertainties of supply, unusual inventory build-ups, competition from other fruit drinks, production and disease problems — all required the development of some arrangement, whether cooperative, contractual, or something else to average out price swings and inventory risks, and to coordinate the overall functions of the industry. The January 1967 build-up of orange grove production had every segment of the industry concerned about the industry's ability to maintain profitable price levels of the raw and processed products.

The maintenance of price levels for the raw material and the finished product may be more difficult when less than 10% of the supply is priced on the spot market, another 20% is priced on a cash market over a period of time, and the remaining 71% is unpriced except for contracts over a period of time. The 71% that is unpriced is eventually priced on a "pool structure" that utilizes as one of its pricing bench marks the 10% of the crop that is priced on the spot market. Other benchmarks include futures markets and other quotations.

The reporting of prices also leaves something to be desired. One or two processor price leaders will give their quotations to the Florida Citrus Mutual economist who acts as an "informal cash market" for the industry. Through the use of the telephone and newsletters the cash market is "reported" to the industry. At the retail level, it has been noted that each firm and each store within a firm has widely divergent policies that will affect the price level of the manufacturers' brand and private label orange concentrate. In many cases, Minute Maid and other firms will prepare an advertising and allowance program as well as attempt to show the operating margin advantage to the retailer for carrying their products. In some cases they are successful in establishing a price pattern, but for the most part the hodgepodge of private label competition and discount price activity adds up to a wide disparity of prices and profits, as noted earlier.

Diversified food firms, such as Minute Maid, are anxious to develop a more stable pricing pattern in the industry so that they, in turn, can offer the consumer frozen orange concentrate and related products at uniform prices in vending machines. Also, most ele-

ments of the industry want some market device to protect their inventory positions and dampen price fluctuations. (There are exceptions who like to "outguess" the market swings.)

The new orange concentrate futures market has the advantage of making more public all the pricing elements in the industry and the added advantage of inviting speculative interest to dampen the high and low price extremes. In addition to the futures market, the inventory pool proposal as part of a market order could offer a price stabilizing influence. In January 1967, 4 million gallons of orange concentrate had been purchased for the school lunch program by the Department of Agriculture; this market may point the way for the use of an inventory pool and "secondary market" allocation. Many people in the industry believe that the futures market will provide greater consumption of Florida orange products. The futures market, like any institution and arrangement (unless it is a government warehouse or private pool inventory) is not a customer, it is simply a market aid that broadens the time and geographical dimensions of the commodity.

As stated earlier, successful (profitable) decision making in an industry like the Florida orange industry is the result of management's strategy in adjusting to or changing its external environment. The tools for adjustment and change are the institutions created by or for managers.

The first three sections of this study have described who have used the coordinating institutions and arrangements of the wheat, soybean, and Florida orange industries, as well as how they have used them. The last section of this study will evaluate the use of specific coordinating devices by businessmen as they attempt to integrate their firms' functions into changing agribusiness systems.

Current Trends and Conclusions

XI

Critical Trends for Agribusiness Commodity Systems

THE FIRST four sections of this study have developed the concept of a commodity system and have described the structure and performance of the wheat, soybean, and Florida orange systems, the forces of change affecting them, and the responses of the participants to change. This last section of the study will examine probable future trends and the impacts of these developments on each of the three commodity systems.

Such an analysis should enable the manager to understand and to perceive more clearly the various opportunities for change. This latter ability necessitates the development of strategic long-range planning and a sophisticated management organization which will permit the firm to keep abreast of the rapidly changing outside influences. The organization must be kept flexible enough to change and to generate new and creative options for itself. In some cases the private manager will look beyond the immediate problems of his own firm to see the problems of the system as a whole. Such an analysis should enable a manager to help in the transition to another form of system that is more workable.

A few of the key trends and developments facing the participants in these commodity systems in the future are as follows:

(1) The growth of private labels and new types of market orientation.
(2) The growth of cooperatives and their new uses by both corporate and cooperative leaders.
(3) The new uses of government programs by business managers.
(4) The better utilization of trade associations in both action planning and strategic long-range planning by the private and public manager.
(5) The increasing emphasis on the world dimensions of the food economy.
(6) The further development of vertical and contractual integration.
(7) New uses of futures markets as market extenders.

Each of these and their impacts will be discussed in turn.

THE GROWTH OF PRIVATE LABELS AND NEW TYPES OF MARKET ORIENTATION

As the mass distribution system has developed in the United States through increasing urbanization, changes in transportation, and product innovation, tremendous incentives for mass processing, procurement, and agriculture production have arisen. Each commodity system historically has produced a wide range of consumer food products that have been able to meet changing and diverse consumer wants. The life cycles of these products generally have common characteristics. First, the branded manufacturer innovates and produces a unique product and then establishes a market for it by responding to or anticipating consumer demand. This new product with its unique and differentiated properties usually requires special technology and packaging in its production and makes maximum use of distribution channels in its market strategy. Once technological and product imitation becomes prevalent, the product becomes more of a commodity item, private labels become commonplace, and profit margins for the branded item decrease.

The example of margarine in this study is fairly typical of a life cycle of a branded item. First, advances in technology provided product differentiation, enabling brands to be established in satisfying a need, especially during the butter shortage of World War II. Eventually, knowledge of the new technology became widespread and margarine became more of a commodity and a "private label" item. The branded manufacturer had the choice of supplying private labels or of developing new types of packaging (soft margarine in a "tub," liquid margarine in a squeeze bottle), new types of the product (whipped margarine) or new types of margarine with different tastes and ingredient combinations of corn oil and safflower oil as well as soybean oil. Many of the margarine manufacturers followed the course of new developments and generally expanded the total market for both the branded and the private label products without the normal erosion of profit levels.

The evolution of bread handling in the United States is also typical of the changing nature of our competitive food system. Historically, in the United States, bread has moved from a purely local baker operation to a promoted mass produced product.

Stage One consisted of local grist mills with the women of the family baking the bread. For all practical purposes this stage no longer exists.

Stage Two was the development of the local bake shop which still survives on the basis of unique product qualities or consumer taste preferences.

Stage Three was the development of a branded uniform product that, on the whole, was cheaper to produce than the product of the local bakery. This bread had price appeal and uniformity of quality.

Later specialty breads were developed that catered to the desires of various groups. Such breads included Pepperidge Farm, Arnold, Anadama, and Levy Rye.

Bread has other properties that must be taken into consideration. It has to be baked and distributed daily to ensure freshness. The manufacturing plant must be in close proximity to the market. With improved superhighways, however, close proximity may mean as much as 100 miles away. Bread sales require an expensive daily distribution system that includes high commissions to delivery operators. Some of these delivery costs have been reduced by the development of drop-shipment deliveries from wholesale bakeries to central distribution points, but on the whole, these high distribution costs led to

Stage Four which is the food chain's private label bread operations that enable the chain to reduce the cost of handling and selling bread compared with the practices of wholesale bakery operations.

In addition, stage four received additional incentives from the Robinson-Patman Act because wholesale bakers found it difficult to make price concessions to large retail outlets, whereas retail food chains operating their own bakeries were in a much more flexible pricing position when selling private label bread to their own retail outlets.

As has been pointed out earlier, concentrated orange juice varies considerably in quality, and consumers develop certain preferences for a particular brand. For a retailer to overcome this preference, a severe price cut in a competing product is necessary, or a unique product has to be developed. There are also many types of product competition, such as fresh oranges, canned juice, reconstituted juice, and synthetic products. From a market structure point of view, there is a limited geographical area of production. In this unique food item many of the main processors have had to develop grower cooperatives in order to obtain the necessary quantity and quality of oranges. The quality and availability of the product are not consistent from year to year, resulting in wide quality and price variations which are of utmost importance in formulating merchandising policies. Price consciousness is important in the purchase of orange juice in general, and by the same token it is important in the choice between brands. Nationally about 35% of all frozen orange concentrate is sold under retail food distributors' private labels. Nationally advertised manufacturers' brands sell 25% of the total, and the remaining 40% of sales are primarily packer labels. One must also note that a specific retailer may have more than a single private label orange concentrate product. One private label product may appeal to one group of consumers on the basis of its taste; another to consumers who may want a product of uniform quality.

The product life cycle of orange concentrate is intertwined with the changing nature of the total commodity system of which it is a part. The original product came into being as an offshoot from the development of a process for dehydrated orange juice powder destined for military use during World War II. The Department of Agriculture and the Experiment Station of the University of Florida were also involved in developing an orange concentrate and suggested the cutback of single strength juice to reincorporate the aromatic and volatile components. The Minute Maid Company and The Snow Crop Corporation established a national market for the product, of which 85% of the sales were manufacturers' nationally advertised brands. Technology became accessible to competitors when the USDA laboratories provided free research to all firms. This resulted in products uniform enough to achieve a nondifferentiated status and led to a decline in the premium for nationally advertised brands. Distributors' private labeling expanded rapidly thereafter.

Once national markets became established by the branded manufacturers and knowledge of technology became widespread, all three commodity systems had "production pressure" to reckon with. In the cases of bread, margarine, and frozen orange concentrate, there has usually been excess capacity in the production of the raw products: wheat flour, soybean oil, and orange concentrate. Many manufacturers were anxious to make use of idle plant capacity and therefore offered private label products to food chains on a contribution to fixed investment cost basis. This competitive activity put pressure on those manufacturers to develop new, more easily differentiated food products. In fact, most manufacturers' brand firms have broadened their product lines to include new related food products that are more easily differentiated. In the case of margarine, new products and new packaging were achieved rapidly. In the case of frozen orange concentrate, most innovation has taken place with the development of synthetics. In the case of bread, a whole new frozen dough process has helped to broaden the variety of bread products available to the consumer.

Any weakness in the distribution or processing system results in the development of methods to change the food system. In the case of bread this enabled retailers to integrate bakery operations and save as much as 3 cents per one-pound loaf by avoiding a high cost delivery system.

As bread, margarine, and frozen orange concentrate became available as private label items, certain patterns emerged in the pricing and handling through retail distribution. These patterns reflected the influences of the total environment of the wheat, soybean and Florida orange commodity systems. Thus we have three generally distinct patterns.

In the six bread retailing operations studied, the gross margins were highest for the manufacturers' labels; the retailing expenses per unit were highest for the retailers' private label; and the resulting net margins were highest for the manufacturers' brand bread. In orange concentrate operations the retailers' gross margin, allocated costs, and net margin were all highest for the manufacturers' brands. In margarine, gross margins were approximately equal between private label and manufacturers' brands, allocated retailer costs were higher for the manufacturers' brands, and net margins were highest for the private label.

Why did these three patterns emerge? In the case of bread, a costly distribution system encouraged the food chain operators to manufacture and distribute their own private label bread. The general policy was to bill their retail outlets at a price high enough to show good manufacturing profits, and low enough to undercut the manufacturers' brands by 4 to 5 cents per loaf in order to sell large unit volumes of private label bread through their retail outlets. This one example also suggests that retail food chains that manufacture their own private label products may expect lower net margins for their private label products at retail than

they would if they purchased private label products from outside manufacturers.

In frozen orange concentrate, manufacturers' brands have demonstrated that in general they provide more net margin for the retailer than do private label products. An exception to this generalization is the food chain operator who is able to judge the volatile price swings of the market better than his competitors do, and makes a procurement profit.

Manufacturers' brands of frozen orange concentrate provide greater profit to the retailer than private label because of the ability of some brand manufacturers of brands to differentiate their products and to maintain quality through vertically integrated supply relationships. On the other hand, some retailers have developed a private label product of similar quality through contractual relationships. The premium that the manufacturers' brands earn is shared by the manufacturer with the retailer. There is no altruism here. The retailer puts pressure on the manufacturer of national brands through the use of private label brands in order to encourage this "sharing" with all retail outlets. On the other hand, the retailer has had to cut his private label price by an average of 5 cents per can in order to move large volumes of private label orange concentrate.

In the case of margarine, information about the new technology for the deodorizing and hardening of soybean oil was widely disseminated. Government laws on coloring became less restrictive, excess manufacturing capacity developed, and soybean oil margarine became a commodity closely tied to the soybean oil commodity markets. Nevertheless, private label retailers' brands had to be priced at 10 cents a pound under the leading manufacturers' soybean oil margarine brands in order to move a large unit volume of private label margarine. The high net margin for private label brand seems overstated because of the higher allocated retailing costs attributed to the manufacturers' brands by the six food chains in this study. The commodity orientation of margarine, however, puts a premium on single line manufacturing runs, transportation savings, and a wise use of soybean oil futures markets as well as margarine markets — all of which may also explain part of the favorable private label net margins for margarine as compared with the net margins for the manufacturers' brands.

In each of these cases it is perfectly clear that price is the primary appeal for the private label brands of bread, frozen orange concentrate, and margarine. A 5-cent discount on a 23-cent loaf of bread, a 5.5-cent discount on a 30-cent can of orange concentrate, and a 10-cent discount on a 29-cent pound of margarine indicate the magnitude of these price discounts. The price discount has had to be a substantial one in order for the retailer to obtain his major volume objectives.

There are several significant trends evident in the three product patterns of bread, margarine, and frozen orange concentrate:

(1) Irrespective of profitability food retailers will continue to carry private labels in order to be competitive with the private labels of competing food retailers, to provide a low cost image for the store, to provide price pressure on the national brand manufacturers, and to provide a traffic builder product at a reasonable price.

(2) Private label merchandising will probably expand in the future. As the U.S. mass food market expands and becomes concentrated in fewer and larger firms, more products will become suitable for private labeling. Food retailers are finding it more difficult to expand horizontally and have therefore been more experimental, shifting into food manufacturing as an alternative investment. Furthermore, the pricing problems of the national brand manufacturers under the Robinson-Patman Act provide an additional incentive for private label manufacturing by the food retailer.

(3) In general, manufacturing industries with excess manufacturing capacity and excessive raw material supplies tend to contribute to the growth of private label brands. During times of a shortage of either manufacturing capacity or raw materials, as a result of war or a freeze in a geographically concentrated crop such as Florida citrus, an increase in the proportion of manufacturers' brands occurs.

(4) The private label mechanism in all three commodity systems enables the small independent food manufacturer (with labor's cooperation) to have access to a mass market with minimum sales expense and to have the benefits of long production runs on a single specified product. The continual harassment of the larger manufacturers' brand firms by these small firms will put added pressure on the large manufacturers' brand firms for increased innovation and/or lower prices.

(5) The rise in the U.S. standard of living, the unique desires of the many segments of our population, and the imagination and innovation of U.S. food processors responding with new products and new services means that branded items will remain the dominant force in the growth of the grocery products industry. However, the control of shelf space by the retailer and the efficiencies of vertical or contractual integration will constantly serve as a defense against excessive product proliferation and will tend to hold down prices and profit margins. It will also stimulate the development of new differentiated products.

(6) The great diversity of these commodity systems, the multitude of institutions, arrangements, and social customs, and the manifold wants of the consumer seem to dictate a food system where both the brand manufacturer and the private label distributor will be successful.

The revolution of the food system in the United States has developed a great variety of strategies in each product line and has allowed each of them to be profitable. This seems to indicate that each firm in the U.S. food processing system has the choice of finding its place in satisfying a consumer product or service need, or of being a low priced competitor of a nondifferentiated product, using price as the main competitive weapon in seeking to be chosen by the consumer. If a firm cannot succeed in either of these broad alternative strategies, or a combination of both, then, of course it will no longer be a part of the food system.

(7) Private labels and manufacturers' brands are but one facet of a changing food system. Their successful use in serving the ultimate food consumers' requirements is related not only to the status of the consumer they are serving, but also to the size, number of firms, and coordinating arrangements of the commodity system of which they are a part. The legal, technological, and organizational aspects of the commodity systems that produce these products are as important as the differentiable qualities of the products.

In addition, once it becomes difficult to maintain product differentiation, then one of the strategies open to managers is to broaden their operations into products that are more easily differentiated — for example, orange concentrate into orange drinks ("Hi-C") and into the total "drink market," the merger of Minute Maid and the Coca-Cola and Duncan Foods operations (coffee); bread and flour operations into snack foods and cake mixes; and margarine into new shapes, consistencies, and flavors of margarine and other spread products. Conglomerate mergers have been common in all three commodity systems in order to broaden the companies' ability to satisfy the unique and changing food desires and life styles of the ultimate consumers.

THE GROWTH OF COOPERATIVES AND THEIR NEW USES BY BOTH COOPERATIVE AND CORPORATE MANAGERS

The nature of the products, the status and widespread knowledge of technology, and the political and economic development of the commodity systems involved have produced slightly different patterns of cooperative growth. In the case of wheat, low income levels for wheat farmers led to cooperative and governmental programs that put producers into the grain business. Once in the grain business the cash flow advantages of "owner-customer" organizations led to growth by merger.

In the case of soybeans, cooperative grain elevators were already in existence from their original establishment in the farming areas. The price swings of the soybean crops led to cooperative pooling. The dissemination of processing technology, the pooling arrangements, the use of soybean meal by farmers supplying soybeans to the cooperative, along with cash flow advantages, led to cooperative growth in the soybean industry.

The merger activity in both the wheat and the soybean industries has added to the management talent of the combined firms. In addition the *cash flow* advantages of the owner-customer cooperative form of enterprise have led to nonfarmer cooperatives and quasi-cooperatives in both systems. In both the wheat and the soybean industry systems, unique product developments of a differentiable nature were by and large left to the noncooperative firms. In the orange industry system, the fact that orange concentrate processing is a one-step process from grower to consumer has put the cooperative processor into direct competition in the consumer market. In spite of his lack of consumer knowledge, the presence of price and production uncertainties and cash flow opportunities have led the cooperative manager to expand his processing operations in the industry, but primarily on a "commodity" private label basis.

In each of the above commodity systems the extension of the producer's activities forward into marketing and processing and backward into procurement was motivated by improving incomes to the producer through lower procurement and marketing costs, spreading price risks, new marketing opportunities, and/or diversifying the farmer's investments into related functions that were more profitable than his farming operations.

There are several significant trends evident in the use of the cooperative form of organization in the wheat, soybean, and Florida orange commodity systems:

(1) The cooperative form of enterprise will continue to be an important coordinating device in the wheat, soybean and Florida orange industries. From the producers' point of view, it is the major device.[1]

[1]It is a major device for American agricultural producers generally with some 20% of all farm procurements purchased

Some 80% of all U.S. farmers are members of one or more cooperatives. The cooperative form of enterprise will expand because it provides both a major procurement entity for the purchase of farm inputs economically and efficiently and a method of providing large quantities of uniform raw products for the food system.

(2) As cooperatives expand their operations, the requirements for sophisticated management skills increase. In a market that is short of top managers more cooperatives will use the merger route to bring top managers from other organizations into their operations. Also the nature of the cooperative organization is changing with the development of a mixture of both corporate and cooperative subsidiaries in order to provide flexibility in operations and to provide management incentives.

(3) Corporation managers are now making more use of the "cooperative-corporation" in their organizational structures. The central issue in the use of a cooperative association is what is income to the association and what is income to the owner-patron. Patronage refunds paid in cash or equivalent after the close of the fiscal year (if true allocations based on patronage are in effect additions to price of goods marketed or reductions in costs of goods purchased) do represent income to the patron and not to the association. This allocation is true of the income tax law in general even though it especially fits the cooperative organization. A patron of a cooperative may be an individual, a corporation, or a subsidiary of the same organization. The 1962 Revenue Act states that 20% of these allocations must now be in the form of cash in order for the patron to pay an income tax on both the cash patronage refunds and on those allocated on the books. Keeping patronage refunds in the form of allocations on the books allows the cooperative to build up a capital structure at a faster rate than other types of organizations. This advantage will help the cooperative type of organization to expand more rapidly in all these commodity systems. Such continued expansion may result in a reappraisal of the consequences of this method of capital formation by tax authorities. Typical of the expansion through allocated patronage refunds are regional farm cooperatives where 80% of the equity was acquired in this manner. If tax laws remain unchanged, then both cooperatives and corporations with quasi-cooperative

through cooperatives (some $4 billion) and 30% of all farm sales made through cooperatives (about $12 billion). One out of every five persons in the world is a member of a cooperative. (For a general description of U.S. cooperatives, see Appendix XI-1.)

subsidiaries will make greater use of this method of capital formation especially in the acquisition of related entities.

(4) Cooperative organizations will continue to receive public support by both major political parties, by the Farmer Cooperative Service of the Department of Agriculture, the Farm Credit Administration and the Bank for Cooperatives, and by special emphasis in our Foreign Aid programs. Although public pronouncements by themselves do not necessarily mean expansion of cooperative activities, the services available to them, the specific and special credit agencies at their disposal, and the attention given to them by Land Grant College Extension Services all help to promote their growth.

(5) The AID program has given special emphasis to cooperatives primarily because the developing nations' food systems are relatively basic with one-process food operations, thus providing easy access to cooperative procurement and processing operations. Also, politically it is easier to get local government support for this one type of coordination improvement in the food marketing system. The growing importance of both wheat and soybeans in international trade and the desire of cooperatives to participate in this market directly, would indicate expansion of export activities by farm cooperatives or merger with one of the existing major grain exporting firms.

(6) Although farmer cooperatives in the wheat, soybean, and Florida orange systems have integrated backward into farm supplies and forward into processing, they have been only partially successful in merchandising finished food products through the ultimate retailer. As noted in the Florida orange study, their sales to the chains are for the most part private label sales. That is not to say that some cooperatives have not developed product differentiation skills — Sunkist, Ocean Spray and Welch's Grape Juice have excellent franchised products (the latter firm, however, was acquired by the Grape Growers Cooperative after developing a franchised product) but, on the whole cooperative management has been fairly weak in developing merchandising techniques for their finished products. This weakness is recognized and the "new breed" of cooperative management is much more marketing oriented.[2]

Several large-scale integrated farm cooperatives recognize that they are in the food business and that management skills in retail food distribution and merchandising must be developed, acquired or both.

(7) Statements of several farm cooperative leaders in the summer of 1966 suggest a growing demand on the part of the producer to use the cooperative not only as a pooling of purchasing power for obtaining farm supplies and as a uniting of marketing activities in order to average out product price and quality requirements, but also as a means of controlling output at various price levels and of dealing directly with the ultimate food consumer. One suggestion is a "Wagner Act" for the farmer cooperative which would grant the majority of the producers around a processing plant or retail food area the right to bargain for the entire production going to the plant or retail food store. Another suggestion is a purchase of a major food chain such as The Great Atlantic & Pacific Tea Company.

(8) Obviously the future use of the cooperative in the wheat, soybean and Florida orange industries will ultimately be decided by the cooperative and corporate managers who have the ability to maximize the use of this organizational form, given the present position of their firms in the industry and the type of governmental programs, tax incentives, public policies, and future coordination requirements of the food systems of which they are a part. Like all other elements of a commodity system, cooperatives have to be put in the perspective of the changing environment of the total system.

NEW USES OF GOVERNMENT PROGRAMS BY BUSINESS MANAGERS

In all three commodity systems that we have examined, the growing interdependency of the segments, the ever increasing need for more coordination within and between commodity systems, and the need for overall action and policies in terms of the total marketing system have changed the role and perspective of public policy makers.

In the case of wheat, the chronic income problems of the wheat producer and the resultant price support program that led to government wheat surpluses, which then produced government wheat storage operations for the warehousing of the surpluses and government export programs for "getting rid of the surpluses," are indicative of the chain reaction effect of a patchwork government program on a complex, interrelated domestic and world wheat system. In each case the underlying problem was an imbalance between supply and demand. Although a specific program may have been developed for one segment of the commodity system, that is, the farmer, the pro-

---

[2] Many cooperatives handle as much as 50% of food products *not* grown by their members in order to be an effective market organization in the food business by offering a broad product line of goods and services.

gram's impacts and resultant administrative machinery affected each stage of the vertical wheat structure from farm-supplier to ultimate distributor and consumer. In essence, government wheat programs were and are agribusiness programs rather than farm programs even if their originators conceive them in a narrower context.

Although acreage controls and acreage diversion programs are being sidelined in the wheat system in the face of immediate and long range world food shortages, the year to year swings between surpluses and shortages will continue to occur even if the market demand is an expanding one. In the face of rising income levels and population growth, and uncertain production operations (years of surpluses and shortages), some type of balancing machinery has to be maintained in order to avoid unnecessary wrenches to any one segment of the wheat system and to avoid a national or international shortage of food. This responsibility for balancing resources in the wheat system over long periods of time has been shared by a combination free market system and a network of 50-odd nations' wheat programs. Inadvertently, the U.S. wheat price support program, storage program, and export program became "balancers" for the wheat system in the United States and price stabilizers in the world wheat markets. This responsibility ultimately becomes governmental when balancing is not accomplished by the market in a way that produces viability in each segment of the system. In most cases it is the producer who bears the brunt of adjusting to major supply and demand changes.

Given the "balancing" role or planning role as a major governmental responsibility, what does such responsibility mean in terms of business and government managers' policies in the wheat system of the future?

(1) First, it means the development of a national reserve inventory for wheat in the United States. Specific provisions such as a formula for releasing the inventory to the market or for putting wheat into the reserve, should be worked out with industry leaders from each segment of the wheat system. Given a certain formula for administering the reserve, private decision makers could make their own plans without fear of arbitrary government procurement or selling practices. Of course in case of a world food disaster, emergency measures may have to be taken that would have priority over a mechanical formula.

(2) In a very uncertain world the existence of food reserves (in terms of stocks of a commodity and of unused fertile acres) in this country may be a public obligation as well as a national defense requirement.

The cost of "inventory management" as an obligation should be borne by the public, not the producer or any other participant of the wheat system. This policy means that government storage operations will continue to be an important part of wheat system operations but not as important a consideration as in the past. The cost of maintaining inventories in the "pipeline" of the wheat system will be carried by the participants of the wheat system and minimized through the use of futures markets, contracts, and other arrangements.

(3) As a "balancer" in the wheat system the government must have legislative authority to make long-run supply and price decisions in order to provide some stability in the decision-making environment of the industry. The new four-year agricultural program is certainly a step in the right direction.

(4) The balancer's role is, of necessity, interwoven with the level of export price subsidies and domestic compensatory payments to producers, and with methods of transferring payments from one segment of society to the producer. The cost of the program to the taxpayer may be so burdensome that part of it will continue to be shifted to the bread consumer in the form of flour milling "processing taxes" (certificates) which increase the price of a one-pound loaf of bread by one cent.

(5) The administrative machinery of a reserve and price support program must make use of the private segment of the wheat system. The businessman must plan for the effective use of this program in his business operation without having the program distract the enterprise from its primary function of satisfying the ultimate consumers of wheat food products in an efficient manner.

In addition to the "balancer" role of the government in the wheat system, there are a host of services that have helped the wheat system function more effectively in the past and will help to improve the business environment of the future. The past and future services include the following:

(1) The development of new hybrid seed varieties that put potential yields of some varieties up to 100 to 200 bushels per acre. In essence the government, together with private seed companies, is an excellent R&D center for the producer.

(2) The development of new products for the consumer market, such as "bulgar," which attempts to make wheat cook like rice but not necessarily look like it, for the overseas concessional markets. Thus, the government is also a new product innovator for the wheat industry system.

(3) The development of a grading system that al-

lows coordinating transactions to occur throughout the vertical structure of the wheat system.

(4) The use of the state colleges as disseminators of research and product information for both private and public entities.

(5) A fact finder and economic intelligence reporter for supplying important crop, weather, transportation, and market information for all participants in the wheat system.

(6) A development agency for new firms and operations, both in the United States and abroad.

The business manager of the future in the wheat system will make better use of the services and coordinating activities outlined above and will also be in a better position to maximize his domestic and international opportunities through an important change in both governmental and business philosophies. The United States and world governments have rediscovered the private sector of the U.S. food economy and have a new appreciation of the complex, ingenious mechanism that it is. The National Commission on Food Marketing, in spite of specific new governmental recommendations, was full of praise for the food systems of the United States. Overseas governmental agencies are now quite desirous of having U.S. businessmen apply their know-how and total market concept to the requirements of various food systems of other countries. The recipient countries' governments are also encouraging greater participation of U.S. food operators as long as they become part of the local food industry. The American businessman is slowly phasing his operations into the international economy, but he requires the major governmental support evident in all three commodity systems that we have analyzed: namely, some sort of stable environment in which to operate, where sanctity of property, contract, and common integrity are part of the system or can be assured by guarantees of the United States and other governments.

Typical of the use of governmental programs in the international area is the recent project wherein Sweden and the International Development Association (an affiliate of the World Bank) will lend $24 million to Pakistan to help finance a grain handling and storage project for wheat and other food grains. This will enable Pakistan to maintain or increase its annual importation of 700,000 tons of wheat, much of it from the U.S.

The soybean system has also made use of many of the same types of programs outlined for the wheat system, but has been in the fortunate position of having a fairly good balance between productive resources and consumption needs. The one exception has been soybean oil, but rising world incomes and population has limited this imbalance problem. The administration of these programs requires not only a high level of business cooperation but a maintenance of integrity in the face of unlimited temptations. The notorious De Angelis case is but one example of the misuse of a government program.

The government services available to the wheat system were likewise available to the soybean system. In the early beginnings of the industry, government educators provided an educational service that was necessary to bring producer and processor together. Government laboratories improved flavor stability and provided oil deodorization techniques in order to broaden the food market outlets for soybean oil. Government institutions tested the value of soybean meal as an important poultry and livestock feed ingredient. Government agencies have worked hand in hand with private associations to open new world markets for soybean and soybean products. The government has made fewer mistakes with policies on soybeans than with wheat policies (with the exception of World War II controls) because the price levels have been more attuned to the market needs for the raw and finished soybean products. The balancing problem for the future will be how to build up the reserve supply of soybeans without disturbing the viability and, so far, excellent performance of the marketing system.

In the case of Florida oranges and frozen orange concentrate, in the past the balancing task was accomplished by a series of fortunate circumstances. The technology for making frozen orange concentrate was developed through a wartime contract when market gluts were developing. The technology had excellent acceptance, and more importantly, so did the product. Since that time, impending market gluts of oranges have been averted by timely freezes, but in April 1967 the 1966–1967 crop forecast was for 147 million boxes, some 34 million boxes above the previous record output. Even more discouraging is the high percentage of new grove plantings which will be coming on the market in the next four years. The industry is already devising an industry price pool as a buffer stock, or balancing stock, for the industry. New market orders and agreements have been suggested as well as a minimum price support to the grower. If such price pools and market orders are developed, the government will then be in much the same coordinating position as it is in the wheat industry, without as storable a commodity to handle. Obviously, if these programs come into being, business managers will have to make use of them or adjust their operations to them. One use will be to level out price swings, thus enabling those firms with high market competence to concentrate their efforts in marketing rather than in advantageous procurement practices. New governmental feeding programs that will make use of frozen orange concentrate are also being developed, such as for school lunches. Export possibilities are limited because of the expansion of lower cost, competing sources of orange concentrate production in many other nations.

The manifold services of the Federal Government are also helping to coordinate the operations of the Florida orange industry. New products, processes, packaging, and better grading systems and production practices, are all being developed by national and state governmental agencies.

In each of these industry systems the unique pattern of the harmonizing of private and government policies depends upon the nature of the imbalances within a system, the historical evolution of the problems and of government programs that have been developed, the perishability of the product, the international competitive position, the philosophy of the business and government leaders, the political importance of the participants in the system, and the economic importance of the food products to the ultimate consumer.

In each case mistakes were made when price levels, premiums and discounts were not consistent with the cost of functions and the product wants of the ultimate consumer. In the case of wheat, the income needs of one million producers and the impact of the thrusting of a "surplus storage" and "concessional market" device on the system could not be ignored. In the case of soybeans, the imbalance of the twin products of the soybean led to a soybean oil storage program. In the case of frozen orange concentrate, the inventory pool seems certain to be established. The government programs of the future are more long range in viewpoint and take into consideration the use of the efficient private sector facilities in the execution of these programs. The service functions are being constantly updated in order to help in the coordination of the production, movement, storage, processing, and distribution of the products of each commodity system.

From these discussions of the wheat, soybean, and Florida orange systems, the reader must be aware of the complete interdependence of governmental and private decision making. This is especially evident when one attempts to place a dollar value on government program benefits in the wheat commodity system (see Table XI-1). Many aspects of these industries have several of the attributes of a public

TABLE XI-1. Product Revenues of Selected Wheat Industry Sectors Compared with
Government Program Benefits: 1963
(In millions)

Industry sector	Various revenue estimates		Government program benefits	Government benefits as % of product revenue estimates
Wheat farmers	$2,100	—*Gross Sales* value of wheat	$600 —Value of wheat price supports	29%
Country elevator wheat operations (cooperative and noncooperative)	$ 27	—*Gross Revenue* for wheat volume handled	65 —Wheat storage payments	30[a]
	65	—Wheat storage payments		
	$ 92	—*Gross Wheat Revenue*		
Terminal elevator	8	—*Gross Revenue* for wheat volume handled	75 —Wheat storage payments	50[b]
	75	—Wheat storage payments		
	$ 93	—*Gross Wheat Revenue*		
Export firms	$ 24	—*Gross Revenue* for wheat volume handled	14.8—Wheat storage payments	38
	14.8	—Wheat storage payments		
	$ 38.8	—*Gross Wheat Revenue*		
Flour millers	$ 17.3	—*Net Revenue*	24.4—Wheat storage payments	141[c]

[a] 30% of *all* country elevator revenue (including *all* grains assembled, cleaned, and stored).
[b] 50% of *all* terminal elevator revenue (including *all* grains assembled, cleaned, and stored).
[c] Wheat storage payments to flour millers in 1963 were estimated to be 141% of flour *net income*.
SOURCE: Author's estimates and USDA, Agricultural Stabilization and Conservation Service publications.

utility. The federal and state governments, with the help and advice of the participants of these industries, regulates:

(1) the location of major inventories;
(2) time of shipment;
(3) percentage of grain to be transported in American ships;
(4) subsidies on products exported;
(5) duties on products imported;
(6) type of merger activity;
(7) income and price programs;
(8) amount of consumer products devoted to school lunch program;
(9) the types of advertising and merchandising product programs used domestically and internationally;
(10) the acceptance or rejection of various freight rate relationships;
(11) the lending of money to erect additional processing facilities;
(12) the support of cooperatives as a matter of public domestic and international policy;
(13) supervision of futures markets;
(14) setting of standards;
(15) when to sell surplus commodities; and
(16) a whole host of service and antitrust operations.

In a land 3,000 miles wide and a total agribusiness segment that accounts for over 50% of the nation's business assets, $170 billion of sales ($20 billion farm inputs, $37 billion farm outputs, and $113 billion consumer food and fiber purchases), and 30% of its labor force, one cannot escape the government services and regulations required to make a complex food economy work. All of the coordinating institutions in agribusiness involve group action — and "any group action in agriculture rests on acquiescence of government if not its involvement . . . and present day agriculture is a creature of government."[3] The government will continue to be one of the most important coordinating elements in determining the market system of the food economy. Its "balance" or "shock absorber" role will also continue to be a costly one. The costs of the Commodity Credit Corporation program for wheat price support (including export subsidies), the P.L. 480 program costs, diversion payments, and interest were $1,981 million in 1962, $1,983 million in 1963, $1,485 million in 1964 and $1,150 million in 1965.

Our descriptions and analyses have also indicated that the government has played an important role in research and development for all phases of the wheat,

soybean, and Florida orange industries. The Extension Service, the market news media, the Farmer Cooperative Service, the Economic Research Service, as well as the USDA Laboratories, grading facilities, health inspections, and so on, have all supplied important services necessary for the maintenance, adaptability, and growth of a nationwide food system.

From this brief summary of the different patterns of government-business interaction in the development of the wheat, soybean, and Florida orange systems, several significant trends are evident in the future use of government services and programs by business managers. These trends are as follows:

(1) Government storage programs will continue to be an important aspect of the wheat system both in terms of wheat and soybean storage facilities in the United States and in terms of new storage facilities in the developing countries for facilitating the handling of food and wheat shipments. On the other hand, there will be a reappraisal concerning where reserve stocks should be stored, both in this country and abroad. This reappraisal will result in the loss of storage revenue for firms in certain regions and locations in the United States.

It will also result in a highly competitive storage rate being set, perhaps even on a bid basis. Some of the results of these same trends in the past show that annual storage and handling costs from 1960 to 1963 declined almost $100 million from $476 million in 1960 to $377 million in 1963.[4] Occupancy levels in some areas are below 25% and the dependency of many firms on storage income in the past has meant some economic adjustments for them. Typical of the effects are those reported by the Seaboard Allied Milling Company in its annual report of May 29, 1965:

Storage and other operating revenue in 1964–1965 totaled $1,744,343, compared with $2,658,893 in the preceding year. . . . As a result of further reduction in both total and government-owned grain stocks held in commercial elevators, your company's storage profits were largely eliminated in the past year. In view of the national administration's continuing emphasis on reduction in grain stocks, through both legislative and administrative programs, the decision was reached to dispose of some of our grain storage properties.

The excess grain storage capacity of several geographical areas has resulted in the suggestion by the management of such facilities that a bid basis be used for storing grain and that they submit bids below the

[3] Breimyer, *Future Organization and Control of United States Agricultural Production and Marketing.* Paper delivered at annual meeting of American Farm Economic Association, Purdue University, August 17, 1964.

[4] USDA, Agricultural Stabilization and Conservation Service, *Storage and Handling Costs Incurred by Type of Storage on Commodities Acquired Under the Price Support Program,* October 18, 1963.

standard storage rates set by the government. One example of such an effort is found in a news release dated August 23, 1965:

> The Department of Agriculture plans to ask for bids to store "substantial quantities" of Commodity Credit Corporation-owned grain in Buffalo, New York, elevators, according to Senator Robert F. Kennedy of New York. Preliminary indications are that 1,000,000 bushels of oats and 2,000,000 bushels of wheat will be offered to Buffalo elevators for storage on a bid basis. Senator Kennedy has been consulting with the Department on utilization of Buffalo grain storage capacity in light of presentations by Buffalo maritime and labor officials that the port's elevators were being neglected in CCC storage operations.[5]

In addition to lowered government wheat storage occupancies and rates, the wheat warehouseman will have less authority over the movement of or first option to buy government grain in his facilities, because the government will need maximum flexibility in dealing with overseas concessional shipments and sales opportunities.

(2) New government programs will provide more freedom and flexibility for all segments of the commodity systems as the government realizes that all participants must have maximum freedom to innovate products, processes, and distribution functions in order to achieve the goal of an efficient and adaptable food system that will satisfy the food requirements of its domestic and international consumers. To provide this additional program flexibility the government has, and will continue to develop, programs that:

(a) provide flexible alternatives for producers to shift among crops without penalizing them through loss of program benefits;

(b) simplify the machinery of government operations by placing more of it in the hands of cooperative and corporate firms;

(c) work more closely with *all* segments of a commodity system especially in the development of an inventory management and reserve plan. This may be closely related to the suggestion of Lauren K. Soth (a member of the President's Food and Fiber Commission) for a "planning guideline" and a National Agricultural Goals Conference;

(d) change the Food-for-Peace Program (P.L. 480) from a surplus disposal to an economic need program consistent with the food and trade requirements of other countries; and

(e) provide laws that prohibit fraud and deception for consumer food products without destroying the opportunity for the food system to appeal to the total life style of the consumer.

[5] *Southwestern Miller,* August 24, 1965, p. 30.

(3) The U.S. agribusiness industry knows how to cooperate with the U.S. Government in building a viable food marketing system. The past cooperation in the domestic market is well documented throughout all the sections of this study. It is the same type of cooperation[6] that is needed in the world agribusiness market so that not only will food needs be recognized, but effective actions to supply those needs will be developed and executed.

The world market lacks both the food and the money to make it a commercial gold mine. Increasing the potential of this market will continue to call for greater cooperation and a four-way partnership arrangement among U.S. agribusinessmen, foreign agribusiness firms, and the governments of both. Government participation will include financial aid, investment protection, tax incentives, and research and development of new food products.

Furthermore, government subsidies of new food products through commercial channels are necessary to avoid the "charity diet" label given to aid shipments distributed through government and private charitable organizations. Donations through the School Lunch Program have avoided the charity stigma; thus they are an important exception to this generalization.

Managers in the world food business must also keep in mind that even though they may need government cooperation and support now, they must plan the present development and distribution of their individual food products with the objective of some day taking over full responsibility for this market. Agribusinessmen who plan their future food policy on a long-range basis will be making a lasting contribution to their individual companies, to the proposed government-industry partnership, and to the food economy of the developing nations.

(4) The development of new types of P.L. 480 programs and variable levies will not be deterrents to U.S. commercial agricultural export trade any more than they have been in the past because businessmen have used these programs as marketing tools. The government administrators, in turn, will continue to utilize the know-how and facilities of the private segments of the food and fiber systems in the execution of these programs.

In summary, the food and fiber programs of the future will attempt to provide greater freedom of ac-

[6] This cooperation was evident and was stressed at an informal industry-government meeting held at the Harvard Business School on May 26, 1966, and summarized by Ray A. Goldberg in a *Harvard Business Review* article, "Agribusiness for Developing Countries."

tion for every segment of the food system. The Department of Agriculture wants to maintain independent and viable business entities in all segments of the food economy. The past programs all provided incentives for efficiency and volume of output, and in no way penalized the efficient farmer, farm supplier, processor, or distributor.

The present programs have been formulated in a similar manner. The above descriptions and analyses indicate that governmental policy is at a turning point. In a way, the Secretary of Agriculture is in a much more untenable position. In current proposals he has to set the price support at levels that will take into account the many price support activities of other countries around the world. In past programs the U.S. price support bore no relation to competitive world markets. Today it is supposed to reflect an estimate of world supply and demand and the many programs affecting that supply and demand. In essence, the Secretary is placed in the position of selecting a price level that would approximate a quasi-free market price. In addition the Secretary has to take into consideration the changing nature of the U.S. wheat, soybean, and Florida orange commodity systems.

The businessmen in the wheat and soybean industries, and, to a lesser extent, in the Florida orange industry have been asked to take on more of the price stabilizing and inventory management functions of their respective firms and industries. Furthermore, they are to cooperate as industry groups (the Soybean Council, Wheat Growers Association, Florida Citrus Mutual) or as individual firms in developing imaginative export programs for their respective products. In addition, they are requested to implement the storage, distribution, and processing functions of the products within the recipient country with, of course, the recipient country's cooperation. In other words, American agribusiness is emerging from a preoccupation with internal high price supports as a means of improving farm income (and the resultant storage program) to a potentially expansion-minded attitude of serving world food and fiber consumer needs with a rational and planned level of minimum commodity inventories.

THE BETTER UTILIZATION OF TRADE ASSOCIATIONS IN BOTH ACTION PLANNING AND STRATEGIC LONG-RANGE PLANNING BY THE PRIVATE AND PUBLIC MANAGER

The "personality" or pattern of development of a commodity system is probably best illustrated by the type of trade association that the various participants have created to help coordinate the many functions

of the system. The trade association, in most cases, represents a piece of coordinating machinery that reflects the central character of the major managers of an industry system. Just as "the central character of a business organization and the individuality it has for its members and its various publics may, in the instance of mature and highly developed corporations, be determined with some clarity," [7] so may the character traits of mature and highly developed trade associations. These association "personality traits" give some broad indications as to the nature of the total environment of the system. Like any good coordinating device, it is a two-way mechanism obtaining inputs from individual firms operating in the various segments of the system and using these inputs to arrive at some general comprehension of the desires and needs of the industry system as a whole. At the same time it provides a general summary and a projection of the present and future state of the industry in order to provide an industry intelligence system for use by individual public and private managers in formulating strategic long-range planning.

It is the latter functions, the intelligence system and the development of industry action alternatives, that are most important for the individual private manager who has very few formal procedures for influencing or comprehending the total system's attitudes or actions.

The same intelligence system functions of associations are also important to the public manager who wants to get a total commodity system perspective in order to improve his formulation and administration of public policy.

The numerous trade associations described in the wheat, soybean, and Florida orange sections of this study have a variety of intelligence, service, and action operations for their respective commodity systems. The functions of these associations are extremely varied and include: price barometer, product innovator, export market developer, grade and standards instigator, market structure innovator in terms of suggesting futures markets and inventory pools, trade representative before various governmental bodies, industry advertising leader, and the hiring of outside consultants to analyze overall industry requirements.

How the business executive utilizes his trade association in part determines the performance of this type of coordinating machinery in meeting the criteria of: (1) providing flexibility and adaptability for agribusiness firms, (2) establishing price stability, (3) enhancing the competitive environment, and (4) encouraging industry innovation. A recent doctoral dis-

[7] Learned, Christensen, Andrews, and Guth, *Business Policy: Text and Cases*, p. 18.

sertation bears indirectly on the matter of the use of a trade association by an executive: "It is concerned with the way in which top management gains relevant information about events occurring outside the company in order to guide the company's future course of action." [8] Basically, Dr. Aguilar is concerned with how top management "plugs into the industry structure network" and how "information which is received from different sources is integrated within the company." His conclusions, drawn largely from the chemical industry, indicate three shortcomings: (1) lack of effort in a comprehensive manner by the company to "plug into the network," (2) lack of concern with broad environmental issues affecting the firm, and (3) lack of information integration within the firm. In all three of our commodity system examples, the trade associations provide a valuable service of keeping the individual firms "plugged into the network" and of examining the broad environmental issues affecting the firms. The very quasi-public nature of the food industries forces food executives to be aware of their external environment.

Of the three examples of industry association coordination, the Florida orange system stands out for its excellent use of these types of coordinating machinery. This success is partly due to the fact that the orange crop (especially the juice-type) is largely concentrated in one state, and the existence of the Florida Citrus Commission and the State Agricultural Colleges makes it much easier for trade associations to deal with and anticipate the problems and opportunities of the industry. However, these associations, especially the Florida Citrus Mutual and the Florida Canners Association, have been outstanding and farsighted in identifying and analyzing the critical issues facing their industry, and they have suggested alternative and practical programs of action. Part of this success is due to the excellent association leadership and part to the representation and interest of the top executives of the industry in their association.

The soybean industry has also been recognized as an industry that was farsighted in its development of trade associations. The Department of Agriculture and the soybean industry in general give much of the credit of soybean and soybean product export expansion to the Soybean Council and its persistent efforts to find new uses and to improve the products of the soybean for overseas market development.

The wheat industry, until recently, was made up of many factions that had a relatively narrow focus on the critical problems facing the industry. In 1965, however, a new National Wheat Council was formed which rep-

resents all the major segments of the industry and which will work closely with the Department of Agriculture in formulating improved public and industry policies. In addition to the narrow focus of many minor trade associations in the wheat system, many of the top executives delegated to act as their representatives at these associations were men who had very little to do with long-run policies. Hence much of the information they received was not integrated into the action of top management in individual firms. Furthermore, the lack of knowledge on the part of industry representatives meant poor formulation of trade association policies.

Trade associations aid a firm's flexibility and adaptability in adjusting to or changing its commodity system because the small firm is given access to broad information systems and group representation that it could not afford on an individual company basis. Trade associations do aid in promoting price stability.

The development of a pricing service by the Florida Citrus Mutual Association has been quite helpful, but the practice is open to criticism of a potential seller bias. (The development of a futures market may improve the pricing service offered by the Florida Citrus Mutual; see page 178.) The price-making activities of the Millers' National Federation resulted in Federal Trade Commission action, and since that time association price activity has not influenced prices. The soybean associations are not active in price operations.[9] The availability of cash and futures markets for all three soybean products (soybeans, meal, and oil) requires no added services by the association.

The associations have definitely improved the competitive environment of all three commodity systems by the dissemination of information concerning new production practices, new products and new markets. In addition, by allocating funds for product research and market promotion new innovations have been developed in all three industries — but the Florida orange and the soybean associations have out-paced the fragmented wheat associations. The Florida orange industry, for example, is using $18 million of advertising outlay to promote orange juice in 1967. This amount represents some 10% of the value of the crop on the farm. Other potential activities of Florida associations are set forth in Exhibit XI-1.

Perhaps the main implication that can be drawn from the comparison of the three commodity system association activities concerns the association leaders, who in recognizing the fact that their policies progressively have more influence in changing the environments of

[8] Aguilar, *Scanning the Business Environment.*

[9] The one exception is the Webb-Pomerene soybean oil export group. This group should re-evaluate the wisdom of an arrangement that could easily be charged with "price understanding."

EXHIBIT XI-1

Florida Citrus Mutual Trade Association Activity:
Plans for 1967 Season

What the Industry Must Do *Now* In Order
To Profitably Market This Season's Crop

1) DEVELOPMENT OF SECONDARY MARKETS

The immediate goal is to DEVELOP SECONDARY
MARKETS by arranging for Governmental purchases of 10 to 15 million gallons of frozen concentrated orange juice for the National School Lunch
Program, or other available outlets. Secretary Freeman has been alerted to our situation, and our formal
request is in his hands. . . .

2) INVENTORY POOLING

An important Industry Committee appointed last
season to study programs of supply management met
October 12 and approved in principle a proposed
program to work for a marketing order that would
enable the industry to "set aside" a portion of the
orange crop for the development of secondary markets, especially the school lunch program. While a
Marketing Order program would take many months
and probably not be effective this season, a voluntary Marketing Agreement program embodying the
same objectives could be accomplished this season.
Economic studies show that by removing 10% of the
crop from primary commercial markets, over-all returns for the orange crop can be increased by at
least 20%!

3) 8-OZ.

We must, this season, make a major move to introduce the 8-ounce container on a volume basis to the
consumer for this vital reason: every purchase of an
8-ounce can, instead of a 6-ounce container, means
the use of ⅓ more oranges without even increasing
the number of consumer units sold.

4) ADS

The industry advertising and promotion budget for
this season is estimated at a record-breaking $17 mil-
lion, with some $6 million earmarked for orange con-
centrate promotion. A forceful campaign, backed by
this appropriation, should create important sales increases for citrus fruit and products.

5) WE'VE GOT TO WIN BACK
THE CANADIAN MARKET

Salesmen of fresh Florida citrus made a missionary
trip to Montreal in August to begin planning with
the Canadian trade ways to win back the fresh market for Florida. Trade Luncheons will be held in
Toronto and Montreal next month. We must win
back a large percentage of our Canadian fresh business from California, South Africa, and Israel. Fur-

ther, in 1961–62 we sold nearly 4 million gallons of
orange concentrate to Canadian customers, but since
then Argentina, Brazil, and others have captured
much of our market. Canada is our best opportunity
for increasing exports of frozen orange concentrate.

6) MILITARY CUSTOMERS OFFER
GREATER POTENTIAL

With about 3 million men now in uniform, military
purchases of fresh and processed Florida citrus can
be significantly increased this season. The industry
must work together to develop this potential and
make military authorities aware of the "good buy"
that will be available this season.

7) OTHER PROPOSALS MUST BE EXPLORED
THIS SEASON SUCH AS:

What can we do to enlarge the institutional market
this season?

Will sweetened concentrate increase consumption of
orange concentrate and help us break the "30% barrier"?

Should it be made mandatory that all retail concentrate be packed in easy opening cans (when fully
available from can manufacturers)?

Are we missing opportunities to expand the vending
of orange juice?

Should we ask for lower assessed valuations on our
groves by Tax Assessors?

Should we eliminate pulp washing from concentrate
for manufacturing?

Will the "Haley Bill" remove the tax incentive that
has caused some of the new planting in South Florida?

their total commodity systems, will provide more effective industry leadership than will those leaders primarily interested in one small, narrow segment of their
commodity systems. In addition, the role of a trade
association may depend not only on its objectives but
also on the effectiveness of its activities.

There are several significant trends evident in the
development of the types of trade associations utilized
by private and public managers in the wheat, soybean,
and Florida orange commodity systems:

(1) Managers in the wheat system recognize that
they can no longer afford a disjointed segmented industry association approach. The vast changes affecting
the domestic and international wheat system call for
broad perspectives by every trade association in the
wheat system.

(2) As industry operations become even more interrelated and complex, some vehicle for developing environmental intelligence is needed in order to make a
particular commodity system an effective competitor

with other systems in supplying the food requirements of domestic and foreign consumers. Firms in such a commodity system must be willing to provide common information to a neutral association in order to develop meaningful data about the many market, product, and environmental changes within and outside the system.

(3) The political and economic interest in the food system in this and other countries requires some association activities that can provide an interchange of information that is essential to making intelligent, strategic long-range plans for private firms and public entities. A reserve policy, an export program, a compensatory income increase, a major transportation change, an inventory pool, and a futures market all deserve an across-the-board association approach rather than from the narrow perspective of one segment of an industry.

THE INCREASING EMPHASIS ON THE WORLD DIMENSIONS OF THE FOOD ECONOMY[10]

The changing dimensions of international and domestic agribusiness have resulted in three main consequences that affect the U.S. businessman in the wheat, soybean, and Florida orange commodity systems:

(1) The change in the basic policies of the United States and the recipient countries, which now place greater emphasis on the private sector of the agribusiness economy.
(2) The need for increased production of food and farm supplies in the United States.
(3) The need for an integrated approach to the world's developing and developed food economies, which recognizes that all parts of the agribusiness system (farm supplies and operations, food processing, and distribution) must fit together.

Not only must all parts of the food system expand in a coordinated way, but the system itself must have a strong infrastructure of transportation, credit, storage, communication, and education, as well as stable political and social structures.

The three consequences cited provide outstanding challenges and opportunities to the American businessman who is active in world food production and distribution. Already he is beginning to receive priority in economic planning throughout the world. In the United States, for example, a reappraisal of world food policy has occurred for a number of reasons:

(1) The recognition that inadequate diets lead to physical and mental damage to the population of the less-developed countries.
(2) The projected explosion of world population and the resultant aggravation it will cause to an already serious world food situation.
(3) The limitations and inadequacies of the Food-for-Peace Program (Public Law 480).
(4) The opportunities to make better use of our domestic agricultural facilities.
(5) The chance to provide self-help programs to the developing countries by furnishing a better mix of food supplies and technical aid so that viable total economic systems can be established.
(6) The realization that North America is the only part of the world with an inventory of food supplies, and therefore that these supplies must be considered as world food reserves.
(7) The realization that our agricultural plant does not have unlimited production capacity and that a time may come when we will be unable to close the gap between world food needs and our productive capacity.

The U.S. world food policy is actively changing with increasing emphasis on an integrated package of self-help programs. This has provided a new climate for expansion in every segment of international agribusiness.

The new environment for overseas agribusiness investment has specific relevance to the wheat, soybean, and orange industries.

In the wheat and soybean commodity systems, the importance of the changing world food market environment is already being felt because over half of the domestic wheat production[11] and 41% of the soybean and/or soybean product production are exported.

In the case of wheat, over three-fourths of wheat exports are in the form of concessional sales (under P.L. 480 shipments). Undoubtedly these sales will only continue insofar as they lead to the self-help development of the food systems of developing countries. Eventually such sales will be related to additional protein nutritional needs with lysine and other amino acids being added as supplements to the wheat. In addition to selling the wheat, U.S. businessmen will play a more important role in planning and developing the wheat and flour processing systems of these countries by providing technical know-how, investment capital, storage, transportation facilities, and technology to improve handling and to cut down waste. In the long run this will lead to multinational companies, will act as a stimulus to indigenous wheat output if climatic condi-

[10] Much of the information for this section of the study has been summarized in Goldberg, "Agribusiness for Developing Countries."

[11] The wheat exported was obtained from both current production and from inventories that helped to reduce the level of government wheat stocks.

tions are suitable, and may lessen or even reverse a developing country's dependence on wheat imports.

This apparently has been the case in Mexico where the extension of new flour mills in recent years has contributed to the change in Mexico's net balance of trade in wheat from large net imports (with some 38% of the national wheat flour consumption imported during the 1941–1952 period) to that of self-sufficiency since 1955–1956 and of net exports subsequently. The same motivation appears to have underlined the establishment of a large Nigerian mill and of a mill in Sudan.[12]

Just as U.S. wheat managers are playing an important role in the total food systems of their international consumers, so are managers of non-U.S. firms beginning to develop multinational entities of their own. For example, Ferruzzi Enterprises of Ravenna, Italy, plans to build a large grain export elevator at Myrtle Grove, Louisiana, and perhaps a large flour mill as well. Ferruzzi's organization is the largest importer of feed grains and soybeans in Italy, accounting for about 50% of Italy's grain imports and operating 14 grain elevators.[13] Such backward integration into U.S. operations by importing firms from other countries will undoubtedly expand as the United States plays an even more important role as the bread basket and feed grain supplier to the world food economy.

Similarly, rising incomes and increased world demands for livestock and vegetable feed products will call for additional soybean exports and soybean processing operations overseas. The climatic limitations on the production of this crop will probably limit major production areas to the United States, mainland China, Brazil, Soviet Far East, Canada, and Mexico, but indigenous processing capacity will expand throughout the world to provide local soybean meal and oil supplies to an expanding livestock and human population.

The internal price support and import and export subsidies of wheat and soybean trading countries affect the patterns of world wheat and soybean trade. In addition there are special internal product specification regulations. In many cases these regulations determine the percentage of locally grown wheat that must be used in flour, in oilseed crops, and in processing. In fact, before many U.S. firms can build food processing facilities overseas they usually make public or private agreements with the local government and agree to utilize a certain percentage of local grain before they get a building permit.

In 1964 the Department of Agriculture thought it had found an equitable procedure to break through the nationalistic policies of importing and exporting countries. The principle was "market sharing." The United States signed an agreement with Great Britain to maintain the U.S. percentage of wheat imported into that country and to maintain this same percentage position as the total wheat market expanded in England. During 1965 this policy proved to be unworkable and our wheat shipments to Britain decreased substantially. The British were to attempt to remedy the situation by changing internal policies, but internal political pressures prevented this. The United States again is moving away from a country by country market-sharing principle to some form of overall international pattern under a multinational agreement.

Just as the wheat commodity system is greatly affected by export and import programs so is the structure of the soybean system. The P.L. 480 program for soybean oil has been the safety valve for the domestic growth of the soybean industry. The creation of a Webb-Pomerene cartel to compete in international trade raises many problems. The cartel may be necessary to enable smaller firms to limit their commodity risk in selling large quantities of oil to overseas markets (although a futures market does provide excellent hedging opportunities). Such a cartel must eventually affect domestic prices. Furthermore, if businessmen discuss the value of soybean oil at Rotterdam, it takes very little ingenuity to subtract appropriate freight and handling costs to come to some common agreement on domestic oil prices at Decatur, Illinois.

The increasing tariff barrier of the Common Market on soybean oil and the reluctance to maintain duty-free provisions on meal and oil may mean that additional trade walls will be erected against this industry, which is becoming more and more dependent on the export market. On the other hand, the world needs for soybean and soybean products are so great that these barriers should not prove to be too limiting to the future export expansion of this industry. Undoubtedly, most countries will attempt to expand their local processing operations even if they are unable to grow local soybean supplies.

The Florida orange industry has had limited expansion overseas because of its high cost location compared to competing world sources of supply. Many managers in the Florida orange industry look upon the changing world environment as a threat to the American concentrate market. Typical of the successful efforts to protect this market was the appeal to deny Panama and the Virgin Islands duty-free entrance of citrus products to the United States described in Section IV of this study.

---

[12] Szarf, "Modern Flour Mills in Developing Countries," *Monthly Bulletin of Agricultural Economics and Statistics*, June 1966, p. 14.

[13] *Southwestern Miller*, March 1, 1966, p. 28.

In addition to the type of tariff activity indicated above, the Florida Citrus Mutual has been most anxious to keep citrus fruits and products on the "Exceptions List" of the Kennedy Round of tariff and trade negotiations. The attitude of Mutual was expressed by its Executive Vice President, Robert Rutledge, as follows:

Mutual, along with other industry organizations, has made a strong plea for citrus fruits and products to be placed on the Exceptions List. We are hopeful, of course, that the information and the argument which we have presented will convince the President that any reduction of import duties for citrus fruits and products would jeopardize our industry.

Mutual's all-out effort to maintain our present tariffs is based on the premise that foreign citrus producing nations have the potential to take over a large part of our domestic markets, if our import duties are lowered. Here is a very recent development which substantiates this fear. The Foreign Agricultural Service of the USDA reported on September 7 that citrus growers in the State of Sonora, Mexico are interested in the planting of citrus trees and vineyards in that district. The report of the U.S. Consular Officer had this to say:

"Since water pumping restrictions were imposed on the coast of Hermosillo, growers have been on the lookout for crops less dependent on water and with a cash yield high enough to replace wheat and cotton. Most of the interest seems to be centering on citrus fruits and grapes. Already thousands of citrus trees, mostly orange, have been planted, and studies are underway to plant many more. The United States, of course, is being considered as a potential market for these crops."

It is no wonder that Mutual has spearheaded the drive to maintain our present minimum rates of import duties for citrus fruits and products.[14]

In the past the problem of expanding world trade of agricultural commodities was basically one of balancing national interests. As Dale E. Hathaway stated, "We have now reached the point where agricultural policies are too important to be left to national agricultural interests."[15] New policies of market sharing, coupled with assurances with respect to internal national production and marketing programs, seem to be in the forefront of current international discussions. Overshadowing these discussions is the food shortage emerging in most of the less-developed regions of the world.

The USDA has encouraged private firms, trade associations, and state associations to develop additional marketing programs for the expansion of overseas markets. But such national cooperation is not enough.

The businessman in these respective industries will have to expect major international agreements covering the major product commodities of the world to be enacted in the next decade. The availability of food and commodity price stability, next to war and peace, are the important challenges facing the United Nations today. American agribusiness managers will have to reckon with these challenges in determining their overall policies in formulating strategies consistent with the potential environmental changes facing their respective commodity systems.

One example of the new emphasis on business and government cooperation in improving food systems in developing countries was an informal meeting of U.S. business and government leaders held in the spring of 1966. Recognition of the necessity for effective government-industry partnership in the world agribusiness market was underscored by the high caliber of the committee members.[16]

In tackling the common problem of world food needs, the participants arrived at a number of conclusions pertaining to U.S. industries and government.

(1) New legislation proposed in Congress would shift the emphasis from surplus disposal to integrated self-help programs. Meanwhile, various program guidelines are being changed to ensure more emphasis on quality of food and on the importance of the total agribusiness approach to the developing nations. This broad approach recognizes the fact that the food-processing industry is a key factor in the growth of the total economy of the developing countries.

(2) The U.S. food industry must accept and build on the desire of people and governments to be as self-sufficient in their food operations as possible, and to be an important part of their own local economies. A foreign agribusiness company must recognize this and must utilize the resources of its local economy as fully as possible.

[16] The Committee members included: R. Hal Dean, President, Ralston Purina Co.; Aaron S. Yohalem, Senior Vice President, Corn Products Company; Augustin S. Hart, Jr., Executive Vice President, Quaker Oats Company; Raymond Fiedler, Vice President, Archer-Daniels-Midland Company; Dr. Frank C. Hildebrand, Vice President, General Mills, Incorporated; Robert Callaghan, Assistant to the Director of Research, General Mills, Incorporated; Charles Overbeck, Vice President, General Foods Corporation; L. Edward Klein, Assistant General Manager of International Division, Monsanto Company; Edmond H. Fallon, Executive Vice President, Agway, Incorporated; Dr. A. M. Altschul, Head of Task Force to Develop New Sources of Protein Foods for Developing Countries, U.S. Department of Agriculture; Herbert J. Waters, Assistant Administrator for Material Resources, Agency for International Development; Donald W. Hoaglund, Assistant Director-Development, Finance and Private Enterprise, Agency for International Development; Miss Trienah Meyers, Staff Assistant to the Administrator, Economic Research Service, U.S. Department of Agriculture.

[14] *Florida Citrus Mutual Triangle*, October 14, 1964.
[15] *The Grain Review*, Winnipeg, July 1965, p. 5.

(3) The production and marketing sophistication of private companies is indispensable to the success of a world food program. In a number of developing countries the local governments are often ineffective in their own rural areas, and nongovernment centers are necessary to get the job done.

(4) Aid programs must be administered in such a way as to persuade the developing countries to place a high priority on the building of viable internal food systems, rather than on using aid food as a crutch or on investing in more glamorous industries at the expense of their food economies.

(5) To the fullest extent feasible, food products should be within the commercial price range of low-income consumers.

(6) A whole spectrum of food products should be developed to attack the problem of protein malnutrition. These should not be given away except in school lunch and similar programs, because otherwise they might take on a charity image which inhibits consumption. Dr. Aaron Altschul of the Department of Agriculture has ranked these products according to their availability to the mass market, and translated them into action terms:

(a) Provide diet improvement in a form that will have maximum exposure to the world population by adding amino acids to cereal grain.
(b) Provide cereal, vegetable, and fish protein mixtures in simple form.
(c) Develop processed cereal and protein mixtures.
(d) Develop beverages with a high protein content.
(e) Develop various types of specialty snacks, desserts, spreads, biscuits — all easily added to school lunch programs.
(f) Develop textured foods out of soybean, cottonseed, and other protein materials.

(7) The government should encourage cooperation with the Food and Agriculture Organization of the United Nations in its effort to interest specific companies in the private sector to engage in business in the developing countries.

(8) The government should let private companies assume greater risks as countries become more advanced and viable, but it should also actively participate in covering risks of companies in the most underdeveloped countries by creating special programs. In these countries the government could perhaps take a major part of the risk and allow the private companies to receive management fees and options to purchase the government's interest over time. Specific suggestions for the latter type of situation include (a) outright construction of plant and equipment by the government with leaseback provisions to private enterprise,

and (b) a share in product research and promotion cost.

(9) The government should build on enterprises that already exist in the developing countries and/or encourage new companies to link up with existing food operations.

(10) The government should provide greater clarity of its organization (showing which officials to contact, for example), as well as greater consistency in its programs.

(11) Industry should accept the obligation for social and financial responsibility in the developing nations' economies.

(12) Industry should do a better job of preparing its proposals for the government.

(13) Industry and government should jointly accept the educational job of informing the public, not only of the world food crisis, but of the combined efforts required by industry and government to meet the challenge.

(14) Consortia comprised of several agribusiness companies would seem to hold promise in the development of integrated food ventures in several of the developing nations.

(15) Any policy, either private or public, must be thought of in terms of long lead times because of the length of time necessary to develop appropriate production and marketing systems.

THE FURTHER DEVELOPMENT OF VERTICAL AND CONTRACTUAL INTEGRATION

As in the other major trends described in this section, a different pattern of vertical integration exists for each of the commodity systems analyzed. In the case of the wheat system, a high cost distribution system from baker to retailer encouraged the development of vertical integration into bread manufacturing by retail food firms. There are limits to such vertical integration by the food retailer because he must have enough retail outlets in a compact geographical area to support an efficient bakery operation. Retailers who do not have such geographically compact food chains have resorted to common ownership of a bakery or to long-term contracts with a particular supplier. The improved efficiencies of such a vertically integrated or contractually integrated system have continued to put pressure on the national and local bakery operations to develop new forms of distribution systems that can be competitive, as, for instance, store-door drop deliveries.

Other segments of the wheat system have integrated backward or forward to reduce costs while improving procurement and market operations. This is true of export firms, flour millers, and grain elevator operators. Because of the many complex parts of the wheat system, vertical integration seems to encompass only two or three major segments at any one time. For example, farm cooperatives are primarily active in marketing their grain through country and terminal elevators and to a limited extent through their own export operations. Flour millers that have country elevators are not too involved on the whole in the export of wheat (with the exception of Archer-Daniels-Midland). Flour millers that have their own consumer bakery goods products seem to be withdrawing from the commodity aspects of the flour business (for example, the closing down of the nine General Mills flour mills). With the exception of Nabisco and Sunshine, national bakers have not integrated backward into flour milling to any great extent. The coordination that does exist throughout the system consists of a great variety of central cash markets, futures markets, and long-term contractual arrangements.

In the soybean system a similar pattern of limited vertical integration exists because of the complexity of this system. However, the major exception is the common ownership of grain elevators, soybean processing plants, and feed mill operations that make use of one of the major products of the soybean, that is, soybean meal. The diversity of the consumer products of the oil — salad dressings, mayonnaise, unique types of margarine — seems to provide a natural division between consumer differentiated product operations and the commodity operations of handling and processing the raw materials. Only when there was a shortage of soybean products did the food manufacturers integrate backward to the basic processing of the raw soybean. After the wartime shortage was alleviated, soybean processing plants were sold by many food manufacturers. Similarly, farm cooperatives and other commodity handlers and processors have only limited vertical integration forward into the manufacture of soybean consumer products. However, the development of simulated "synthetic" protein products made from soybean meal provided an additional incentive for commodity firms to produce "chicken," "beef," and "bacon" products for the ultimate consumer made out of soybean meal. Archer-Daniels-Midland, General Mills, and Central Soya are all moving in this direction. At the same time many of these products are sold to food manufacturers who have already developed a franchised market: for example, "smokey crisp" peanut butter containing soybean meal "bacon" has been utilized by the Corn Products Company in its Skippy Peanut Butter.

As in the wheat system, other coordinating machinery exists in the soybean system to help integrate the functions performed in supplying food products effectively to the ultimate consumer. These are central cash and futures markets, as well as unique long-term contractual arrangements, in an industry carrying such diverse products as soybeans, soybean meal, soybean oil, and margarine.

Because of the well-known one-step-processing technology in the Florida orange industry, this system has the greatest amount of vertical integration. The dependence on large, uniform supplies of orange concentrate by the processor and the dependence on processing capacity as a marketing device by the grower have led to both backward and forward integration in this industry. The wide use of the cooperative business arrangement seemed especially well suited to a six-month harvest season with widely fluctuating price levels for raw oranges and processed concentrate. The increased emphasis on market orientation by participants in the industry would seem to encourage cooperative firms to work more closely with the differentiated product-oriented firms. The tremendous impact of particularly large Florida orange crops may mean more government programs, which in themselves may become integrating devices. Even though there is vertical integration in the Florida orange industry up to the food retailer level, only one food retailer has its own orange concentrate facilities. Integration at this level in the vertical structure is usually obtained by annual contracts. The development of a frozen orange concentrate futures market in the fall of 1966 is another coordinating device that will be used by the various segments of this commodity system.

There are several significant trends that will affect future vertical and contractual integration in these commodity systems:

(1) The recent antitrust rulings on mergers in food retailing would seem to indicate that food retailers may transfer funds from retailing into the manufacturing of more of their own products, assuming that these products are suitable for mass distribution and that they provide either production or distribution savings as in the case of bread. In the past Dr. Allen Paul of the Department of Agriculture stated in an analysis of Federal Trade Commission data for 1960–1961:

The main expansion into food manufacturing was by the six largest retailers; the other firms hardly counted. In the case of the six largest firms, the commitment of equity to food manufacturing was about one-quarter of their overall commitment to horizontal and vertical expansion, and nearly a tenth of the equity commitment by others to supply them with more manufactured foods (the main areas of expanded investment were bakery goods, meat products and dairy products).[17]

On the whole, even though return on investment has been declining for food retailers, retail food operations have proved to be more profitable than food manufacturing enterprises. Dr. Paul estimates that it takes about twice as much equity to generate a dollar's worth of sales from food manufacturing as it does from food retailing.[18] Mueller and Garoian in their book, *Changes in the Market Structure of Grocery Retailing,* also indicate that in general vertical integration into food manufacturing would decrease the profits of such vertically integrated grocery retailing firms.[19] On the other hand, return on investment from some retail food manufacturing enterprises has proved much more profitable than the retailing and wholesaling food segment of the business. One example of such success was reported in the September 21, 1964 issue of *Barron's*:

Super Valu has found an even more satisfying method of fattening the bottom-line figure, while improving the competitive position of its affiliates. Briefly, it is greater stress on manufacturing its own products. This idea is not brand new, since virtually every sizeable distributor has captured plants that turn out coffee, jams and jellies, baked goods, ice cream and the like. However, the potential has yet to be fully exploited. Russell W. Byerly, President of Super Valu, reports that its manufacturing and packaging department operates about 2.5% of company sales, but *10%* of net profits.

It would seem that the profit picture of vertical integration is a mixed one. The inflexibility of common ownership, the heavy overhead costs, the red tape, the slowness to adjust, and the inability to have a compact market area for the most efficient production plant are disadvantages that have to be weighed against the advantages of having either a sure and cheap source of supply or a "captured" market for a firm's output, thereby reducing some of the "business risk," enhancing the opportunity of innovation, and improving the allocation of resources (provided, of course, one has the *management* to "coordinate" these activities).

(2) The expansion of private label activities of the food chains (as outlined earlier in this section of the study) also would encourage additional vertical or long-term contractual integration for such products as bread, margarine, and frozen orange concentrate.

(3) The use of the cooperative type of business or-ganization and some of its cash flow advantages would indicate an expansion of this method of vertical integration.

(4) Although some writers have been concerned that vertical integration may mean the destruction of the family farm, this writer does not believe this to be so for two reasons:

(a) Much of the vertical integration in the food economy is the result of farm cooperative integration — the family farmer is doing his own vertical integration.

(b) The investment of approximately $253 billion in physical and financial capital in agriculture is too big an investment, in general terms, for the $13 billion return received by them (including direct government payments).

Even if one includes the average annual capital gain in land values from 1950 to 1960, which amounted to $3.5 billion, or an estimated $2.5 billion after tax value,[20] in addition to the $13 billion of net income, this amounts to only a 6% return on investment. This is hardly a return which would encourage vertical integration. As noted in the Florida orange section, there are returns for specific crops which are attractive. When this investment is attractive, and a certain source of raw material is most important (as it is in the volatile orange concentrate industry), one would expect backward vertical integration into farming activities. This is evident by Minute Maid's ownership of 30,000 acres of orange groves and the strong position of farm cooperatives in this industry.

The capital requirements of agriculture do necessitate a great deal of coordination with many forms of financial institutions, but these credit arrangements fall short of common ownership (vertical integration). The total dollar volume of the credit supplied is $123 billion: $80 billion of lease arrangements for land and $43 billion of outstanding credit financed by life insurance companies, Farm Credit Administration, commercial banks, and individual and merchant lenders.

(5) Finally, vertical and contractual integration do add to the competition of a commodity system by placing the firm in a better bargaining position in dealing with the vertical market structure and in a better competitive position when competing horizontally with other integrated or independent procurement and marketing firms. Vertical and contractual integration do expose the firm to the opportunities of greater innovation, and to the broad application of an innovation

---

[17] *Examining Selected Features of Commodity Markets Through Balance Sheets,* speech by Allen B. Paul.

[18] *Ibid.*

[19] Page 149.

[20] Cochrane, *The City Man's Guide to the Farm Problem,* p. 123.

once it is achieved. Furthermore, the management of a vertically integrated firm is exposed to the total commodity system of which its firm is a part and to the many alternative arrangements and institutions available to the firm.

In spite of the many advantages of vertical integration, many independent firms have been more successful than some of the integrated firms in the wheat, soybean, and Florida orange systems by retaining the flexibility and adaptability of independent action and, at the same time using other types of contractual integration to help them to adapt to or to change the structure of their commodity systems.

NEW USES OF FUTURES MARKETS AS MARKET EXTENDERS

There have been numerous studies on futures markets concerning their success, failure, and cost. An unpublished doctoral dissertation by Charles S. Rockwell of the University of California was discussed in a paper by Dr. Roger W. Gray.[21] According to Dr. Gray, Dr. Rockwell studied some 25 futures markets and determined that the net return to the participants who comprised the long open interest in these markets over a 16-year period was approximately zero. The significance of Rockwell's findings is that there appears, on the average, to be no risk premium paid for the use of the futures markets by the commercial hedgers.

In the wheat, soybean, and Florida orange sections, the use of the futures market was discussed as a coordinating element for the firms in these systems. Basically, the futures market by dampening price swings, reducing inventory risks, and providing a means to finance inventories enabled the businessman to concentrate on the manufacturing and distributing functions of his firm's operations. The means of achieving these advantages was a proper assessment of the relationship between the cash and futures market prices — the basis. The basis is the result of supply and demand conditions at a given time, which is affected by the quality, location, transportation, and available storage factors affecting the commodity, in relation to the futures market price at a given futures terminal market location.

The basis should reflect the supply and demand factors as well as the cost of storing, handling, insuring, and transporting a deliverable commodity from a given moment of time to the futures market time period and terminal market location. But these factors are con-

stantly changing, and therefore one cannot hedge against a basis change. Actually a good procurement executive should make a profit on the basis. For example, assume the price of March 1966 futures soybeans is $2.50 a bushel at Chicago on November 22, 1965 and the cash price at Decatur, Illinois, is $2.30 a bushel, or a basis of 20 cents under March soybeans. If the procurement officer believes this discount is too great because of a lack of storage space at Decatur, he will establish his soybean basis at this time by buying cash soybeans at $2.30 a bushel and selling a March contract for a similar quantity at $2.50 a bushel. Later on, the basis narrows and he still has a good crushing margin between the price of soybeans and soybean meal and oil; he then will remove his hedge. Let us assume that cash soybeans have gone down 5 cents a bushel and March soybean futures have declined 15 cents a bushel. The processor will then sell cash soybeans at $2.25 a bushel and will purchase back his March futures contract at $2.35 a bushel. The basis has narrowed from 20 cents under March to 10 cents under March. The processor has lost 5 cents a bushel on his cash transaction and has made 15 cents a bushel on his futures transactions, or a profit of 10 cents a bushel. Because margin requirements are very small for commodity trading (approximately 10 cents a bushel for soybeans), the processor in effect has netted a 100% return on his investment in inventory "protection." If the basis is too narrow, according to the processor's analysis, he could go "short the basis" and proceed in a reverse fashion to the example outlined above.

The significance of the use of the basis by the industry is that the businessman is only concerned with the horizontal spread between the cash and futures price and not with the vertical price movements, as such for either the cash or futures soybeans contracts. A different type of operator was Mr. De Angelis who was primarily interested in the vertical price movement. The De Angelis fiasco indicated some weaknesses in futures market regulations. In the case of the policy of one produce exchange, contracts were not kept open after the De Angelis case became known, and some users of this market lost confidence in the market to stay open when they needed it most. On the other hand, the Chicago Board of Trade did maintain its futures market operations and not one warehouse receipt in a warehouse regulated by the Chicago Board of Trade was found to be fraudulent. (Some traders believe that it was too much to ask of a futures market to absorb nine months' trading activities in one day as occurred in the soybean oil and cottonseed oil markets during the De Angelis affair, and that a moratorium

[21] *Fundamental Price Behavior Characteristics in Commodity Futures,* address by Dr. Roger W. Gray.

protecting both the buyer and the seller should be declared.)

In spite of the ability to weather Mr. De Angelis' activities, the directors of the Chicago Board of Trade felt that they should have *prevented* such a situation from arising. With this view in mind, a committee was formed known as the Ferguson Committee (see Appendix XI-2, Exhibits 1 and 2). This committee was charged with the task of making recommendations with respect to margins, capital requirements, warehouse procedures, exchange jurisdiction, and government cooperation. Some of the recommendations proved to be controversial, especially margins affecting floor trades activity. Some directors felt quite strongly that unless the Board of Trade took positive action on floor trading margin control, the Department of Agriculture would. This view was expressed by Mr. Bernard P. Carey, Chairman of the Board, Chicago Board of Trade:

There are those who mistakenly consider freedom to be synonymous with license. I am not one, as I view freedom as being directly tied to responsibility. I feel the more responsibility that is self-imposed, the less restraint that will have to be imposed by outside forces. Therefore, it would appear that self-discipline is essential.[22]

In addition to the De Angelis affair which sparked this proposed legislation, an investigation by the Commodity Exchange Authority of a 1963 wheat transaction on the Board of Trade charged that Cargill "temporarily cornered the wheat market on May 21, 1963" (see Appendix XI-3). As of the fall of 1967, the case had not been decided but the Board of Trade had itself intervened on Cargill's behalf, indicative of considerable difference between trade and government conception of "manipulations."

In the Florida orange study, a futures market was suggested as an additional market coordinating device that might be used in conjunction with other market arrangements, such as pooling, cooperative contracts, and a proposed cooperative inventory pool of orange concentrate that would act as a buffer stock for the industry.

Such a frozen orange concentrate futures market was established on October 26, 1966, by the Citrus Associates of the New York Cotton Exchange. During its early days of trading a satisfactory trading price "level" was difficult to obtain (see Exhibit XI-2). The market opened at 29.70 cents per pound of orange

[22] Annual Membership Meeting, Chicago Board of Trade, January 1965.

EXHIBIT XI-2

WALKER & COMPANY
470 ATLANTIC AVENUE
BOSTON 10, MASS.
TELEPHONE: LIberty 2-5814

MEMBERS:
NEW YORK COTTON EXCHANGE
NEW YORK PRODUCE EXCHANGE
MEMPHIS COTTON EXCHANGE
WOOL ASSOCIATES N.Y.C.E.
NEW ORLEANS COTTON EXCHANGE
LONDON WOOL TERMINAL MARKET ASSOC.
Oct. 28, 1966

CITRUS REPORT

This is the first of Walker's citrus letters. Each week we will publish the high-low-close of the citrus futures prices, and describe the market's activity and news.

This market began on Wednesday at 12:30 P.M. with a well attended and traded opening. Prices gained throughout the day and the market closed more than a penny above its opening levels. On Thursday this strength continued, and prices had soon advanced the daily limit (2 cents). On Friday the market again advanced the limit for the week up a total of 5 cents from 30 to 35 cents.

As with all new commodity futures markets, this market is seeking a trading level. Since the first month traded is January 1967, prices must reflect the outlook for the 1966–67 season. With a record crop predicted (139 million boxes), citrus futures prices are currently well below last season's levels. However, the carryover of concentrate from last season is some 20% lower, and there always looms the specter of loss due to weather.

	January	March	May	July
Opening for week	2970 T	2975 T	3000 T	2950 B
High for week	3480	3505	3535	3125
Low for week	2970	2975	3000	2995
Close for week	3480 B	3505 B	3535 B	3580 B

solids. By the end of the week the January 1967 contract had advanced 5.10 cents to 34.80 cents. Also a carrying charge was maintained from January to July of 1.00 cent per pound. As the futures market developed, one processor was able to use the futures market as a market extender. The price of cash fruit compared with the May and July futures prices was low enough for the processor to hedge his cash purchases and rent a processing plant on a toll basis and still make a satisfactory profit. In addition, the Florida Citrus Commission at first insisted that futures traders in Florida would have to be licensed by the Commission. After two weeks of trading the matter was settled so that only brokerage firms with Florida branch offices had to be licensed by the Commission. The major features of the market are as follows:

Citrus Futures Trading Facts

Market: Citrus Associates of the New York Cotton Exchange.

Market Hours: 10:15 a.m. to 3:00 p.m. E.S.T.

Contract Unit: 15,000 pounds of orange solids 3% more or less.

Price Quotations: Fluctuations are recorded in 5/100 cents per pound representing $7.50 per contract. A fluctuation of 1 cent represents $150.00 per contract.

Trading Limits: 2 cents per pound above or below the lowest price in the closing range of the previous day.

Delivery months: January, March, May, July, November, and December to a year ahead.

Deliverable Grades: U.S. Grade A Frozen Orange Concentrate, Brix Range 51° to 65° inclusive, USDA score 92 and above, Brix ratio within 13–19.5.

Deliverable Form: 50–55 gallon drums as customarily accepted in the trade.

Deivery Points: One of the Exchange Licensed Warehouses in Florida.

Commission Rates: (Round turn, nonmembers) Regular: $30.00 Straddle: 45.00

The analysis of the Florida orange industry did indicate that approximately 50% of all frozen concentrate inventory was stored in 55 gallon bulk drums that could constitute a deliverable supply for a futures market. Furthermore, trade practices were such that processors did utilize each other's processed product. In addition, suitable warehouse facilities were available that could be considered as part of a regulated warehouse system. Also, because so much of the product moved on a noncash basis, it would be desirable to have as open a futures market as possible to provide an equitable price barometer for the industry. Such a futures market would also take some of the pressure off the Florida Citrus Mutual, which has attempted to provide the industry with an impartial pricing system. Nevertheless, it does represent one major segment of the industry and would, therefore, be open to the criticism of being potentially biased. The current frozen orange concentrate futures market seems to be able to attract outside speculation to cover the short sales of futures contracts by current inventory holders. Such a futures market should certainly improve the ability of participants to finance inventories. In addition, with the assurance of the Commodity Exchange Authority supervision and the option of developing the market on a *trial* basis, it would seem that the industry had everything to gain and nothing to lose. Furthermore, if an inventory buffer-pool is established, a futures market would provide an effective forward pricing mechanism.

In spite of the adverse publicity of the De Angelis affair most executives in the soybean industry are quite pleased with the overall functioning of the futures markets for soybeans, soybean oil, and soybean meal. Typical of their statements is the following comment by Dwayne Andreas, Executive Vice President of the Archer-Daniels-Midland Company and former Chairman of the Board of the Honeymead Products Company:

Just what basic function has the existence of futures markets in soybeans and the soybean products performed on behalf of the economy as a whole? I believe that the most important effect of their existence is that it has converted the crushing business from a basically speculative business to a manufacturing operation. The crusher who now has this price insurance available to him, concerns himself primarily with the margin of profit he can get by actually crushing the soybeans. Prior to the time he had this price insurance it was necessary for him to be a speculator at almost all times for, in order to capture the soybeans in his area, he would have to buy the beans when the farmers wanted to sell them and pay the market price. He would have to hold the beans until such time as the oil buyer wanted to buy the oil and the feed manufacturer wanted to buy the meal. Only rarely did these three transactions take place at the same time. Thus, he was nearly always in a speculative position.

The speculative characteristics of his business tended to over-shadow the manufacturing side. It was necessary for the crusher to maintain a large working capital which sometimes was idle. He needed it for two reasons. One, as a reserve against possible speculative losses and secondly, to finance his inventories. Under the present arrangement, with inventories hedged at all times, it is a simple matter for a well-managed concern to borrow money from banks for the purpose of carrying inventories and pay only the prime rate. This makes for much more efficient use of capital. I have noticed, too, that there has been a marked tendency on the part of top executives in this industry to pay more attention to manufacturing efficiency. This is the result not only of the fact that the speculative function has been passed on to speculators but the narrowing margins have indeed made it an absolute necessity. If it is true that the existence of this futures market has taken the speculative characteristics out of the crushing business, thereby making it possible for crushers to narrow the spread between the raw material and the finished products, certainly our economy as a whole benefits to that extent.[23]

Just as the Florida orange industry is expanding its market coordinating devices by adding a futures market, so is the soybean commodity system. In September 1966 the New York Produce Exchange developed a soybean futures contract, marking the first time in 30 years that grain futures were traded in New York. The new contract is in a 2,500 bushels trading unit, with warehouse delivery permitted at Ohio and Mississippi river points, with base points at St. Louis, Missouri, and East St. Louis, Illinois. This will provide even broader dimensions to the futures trading alternatives for participants in the soybean system. Because of the dominant position of the United States in world trade, these futures markets are being used by managers of soybean operations around the world.

Other executives in the wheat and soybean industries also have indicated the great need of futures market operations. Walter Goldschmitt of Continental Grain stated:

Because of our 100 million bushel capacity and overall domestic and world grain merchandising activities, we handle quantities of grain at relatively low margin and must at given times be owner of considerable quantities of grain, both in store and in the pipelines.

If we did not have means of shifting risk of ownership, a mere one cent change in the market could alter considerably the appearance of our balance sheet. We simply could not operate with high volume, low margins, and bear heavy risks.

We must shift these risks, and we do so by hedging. We do this automatically whether the price be high or low.

If we did not hedge and had to bear the brunt of commodity market fluctuations, I am certain we would not be able to interest financial institutions to make funds available to us to carry our large inventories. In fact, we could not exist.

What is true for us in degree is true for all grain elevator operators.[24]

In actual practice, the futures market is only one of many devices to hedge inventory positions. It is by far the most important and most liquid hedging device, but domestic and government export programs that maintain domestic and world price levels are also used by the grain trade to limit inventory risk. Government sales of grain by law at a formula percent of parity plus storage charges or at market, whichever is higher, are also at predictable price levels and tend to act as price ceilings for a commodity which is part of government inventories. (This policy may be utilized for aluminum and copper in the future.) Other inventory adjustment aids of a public and private nature have been developed. One notable example in recent years was the transitional certificate given to flour millers when the government price support program was drastically changed, causing a market price drop of 50 cents a bushel.

A comparison of the Chicago wheat and soybean futures market data obtained from the Commodity Exchange Authority provides further insight into the different uses made of futures markets by these two commodity systems.

(1) The amount of open interest in soybeans was approximately three times that of wheat, even though soybeans approximate only three-fourths of the size of the domestic wheat crop, thereby indicating greater speculative interest in soybean as a "glamour" crop and also more utilization of the soybean futures by processors (usually in connection with the soybean meal and oil markets).[25] In the past wheat prices tended to rest on loan levels, whereas soybean prices have been little influenced by the loan. Hence they were more volatile and have created a greater hedging need, attracting greater speculation.

(2) A corollary of the above statement concerns the large percentage of soybean contracts which are held by speculators and small traders in soybean futures compared with the wheat futures.

(3) Also, soybean processors seem to be a more significant factor in soybean futures markets than are flour millers in the Chicago wheat futures market.

(4) Even though exporters in the wheat market are a small factor in the futures market when compared to the amount of wheat exports shipped, soybean exporters are an even smaller factor in the soybean market because of the heavy influx of speculative trading.

(5) A comparison of the Chicago wheat futures data with the wheat futures data of the Minneapolis and Kansas City markets indicate the fact that Chicago has much more participation, thus enabling the hedgers to enter and exit from the market with the minimum impact on it. Also, the Minneapolis and Kansas City markets are predominantly used by the flour millers. However, in 1962 and 1963, exporters did make more

---

[23] The Chicago Board of Trade, Symposium on Futures Trading, 1961.

[24] *Ibid.*

[25] The author was unable to obtain similar data for the soybean oil and meal markets from the Commodity Exchange Authority because of the De Angelis investigation at the time this study was in process.

use of both of these markets as dollar exports of wheat increased.

In essence the data indicate a wide variety of uses of the futures market. The combination of different futures markets for different classes of wheat and the use of futures by product markets (such as oil and meal) improve the flexibility of this marketing tool by the firms engaged in the wheat, soybean, and related industries. In addition, as world markets become more important, and as importers gain the knowledge of futures operations and the use of them in their inventory procurement and management decision making, one would expect the volume of trading of these futures markets to expand and become continually more global in the application of firms to a variety of business procurement and inventory operations.

In the interviews with various executives in the soybean, wheat, and Florida orange industries, several constructive suggestions were made concerning futures market operations:

One group of executives have decided to add to their warehousing facilities to protect themselves against the lack of deliverable qualities or quantities of a commodity in certain futures terminal market locations.

Another executive stated that there must be a new approach to futures trading. He said that his company still buys four times as much wheat in July as they would grind in order to get the type and quality of grain they want, when and where they want it. On the other hand, he could not accomplish this procurement operation as efficiently, or with less risk, if it were not for the wheat futures market. The author suggested the possibility of multiple delivery points, but this was not acceptable to him because of the uncertain location of his futures market supplies.

Yet another flour milling executive felt that the wheat futures market, especially in Minneapolis, should relax the requirements as to deliverable grades so that it would be a more liquid market. As he stated, "Naturally, I would like to buy all my requirements on a futures market, but I don't believe this is the purpose of the market."

Other executives in merchandising activities have been most pleased with the ability to transfer types of inventories and locations of inventories by merely exchanging wheat futures contracts among the several wheat commodity exchanges and the various firms that utilize them.

Other managers indicated that their procurement officers are much more sophisticated in their use of futures markets, and have used them in their overall inventory procurement and management operations. On the other hand, some firms, including vertically-integrated ones, admitted that the futures market operation was little understood by management, that there were loose bookkeeping controls on the operations within the comptroller's office, and even more important, that there was such poor communication between divisions of the company that at the time of closing they found they were on opposite sides of a futures trade in a thin market.

The futures market in the wheat and soybean industries has been a valuable aid in enabling firms in these industries to minimize inventory risk, take advantage of that knowledge of markets, enlarge the financing opportunities, make possible transference of inventories without physically moving the commodity, and provide an enlarged time dimension necessary for long-term commodity commitments and world-wide trading activities. It should be a potential marketing management tool for the Florida orange system.

The future of the futures market seems to be one of continued expansion as new uses of it are developed by various commodity groups: live cattle, live hogs, fresh eggs, slaughtered beef, fish meal futures, to name a few of the new or potential ones.

With over $60 billion of transactions a year and with the impact of the futures market on the internal operations of many firms, a constant re-evaluation of the procedures and safeguards of trading is needed. If floor traders and others who are most important and most needed in the futures market take a short-sighted view of not margining closing balances for the sake of short-term liquidity, then the government will have to take a more active role in the futures market which, in turn, may lessen its rapid response to market conditions.

Finally, potential international commodity agreements, potential frozen orange concentrate inventory pools, the development of operation research tools, and new philosophies of procurement and inventory management operations that are more a part of the total business strategy of the firm will undoubtedly expand the use of the futures market. One view of the potential future of futures markets was well expressed in a communication from Leonard A. Bernstein, Commodity Economist for Merrill, Lynch, Pierce, Fenner & Smith, Inc.:

If I read the future correctly, the greatest single factor which will help futures market trading will be the broadening application of scientific management. Until fairly recently, hedgers were concerned primarily with the avoidance of risk. That is, having been "stuck" with inventory by marketing necessity or poor judgement, the hedger used the futures market as an "outlet" for burdensome supplies. Under scientific management, the futures market will be included in the whole context of procurement, production, warehousing, distribution, pricing and accounting. The futures markets represent an alternative which has not been thoroughly explored by management. Instances of management familiar with futures markets are small relative to those firms which are not familiar with futures market potential.

There are two major forces re-enforcing my belief in the growth of futures markets. First, the tremendous proliferation of computers has opened many doors. Large organizations which had no Operations Research groups a year or two ago are now organizing such staffs. Many more will do so in the future. It is only a matter of time before futures markets enter into the field of study of this scientific group. We know of pioneering efforts. It seems unbelievable that futures markets will not benefit from this expanded applied scientific approach.

The second major reason for my belief in the growth of futures markets is the ever-expanding attention this institution is receiving in the academic world. More and more schools are acknowledging this area of study. In time, the growing interest means an ever-increasing flow of graduates familiar with futures markets and familiar in a sophisticated way. This trend will not only spur Operations Research effort, but will also increase the acceptance rate of newly developed techniques.

I envision that scientific management will ultimately employ scientific decision rules as fruitfully as they have linear programming. Concepts born only in World War II are now indispensable to industry. In fact, there is no reason why futures market operations cannot be incorporated into one or more of the equations of a linear program.

Futures markets, as any industry, will survive, thrive or die depending upon its ability to provide a wanted economic service. The "concept" is surely desirable. Risk avoidance and inventory policies are a matter of present concern and will be as long as we remain a capitalistic society. However, futures markets psychology is too much geared to risk. Is it possible that a new emphasis might develop? Such as pooling of resources by an industry with the speculator underwriting the residual price risk of the inventory pool. With technology standardizing many parts, perhaps the futures markets of 2000 A.D. will facilitate the flow of standardized parts between different companies of the same industry or from one industry to another. For example, in a simplified way, if Company A can make a standardized steel rod cheaper than Company B, but Company B is a more efficient producer of steel balls than Company A, the overall efficiency of the industry would benefit if the switch could be arranged. This transfer would be simple enough, but how much more complex it would be for many firms in many industries. To do this, perhaps a greater degree of standardization would be required than now exists. However, there is a trend toward standardization and, perhaps, a futures market of this kind is not so far-fetched.

The futures market as an important market coordination does fit the unique market development of each commodity system analyzed.

It does provide the firm with additional flexibility in carrying out its procurement function and inventory management operations, especially over long periods of time. It not only provides flexibility, but it is crucial to survival, as indicated by the bankruptcy of a prominent sugar firm that did not hedge its sugar inventory during the wide price movements that occurred in 1964.

It does narrow the price swings that would occur without the futures market in which to hedge. Although we have no empirical evidence of soybean and wheat price movements without futures on which to base this judgment, studies of other commodities that have and have not had futures markets in recent years, such as onions, have proven to have wider price swings without the futures market.

The futures market can be used by large and small operators alike in spite of some advantage to those operators that have elevator space in terminal locations. A futures market is the market that most closely approximates the competitive equilibrium model's requirements: (a) large numbers of buyers and sellers, (b) a homogeneous product, (c) free entry, and (d) full information for all participants. In addition, the requirement of concentrating transactions in selected contract months helps to prevent the fragmentation of a competitive market into a number of potentially separate monopolistic markets.

By permitting the firm to lessen its inventory price risk, the futures market has freed management to spend more time on product, production, and distribution innovation.

All of the above conditions are meaningful where there is active hedging and speculative interest. It takes time for a futures market to attract such participation. For example, "For a period from 1948 to 1953, hedging was done at a substantial price sacrifice in soybean futures. The average cost of hedging, in terms of price change against the hedger's position, was about 9 cents a bushel. Since that time, as the trade developed, the much larger market has sustained a much larger hedging load with *no* price sacrifice." [26] This market activity requires both hedging and speculative participation.

In essence, the futures market is an important coordinating element in the wheat and soybean systems and holds much promise in its use in the Florida

[26] Gray, "The Attack Upon Potato Futures Trading in the United States," *Food Research Institute Studies*, p. 109.

orange system. In addition other economists have suggested that it may be appropriately used by the government as a price stabilizer. For example, Dr. Hendrik S. Houthakker, Professor of Economics at Harvard, suggested that all government price support activities be centered in the futures market with an end to all other programs.[27] A commodity stabilization agency would have five well-defined price limits: Agency Floor Price, Agency Buying Price, Agency Indicator Price, Agency Selling Price, and Agency

[27] Statement before the National Advisory Commission on Food and Fiber, Minneapolis, October 3, 1966.

Ceiling Price. Such a program with known limits would tend to minimize speculative participation.

As commodity systems get broader in their marketing and procurement activities, as more sophisticated consumer demands call for more numerous specialized functions, intricate, international pricing devices will become more important in the coordination of the many functions of a commodity system. The futures market, as such a device, will play an even more important role in these commodity systems in the future.

XII

Summary and Conclusions

IN SUMMARY, the special characteristics of agricultural industries have led to the development of private policies and public programs which will have a significant impact on their future structure and behavior. The seasonal and unpredictable nature of agricultural production combined with year-round consumption of food products has resulted in supply and demand imbalances. Such imbalances, in turn, have led to wide variations in prices, incomes, and the quantity and quality of product flows. The extreme and rapid adjustments that participants and industries have had to make as a result of sudden shifts in domestic and world food and fiber supplies have in turn resulted in the establishment of devices by both private and public institutions to help alleviate temporary imbalances and enable participants to anticipate and adjust to change more effectively and with less financial and personal risk. Such devices have included futures markets, cooperative entities, trade associations, contractual and vertical integration, as well as a wide range of government programs such as price supports, compensatory payments, international trade agreements, and relief and self-help programs. All of these devices have been used to help participants adjust to supply and demand imbalances at price levels that provide for viable business operations throughout the system.

These devices have become integral and significant features of many commodity systems, they affect one another, and they have led and are leading to major changes in the organization and operation of most agribusiness firms and entities. The new uses of futures markets as market extenders, the growth of new forms of cooperative-corporate entities, the new utilization of domestic and international governmental programs, the further development of vertical and contractual integration, the better utilization of trade

associations, and the development of new product strategies for private labels and branded food items are trends that have emerged from the challenges of serving efficiently (in the face of uncertain supplies) a new mass food market made up of a wide variety of domestic and international market segments. The challenge of serving these markets is made greater and more complex, not only because of the uncertainties of the quantity and quality of supplies, but also because of the intricate and interrelated nature of the coordinating machinery developed for each commodity system.

Management's understanding of the coordination of the physical and human resources of each system; the development of a more efficient and sophisticated infrastructure of transportation, finance, and education; and the formation of a formal and informal communication network to enable management to systematize its industry intelligence system are all essential for the functioning and effective growth of each commodity system. In each commodity system changes are constantly occurring that open up new challenges and areas of growth and at the same time cause facilities, products, and ways of doing business to become obsolete. The existence of excess capacity for certain products and production facilities and of shortages of products and production facilities in other areas is evidence of the constant adjustments the system and its parts are making. Although managers of firms in any kind of industry structure must be aware of their total industry environment, the peculiar characteristics of agricultural industries with unpredictable and seasonal supplies, the expanding interrelationships in the vertical structure from farm supplier through ultimate distributor, the need for a strong infrastructure, the increasing significance of world markets, and the existence and importance of complex coordinating machinery make a systems approach much more critical in the development of strategies for firms in agricultural industries than for firms in other types of industrial structures. Furthermore, in agricultural industries the day-to-day concern with supplies and qualities of farm-produced goods has had a tendency to keep key executives over-occupied with "commodity-trading" activities. Hence, they have placed less emphasis on comprehending and responding to the major changes that affect the basic nature and structure of their domestic and international commodity system. With such a narrow perspective, there is a great danger that managers will lose out on profitable opportunities for the future or become victims of a changing market structure in which their functions have been materially altered.

The wheat, soybean, and orange industry systems were selected to show the wide range of coordinating devices that have been critical in the various stages of the development of these industry systems. Obviously the special characteristics of each system and the types of people involved in these systems determine the nature and strength of the firms and institutions and arrangements that make up the system. Even though the government is important as a major shock absorber and supporter of the market system and sometimes may play a dominating role in price and product flows, the ultimate effectiveness of the system is dependent upon the many private decision makers that perform the necessary functions of producing, processing and supplying food to the ultimate consumer.

A systems approach gives us several ways in which to analyze the importance of interrelationships and the probable effects of different kinds of change no matter what the source of that change — e.g., economic, political, social, technological, or managerial. The manager of a firm, the public policy maker, and those interested in the total system cannot plan advantageously for change unless they understand the critical implications of the potential change that may take place. Furthermore, the adaptability and flexibility of a company policy or a public policy require an understanding of the system so that the decision maker can not only see potential opportunities, but also provide for "escape hatches" if he is wrong.

The utility to private and public agribusiness managers of taking a commodity systems approach is best supported by examining the salient features and trends noted in the analysis of the previous sections of this study. In each commodity system major changes were occurring that affected the entire structure of the system and the alternative opportunities and constraints of the participants.

WHEAT

In the case of wheat, a systems approach to the income problems of wheat producers might have enabled public policy makers and managers to have some indication of the ramifications of their programs on the total vertical structure of the wheat industry. As it was, the desperate need for storage facilities in the face of larger crops, coupled with the loss of some international markets after World War II, called for immediate action by the government. The five-year depreciation write-off provisions and guaranteed occupancies of wheat in storage facilities helped to alleviate the immediate problem of what to do with the wheat but at the same time they changed the total operation of the wheat system for some time to come. The wheat price support program and the resultant wheat storage policies were extremely important in determining the kinds of firms that became dominant in grain procurement and flour milling. Eventually the program led to the construction of excess grain storage capacity with grain elevator managers and flour millers using grain storage income as a means of reducing handling and processing margins on wheat and flour products. The excess grain storage capacity in turn resulted in the development of company strategies that led to increasing the storage and movement of wheat rather than meeting or anticipating consumer requirements. Excess capacity in all segments of the wheat system led to some bankruptcies which in turn resulted in new participants in the system who took over facilities at extremely low investment values, and this in turn is continuing economic pressure in the industry. In addition, international programs were also "producer or commodity oriented." The question was, how do we get rid of the wheat? The P.L. 480 Food-for-Peace Program became a dumping exercise and in many cases may have postponed economic development in some countries rather than encouraging it.

A growing awareness by public managers of the impact of government programs on the total wheat structure and its commodity orientation rather than market orientation led to a change in policy in 1965 with the passage of new wheat feed grain legislation. The compensatory provisions of this legislation still maintain a reasonable income level for commercial wheat producers and at the same time give the market system more freedom to adjust to and anticipate changing market needs. The legislation gives much more freedom of choice for all participants. It also has a legislative life for a four-year period, thus enabling managers to plan ahead without fear of a sudden program change. In addition, price support provisions are low enough to enable domestic and international consumer requirements to be translated into market demand rather than have producers produce for "high price support programs" and government storage bins. Also the government sales price to the market is high enough to permit free markets to work between extremely low and high price levels. The P.L. 480 program is still operated on an uncommitted basis that will undoubtedly have major effects on the market. At the same time, the government is attempting to announce estimated annual P.L. 480 shipments ahead of time to enable managers to plan without necessarily announcing specific arrangements for individual countries. All in all, this new systems approach to wheat programs by the government is enabling managers to develop more meaningful short-run and long-range strategies for their respective firms.

The government's less active role in the wheat system has already resulted in a revaluation of procurement and marketing activities in the wheat system. The "freeing up" of the market system has resulted in less concentrated supplies in the government's hands and has encouraged the private decision maker to resort to new methods of procurement and marketing. No longer can a private firm buy several million bushels from the government in one location of one kind of quality at his own time convenience. This has led some firms to look at country subterminal operations as becoming more important as sources of current supply. It has also led to new contractual relationships with cooperative and noncooperative wheat suppliers. These new contractual relationships have led to contractual and vertical integration which undoubtedly has improved the product flows in the system and has resulted in some procurement and marketing efficiencies. On the other hand, the same vertical integration may have postponed changes in the industry or may lead to certain economic centers of strength which may cause public policy problems in the future.

The new systems approach by the public manager means that private decision makers must undertake a similar approach if they are to understand, utilize, or respond to these programs which affect their firms and commodity systems. Managers in the wheat system must also develop some sort of device to communicate their ideas to the public managers in the system. It was not until 1965 that this industry had a trade association that cut across all the major segments of the industry, and even in 1967 debates were going on as to how to finance and utilize such an association. The existence of government programs for wheat over the past 30 years that have affected all segments of the wheat system has probably made participants in

each segment of the system more aware of the total system than has any private firm, arrangement, or institution.

At the same time that private and public managers were concerned with over-production problems, events beyond the control of the U.S. wheat decision maker changed many of these situations overnight. The droughts in Asia and Russia changed a world wheat surplus into a temporary world wheat shortage. The population explosion together with the current Asian and Mideastern crises have led to a reassessment of the need for U.S. food reserves. The wheat reserve of the past is beginning to seem fairly small for the potential year-to-year fluctuations that may take place. There is widespread agreement that a food reserve should be established. The 1966–1967 government wheat program may set the example for such a reserve whereby minimum and maximum purchase and sale prices are anticipated to be set at levels that will permit the market to adjust to normal fluctuations in supply and demand, with the government becoming the "stabilizer" in periods of chronic shortages and surpluses. Some kind of stand-by controls similar to the ones that participants of the wheat complex are currently utilizing may be needed if major production adjustments become necessary.

As the wheat system changes in response to domestic and world conditions, there will probably be continued growth in the interaction between business and government policy makers. Obviously with public and private managers having a common understanding of the nature of the wheat system, greater cooperation between them is possible. An example of government-business cooperation in the international sphere is the growth of commercial wheat exports. The wheat exporters may constantly look for new market outlets, but governmental policy makers may be needed to gain access for U.S. firms in these markets. To gain access for U.S. wheat may involve obtaining a guaranteed minimum percent of the market at competitive prices, as well as agreeing to U.S. tariff reductions. The U.S. government is also important in the development of concessional markets for wheat. The U.S. government and the P.L. 480 recipient governments will probably be the dominant determinants in the *volume* of concessional overseas market operations, and the wheat exporter will be held responsible for developing and carrying out the terms of trade. The buyer in the concessional market country may be either the local government or a private firm. The businessman may also require more governmental auxiliary services and perhaps an international agency's aid as international markets and sources of supply become more widespread and complex. This may involve new international grades and information services. Domestically, the government's policies in regard to either farm income or reserve stocks will continue to be important factors in determining the wheat structure. Greater cooperation is possible here in determining minimum price levels and the proper and least disruptive procedure in placing government wheat into commercial channels during periods of wheat shortage.

The increasing importance of the world market for the U.S. wheat complex in terms not only of shipping products overseas, but also of helping to construct complete vertical structures from farm supplies to food distribution and infrastructures in some developing nations, will mean new opportunities for exporters and the utilization of additional public and private coordinating machinery that may become critical in the profitable operation of firms in a future U.S. wheat commodity system. Technological transference overseas may involve not only the transfer and adaptation of a specific technology, but also the use of a systems approach applied to the structure of a particular country's wheat system.

Consumer orientation is beginning to replace the concern with product flows by both private and public decision makers as both take a more systematic approach to their industry. This has meant the development of new products that appeal to the changing style of living in this country and in other countries. Many firms are beginning to reassess their overall company strategies. This has resulted in some firms getting out of the commodity parts of their business and has forced a major restructuring of some industries. (The closing of 9 of its 17 flour mills at once by General Mills is but one example.)

A systems approach to the wheat system is beginning to take place in the management strategies of those participants involved in the supporting structure of the wheat system. For example, the change in cost differentials between transporting wheat and transporting flour has had an effect on the location of the flour milling industry. Equally important is the change in the cost of transportation due to new methods of determining rates. The breakdown in milling in-transit privileges and freight break centers has placed many firms at new competitive disadvantages or advantages. With a systems approach to the logistics of this industry, these transportation differentials can be more equitably determined and set by the Interstate Commerce Commission and other parties.

In essence, private and public managers are beginning to take a systems approach as they formulate strategies by which to operate in a rapidly changing wheat system. Undoubtedly new coordinating devices will be needed to help the participants adjust to change. Some of these devices will include a greater international use of futures markets and the development of domestic and international food reserves. Rapid changes due to population and production imbalances, unsettled international relations, weather uncertainties, new nutritional discoveries, new cooperative and corporate managerial entities all will call for rapid adjustments by private and public managers as they respond to change or help to create change. In such an environment the private manager and the public manager really cannot afford to view these potential changes and their reactions to them in any other kind of perspective than that of the total system. Furthermore, as the government policy maker thinks in broader terms, the private policy maker is going to have to think in a similar manner. In addition, unless the private policy maker plans to abdicate his influence on the future development of his system and leave it completely to the government, then he is going to have to find some device which enables the private sector to play a more important role in the formulating of policies for his commodity system.

SOYBEANS

From its inception, the U.S. soybean industry stands as a prime example of the need for a systems approach to a commodity market structure. Neither production nor processing could take place in isolation. The producer wanted some reasonable expectation of a market before he became committed to the growing of soybeans, and the processor in turn wanted a reliable source of supply; and both of them had to have a consumer and industrial market that could and wanted to utilize the major products of the soybean — meal and oil. By taking a broad perspective of their commodity system, the participants in this industry were able to expand their operations and improve the organization of their market structure to the benefit of the firms and entities in the system and to the benefit of the ultimate consumers they serve.

A systems approach to this commodity organization has also been important because of the same types of problems and challenges that are common in other agribusiness industries. The uncertainty of soybean production and harvest bulges have produced similar kinds of coordinating arrangements in the soybean system that were noted in the wheat industry. However, different structural effects have occurred because of the changing market conditions for fats and oil products and for livestock and poultry products which have had such a rapid growth in consumer demand in this and other developed economies.

There are imbalances in the demand for the joint products obtained from soybeans. The changing price relationships between soybean meal and oil were extremely important in determining the profit of the processing industry. In addition, the price of soybean oil vs. soybean meal affected the technology of the industry, whereby processing changed from a hydraulic to a solvent extraction process which obtained more oil from the soybean. By-product imbalances in this industry led to government programs such as the P.L. 480 program for soybean oil which remains (together with a price support program) the major balancing device for the soybean industry.

The growth of the commercial markets for the products of the soybean has led to less income pressures on the soybean producer and to the establishment of a price support program set at low enough levels to enable the market to be operative without having the government become a major "market" outlet for the soybean. The future development of a reserve policy that may include soybeans would mean the eventual build-up of soybean stocks that would help to smooth the price swings in the soybean, soybean meal, and oil markets. At the same time, the probable existence of both the concessional market (P.L. 480) for soybean oil and the reserve for soybeans would mean a continuation of governmental activity in the soybean system. In addition the government would be a major factor in providing access to certain foreign markets. Also, the government would continue to be an important seed and product research resource for the soybean industry. This continued governmental activity and uneven growth in the industry suggests that there will be continued interaction between private and public managers. A common systems approach should lead to a greater harmonization of the key decision-making roles that each will play in the future.

The rapidly changing livestock and cattle population and its increasing needs for soybean meal as a feed supplement, together with the competition soybean oil faces from other types of vegetable oils and fats, have led to many price fluctuations in this industry. In the past, the soybean price support program has been a somewhat minor factor in decreasing price fluctuations in this industry because the price support has been at a level that has usually been below the market price. This has meant that this industry has had to resort to more private or quasi-public coordinating devices to help lessen the production, procurement, marketing, inventory, and processing problems that exist when there are wide fluctuations in supply and demand. The fact that soybeans, soybean oil, and soybean meal futures markets represent over half the volume of futures market activity for all commodities is but one example of the importance of such a coordinating device to this commodity system. The development of pool arrangements by cooperatives and toll charge arrangements and annual contracts for soybeans, soybean oil, margarine, and soybean meal by other firms are other examples of the types of coordinating devices utilized in this industry. A systems approach would seem to be necessary in order to understand the usefulness of these devices to the firms involved.

The importance of freight rates in agribusiness industry systems noted in the wheat industry is also well documented in the soybean industry. The difference in freight rates between meal and oil and between truck, rail, and barge facilities led to captive transportation operations within a firm and to widely divergent processing gross margins for firms in various locations and eventually broke down a formulistic basing-point pricing system. Again a systems approach to the logistics of this domestic and international industry is essential for both the managers of the firms in the systems and for managers responsible for the development of an effective and flexible transportation network.

The private policy makers in the soybean industry have had the advantage of participating in a commodity system that was relatively new in the United States, that was organized in a compact geographical section of the Corn Belt, and that was responding to the protein and oil needs of an expanding and more prosperous domestic and world population. Being a relatively new commodity organization, it seemed less difficult to develop an all-embracing domestic commodity association that provided easy interchange among the participants of the system. In addition, an international soybean council was formed and became a major market developer for overseas markets. The fact that over 40% of U.S. soybean products are exported is indicative of the success of the council.

There are many changes on the horizon that will affect the structure of the soybean system such as the potential major improvement in soybean yields in the United States and the development of new competitive production areas in other countries. At the same time, the quest for additional sources of protein, such as petroleum, urea, fish meal, and high protein lysine corn, and for new sources of vegetable oil will provide competitive pressures that will keep participants in this relatively young U.S. industry complex alert and prepared to adjust their soybean system to change.

Such adjustments can be best made in the broad perspective of a commodity systems approach.

FLORIDA ORANGES

The special characteristics of agricultural industries that make a systems approach so necessary in the formulation of effective strategies by private and public managers is perhaps best illustrated by the Florida orange commodity system. Because of the concentration of the orange crop in a few counties in the state, the production uncertainties of the crop and the seasonal bulges become even more exaggerated in this system. In addition the four- to five-year period for new trees to bear fruit and the 50- to 60-year utility of an orange grove have led to production cycles that become out of phase with consumer needs for long periods of time. Hurricanes, freezes, and the development of a new product (frozen orange juice concentrate) in the past, however, kept chronic surplus conditions from occurring. Therefore, most of the coordinating machinery in this industry was of a nongovernmental type.

In 1967 a 40% increase in Florida orange production has caused a major change in the thinking of private and public policy makers. Temporary programs were instituted, such as the purchase of 14.3 million gallons of orange juice by the U.S. Department of Agriculture for the school lunch program. In addition a growers' group, the Florida Citrus Mutual, has set forth various programs such as marketing agreements, stabilization programs, and a reserve inventory pool to alleviate the current situation and to help cope with additional production increases that are forecast based on the new tree plantings that currently exist in the state. If orange production continues to increase without the "relief" of a freeze or hurricane, pressure will continue to mount for a government acreage control, product diversion, or income supplement program that will help to alleviate the adverse income effects of over-production at the farm level.

On the other hand, there have been some beneficial effects of the production explosion. Many private managers who took the market for orange products to be one based on "price" alone have given more attention to the development of new products and to new methods of distribution. Many of the cooperative leaders in the industry are becoming more market oriented and have given support to methods of differentiating their products and market channels rather than concentrating on how to "get rid of the product." In addition market aids that were once viewed with suspicion are now being utilized by managers in this

system. One such market extender is the frozen orange concentrate futures market, which was instituted in October 1966 and has thus far proved most useful in the inventory, processing, and marketing activities of many participants in the system. Also coordinating devices, such as vertical and contractual integration and cooperatives, are being re-examined as to their usefulness in the face of the new production levels of this industry. Furthermore, new products and additives, as well as synthetics, that broaden the product spectrum of this industry are no longer viewed as "impure." Sugar additives, lemon-orange combinations, synthetic and natural combinations of products are being developed without the fear of endangering the "purity" of the orange product.

The concentration of the crop and the processing industry in a few counties in the state may accentuate the supply and demand imbalances of this commodity system; but on the other hand, the development of coordinating machinery for the system is made easier because of such geographical concentration and having participants engaged in a common endeavor to improve the production and marketing of one crop. With the ease of communication and the development of excellent industry associations, together with the broader perspective of managers in this industry, the participants in this commodity system are in a position to face the challenge of new domestic and international production levels.

FINAL CONCLUSIONS

It has been the central thesis of this study that to deal effectively with the challenges and opportunities of the U.S. and world food economies, managers have to deal with them as agribusiness opportunities and not solely as agricultural problems. A systems approach embracing all facets of an agribusiness commodity system is essential for the development of effective short-range and long-range strategies for the various participants in these commodity systems.

If such an approach is adopted:

(1) *The public policy maker will be in a better position to formulate policies which will be effective for the total system if he develops them in terms of the commodity system and if he understands the implications of his policy for all its parts.*

(2) *The businessman will also be in a better position to develop more profitable strategies for his firm if he can identify his specific area of competence in the broader perspective of his total industry system and take appropriate actions.*

(3) *With a common understanding of the com-*

modity system of which they are a part, there would be more effective cooperation and interaction between the public and the private policy maker.

CHALLENGES

From this recapitulation of the general nature and probable trends of each of these commodity systems, it would appear evident that even if the private and public policy makers are aware of their total commodity systems and the interactions between the private and public sectors there still remain many probable and unforeseen changes that create a substantial element of judgment in adopting any far-reaching private or public program of action. The encouraging aspect of analyzing these industries as integrated systems is that the degree of risk can be greatly reduced through an understanding of the probable ramification to the system and its parts. Such knowledge also provides indications of what parts of a private or public plan require maximum flexibility or "stand-by" readiness to be used by the public or business manager in case of anticipated or unanticipated changes in or outside of the system.

A few of the many critical challenges facing public policy makers are as follows:

(1) To continue to develop programs that provide minimum income protection to the commercial producer without destroying the competitive adjustability of all the parts of the system to respond to market changes;

(2) To develop programs far enough in advance to aid the plans of all the participants in the system but with built-in and known flexibilities for adjusting to major changes;

(3) To provide new services to the domestic and international agribusinessmen who are constantly reaching back in distant places for sources of supply and reaching farther out to develop new domestic and international markets;

(4) To organize government agencies in such a way as to provide greater interchange between business and government and between a wide variety of government agencies so that all will have the broader perspective of an efficient and viable commodity system; and

(5) To develop periodic studies of the total agribusiness system.

Critical challenges facing the businessman are:

(1) To develop an industry intelligence network which will provide the participants with a greater under-

standing of the interrelationships of the parts of the system and the major ramifications of certain types of private and public policies;

(2) To develop better types of trade associations which will be able to communicate industry information to proper government authorities in order to provide statesmanlike leadership in aiding public policy makers in the formulation of policies for the industry system;

(3) To recognize that the very nature of the supply process will mean continued government programs either in active use or on a stand-by basis, and that he has the alternative of adjusting to these programs or utilizing them in his operations;

(4) To be bolder in the use of present and future ways of meshing his firm's operations into his total commodity system through better use of markets, new contractual arrangements, futures market operations, vertical integration, and the use of new forms of business organizations such as combined corporate and cooperative entities;

(5) To broaden his conception of his industry system constantly and to recognize that his firm's and his industry's ultimate market is made up of domestic and international food consumers who think in terms of diverse and changing styles of living rather than in terms of wheat flour, soybean oil, or orange concentrate.

In essence then, through a broad understanding of the nature and trends of their commodity systems, both the public and private manager have opportunities to develop policies and procedures that will improve the performance of their industry and respective entities and better prepare their industry for adjustments to change as they satisfy the ultimate consumers' food requirements. This systems approach to decision making in agribusiness industries is consistent with the outlook for the action of other U.S. industries as expressed in a recent *Fortune Magazine* article:

By 1977 the U.S. should understand more clearly that its highest satisfactions are derived from the way we go about forming our choices and organizing our action, a way that stresses persuasion over force and arbitrary authority, a way that extends to more and more new shares of responsibility for the future.

.   .   .   .   .

[One of] the characteristics of this [philosophy] is an emphasis on information, prediction, and persuasion, rather than on coercive or authoritarian power, as the main agents of coordinating the separate elements of an effort.[1]

[1] Max Ways, "The Road to 1977," January 1967, pp. 93–95, 194–197.

Appendix

APPENDIX TABLE II-1. Agribusiness Flow Chart Data: 1947, 1954, 1958, and 1962
(In billions of dollars)

	1947[a]	1954[a]	1958[b]	1962[c]
Farm supply sales (farm purchases)	$12.90	$16.40	$18.89[b]	$21.00[d]
Feed manufacturing	2.42	2.70	2.96	3.73
Farm machinery and automotive power	3.60	5.80	4.56[e]	5.20
Seed	0.52	0.60	0.38	0.53
Wholesale trade	0.60	0.50	1.73[f]	—[q]
Retail trade	0.80	n.a.	n.a.	—[q]
Transportation	0.96	1.00	0.83[g]	0.90
Power	0.50	0.70	1.11[h]	1.41
Containers	1.00	1.00	0.20	0.20
Fertilizer	0.42	1.20	1.30	1.60
All other	2.08	2.90	5.82[i]	7.43[q]
Ingredients from processed food industry used for animal and poultry feed	2.19	2.42	—	2.99
Oil meals used in animal and poultry feed	0.21	0.30	—	0.74
Farm sales (processing and distribution purchases)	29.40	29.59	33.41[b]	35.92[d]
Food industries	14.54	14.50	18.41	20.00
Oils	0.81	1.00	1.00	1.80
Drinking and eating places	0.79	0.80	—[j]	—[j]
Alcoholic beverages	0.35	0.30	0.30	0.30
Textiles	2.09	2.09	1.50	2.30
Tobacco products	0.78	0.70	1.10	1.30
Wood and paper	0.19	0.20	0.80[k]	0.80[k]
Nonprocessed foods[e]	9.73	10.00	10.30	9.42[m]
Oils from oilseed crops used in soap and paint	0.72	0.80	—	—
Leather processing	0.49	0.70	—	—
Processing and distribution sales (consumers or household final demand)	62.92	76.40	103.63[n]	114.47[o]
Soap and paint	0.95	1.00	2.28	2.50
Leather	2.07	3.00	4.61	5.00
Food industries	21.02 ⎫	27.70 ⎫	⎫	⎫
Drinking and eating places	13.11 ⎬ 45.07	16.40 ⎬ 55.60	61.94 ⎬ 66.51	64.20 ⎬ 73.62
Alcoholic beverages	1.21 ⎪	1.50 ⎪	⎪	⎪
Nonprocessed foods[e]	9.73 ⎭	10.00 ⎭	4.57 ⎭	9.42 ⎭
Textiles	11.36	11.00	21.40	24.60
Tobacco products	1.48	2.80	4.25	5.25
Wood and paper	1.99	3.00	3.58	3.50
Wholesale and retail trade at household level				
On above items	8.50	12.60	—[n]	—[n]
All other[p]	1.50	3.00	3.00	3.50
Processing and distribution sales plus wholesale and retail trade (sales to final consumer)	72.92	92.00	105.63	117.97

[a] Compiled from input-output data and USDA estimates. All amounts are in producer's values with the exception of farm supplies, which include some retail and wholesale price margins.

[b] All values for 1958 are at a producer's level, and discrepancies may be explained by the inclusion of trade margins in the 1947 and the 1954 estimates. Large discrepancies from 1947 and 1954 are probably due to differences in coverage and treatment.

[c] 1962 estimates by author obtained through use of USDA and Census data.

[d] 1962 estimates in producer's values as described in (b) and (n).

[e] This estimate includes the following items (in thousands of 1958 dollars):
    1. Repair and operation of farm machinery excluding petroleum fuel and oil $1,264,074
    2. Depreciation of farm machinery: (a) Autos   436,000
                                (b) Trucks   520,000
                                (c) Tractors   683,000
                                (d) Other farm machinery   1,217,000
                            Total $4,120,074

[f] Trade margin covers wholesale and retail trade margins, retail taxes, and import duties.

[g] This estimate includes the following items (in thousands of 1958 dollars):

1. Transportation margin	$ 544,867
2. Railroad traveling expenses	29,642
3. Trucking livestock not to market	61,562
4. Milk hauling	178,356
5. Airline traveling expenses	14,842
Total	$ 829,269

[h] Power purchases include petroleum fuel and oil for operation and farm machinery, bituminous coal, fuel oil and gas for heating, and electric light and power.

[i] This estimate includes the following items (in thousands of 1958 dollars): (Producers' value)

All other

1. Cotton ginning	$ 169,698
2. Veterinary services and medicines	132,487
3. Miscellaneous farm business expenses	888,515
4. Miscellaneous supplies	85,573
5. Nonlife insurance, other than auto, truck, and federal crop	149,320
6. Livestock marketing charges	111,760
7. Irrigation	101,510
8. Binding materials	43,327
9. Telephone	118,442
10. Miscellaneous expenses of greenhouse, except bituminous coal and fuel oil for heating and gas for heating	37,920
11. Miscellaneous dairy supplies and DHIA fees	42,340
12. Syrup tolls	2,816
13. Grazing fees	8,774
14. Federal crop insurance	11,948
15. Real estate taxes	816,914
16. Personal property tax	239,800
17. Maintenance on real estate	501,973
18. Salt	28,549
19. Pesticides	181,443
20. Advertising other than greenhouse and nursery	1,089
21. Gross rent on SS&L to nonfarm LL excluding government payments	1,434,214
22. Gross rent on SS&L to farm LL excluding government payments	716,202
Total	$5,824,614

[j] The 1958 input-output framework distribution of nonmanufactured food items to "eating and drinking places" is included in the household allocation and will be included under nonprocessed foods.

[k] The entire production of forest products by farmers in 1958 and 1962 extrapolation was considered to be a secondary product and was transferred to Sectors 3 and 12, forestry and fishery products and lumber products, except wooden containers, respectively.

[l] Includes food products purchased by consumers in relatively unchanged form (like eggs or fresh vegetables) and also those consumed on the farm.

[m] Differences in the 1958 and 1962 treatment have considerably reduced this estimate. Values for farm fresh meat sales and consumption are considered as secondary products which are transferred to the meat packing industry. This change reduces the household allocation about $600 million.

Concerning dairy products, farm-processed milk and cream and farm-produced butter were transferred to dairy products manufacturing industries, reducing household allocations about $900 million.

Another, and by far the most important, difference is explained by including the fluid milk industry in the coverage of the SIC group 202, dairy products. This industry, covering establishments primarily engaged in processing (pasteurizing, homogenizing, vitaminizing, bottling) and distributing fluid milk and cream was left to the trade sectors prior to 1958. Revised coverage of group 202 has reduced household allocations about $2 billion.

[n] At purchaser's value (retail and wholesale trade not separated in 1958 study).

[o] 1962 estimate in purchaser's value as described in (n) above.

[p] Includes seafoods, synthetic fibers, and imports.

[q] Included in "all other" category.

SOURCE: Data for 1947 and 1958 obtained from the Bureau of Labor Statistics Input-Output Study; other extrapolations were made by the author with the aid of USDA.

APPENDIX EXHIBIT IV-1

Grain Terminal Association Memorandum re Purchase of Froedtert Malt Corporation

FARMERS UNION GRAIN TERMINAL
ASSOCIATION
ST. PAUL, MINNESOTA 55101
September 14, 1965

M. W. Thatcher
  General Manager

JOINT MEMORANDUM

To: Affiliated Elevator Managers
    Line Elevator Agents
    GTA Branch Managers
    GTA Fieldmen
    GTA Field Auditors
    Line Superintendents
    Farmers Union Presidents of Minnesota, Montana,
      North Dakota, and South Dakota.

I thought you might be interested in having an advance copy of my article in the *GTA Digest* in order that you get a little information, at this time, with regard to GTA's purchase of the Froedtert Malt Corporation.

Cooperatively yours,

FARMERS UNION GRAIN TERMINAL
ASSOCIATION

(signed)   M. W. Thatcher
           General Manager

GTA Buys Malting Operation

If you grow malting barley, your cooperatives will prove to be of greater service than ever before.

I think you know that, because the big news in August was that farmers have moved into the cooperative malting of barley. But it bears repeating. This is one of the great steps forward that farmers and their cooperatives had hoped for and planned for many long years.

The facts are simple enough. The board of directors and management of your GTA had been making barley plans for more than 20 years, and I had told you about that from time to time.

Many possibilities were discussed and passed by. You can imagine the time and careful consideration that must go into making these major cooperative decisions. We knew what was necessary, but not until this summer were conditions right to go ahead.

Today you are the owners of the largest malting barley operation in the nation. Needless to say, it is cooperative all the way. We call it Froedtert Malt Corporation. It is owned by GTA, whose barley patrons will benefit.

The same people who managed operations under the previous ownership will continue in their work. They have agreed to that. They are capable and experienced people, and we are happy to have them with us. Those of you who come to the annual meeting in St. Paul this November will meet the top people from Froedtert. They are on your team now.

The details of this transaction were reported to you at the time it took place. But you may have some questions about why your directors and management took this big step into barley processing.

We have realized for a long time that farmers needed to integrate their barley business in order to have a more dependable and advantageous outlet for this important crop. That was one consideration. There are others.

All over the nation great corporations are merging with greater corporations to become monolithic business giants. Farmers don't have anything that stacks up in size with those business giants, yet you must bargain with them. And you don't bargain with them by long distance telephone; you have to be right in the showroom.

To cite you an example: The second largest grain trading firm in the world has just spent a reported $20 million to gain control of 51 percent of the stock of the second largest concern that manufactures livestock feeds and processes soybeans and other commodities.

That is the kind of integrated competition you are up against. It is tough, intelligent, aggressive and imaginative competition. You must match it.

I am not trying to frighten you. I just want you to understand the facts. Increasingly the big, integrated international firms, engaged in both domestic and export grain selling and all types of processing, are by-passing everybody in the business.

They have inland facilities at each major interior market, and at each port. They jump over the terminal markets and the regional operators who have specialized in amassment of small and large lots of grain, and they by-pass the local elevators to buy directly from farmers. Then they do their own concentrating in their own facilities, process what they want, and export the rest through their own facilities. Many even have their own ships, overseas offices and handling facilities.

These huge international firms consider the whole world market to be their oyster. Farmer cooperatives, to them, are just competitors, and not very big ones at that. They are out to make money, not to protect or benefit you.

Is it necessary for me to say more? That ought to be enough to help you understand that your stake in the future, as farmers and producers, is right here in your cooperatives.

That is why you are in the business of processing barley, soybeans, flaxseed and durum wheat, and why you are making your own livestock feeds. It is why your basic cooperative grain marketing operations are being improved and expanded.

Your cooperative accomplishments have been great indeed, but the greatest challenges and opportunities are still ahead.

The total purchase price for all the new facilities amounts to $10.5 million. The GTA annual report in November will list the plants and their locations.

We borrowed $8.5 million from the Bank for Cooperatives on a mortgage basis payable back at the rate of $50,000 per month. It will prove to be a great investment for our farmer-owners, and I am delighted with this great cooperative step forward.

We look to the future with great confidence for better days for our farmers.

APPENDIX TABLE V-1. Storage Earnings of Major Wheat Firms: 1958–1963

	1963	1962	1961	1960	1959	1958	Total
C-G-F Grain Co.[a]	$17,238,717	$19,376,218	$24,925,192	$28,313,848	$23,470,634	$14,787,434	$128,112,043
Cargill, Inc.	5,831,757	6,335,499	9,474,404	9,808,744	12,103,615	13,226,341	56,780,360
Punta Alegre Commission Corp.[a]	4,884,202	5,277,319	1,233,023				11,394,544
Archer-Daniels-Midland Co.	4,875,545	2,779,579	5,134,987	5,919,132	6,076,898	6,240,199	31,026,340
F. H. Peavey and Co.	4,690,655	4,064,223	4,169,304	5,389,505	5,528,810	5,623,702	29,466,199
Continental Grain Co.	4,059,334	3,728,182	6,190,879	7,198,886	6,835,190	5,833,690	33,846,161
Farmers Union Grain Terminal Assn.	3,700,543	2,390,665	3,945,877	4,089,595	4,781,426	3,328,488	22,236,594
Harvest Queen Mill and Elevator	3,549,156	4,192,956	4,856,361	5,204,045	5,884,495	5,514,064	29,201,077
Farmers Cooperative Commission Co.	3,288,963	3,657,169	3,648,093	4,100,897	4,102,697	2,463,576	21,261,395
Goodpasture Grain and Milling Co.	3,174,619	3,862,106	3,443,859	3,438,872	3,824,297	3,676,577	21,420,330
Farmers Union Coop. Marketing Assn.	3,174,349	2,609,744					5,784,093
Morrison Quirk Grain Co.	2,953,784	2,689,669	2,837,713	3,095,454	2,929,588	1,867,762	16,373,970
Seaboard Allied Milling Corp.	2,806,792	3,060,487	3,299,454	1,435,573	1,139,311	517,396	12,259,013
Bartlett and Company Grain	2,460,069	2,633,232	2,292,708	2,655,823	2,126,983	2,107,568	14,276,383
Producers Grain Corp.	2,342,220	2,209,080	2,200,595	1,876,571	2,621,401	1,644,824	12,894,691
Bunge Corp.	1,821,093	1,852,199	1,696,717	1,992,720	2,318,773	1,839,525	11,521,027
Ross Industries, Inc.	1,790,885	2,158,161	2,018,256	2,337,813	2,569,705		10,874,820
General Mills, Inc.	1,613,516	1,245,985	2,086,142	2,642,146	2,776,898	1,634,936	11,999,623
Standard Milling Co.	1,526,964	1,936,649	2,114,736	1,960,460	2,214,819	2,018,376	11,772,004
Union Equity Cooperative Exchange	1,450,757	2,204,815	3,266,063	4,304,556	6,717,599	6,452,587	24,396,377
Sam P. Wallingford, Inc.	1,393,321	1,577,911	1,827,588	1,950,530	2,292,231	1,627,102	10,668,683
United Foods, Inc.	1,332,153	1,538,491	1,394,062	1,061,306	698,540		6,024,552
Morrison Grain Co.	1,331,129	1,441,197	1,605,397	1,743,050	1,821,811	1,233,801	9,176,385
The Pillsbury Co., Inc.	1,262,402	1,384,877	1,845,459	1,812,037	2,285,802	587,707	9,178,284
Kimbell Milling Co.	1,139,162	1,607,697	1,611,101	1,628,315	2,181,374	1,570,497	9,738,146
Flour Mills of America	1,082,728	1,169,580	905,700	949,922	615,603	602,607	5,326,140
Westcentral Coop. Grain Co.	1,061,546	1,036,728	1,108,817	1,310,131	1,363,088	1,522,930	7,403,240
Louis Dreyfus Corp.	1,057,940	602,365	816,077	1,144,541	873,042	522,504	5,016,469
Osborne-McMillan Elevator Co.	1,032,931	959,834	1,070,239	1,074,867	1,205,173	1,204,573	6,547,617
Farmers Grain Dealers Assn. of Iowa	1,032,517		1,341,112	1,302,483	1,328,074	1,134,365	6,138,551
Uhlmann Elevators of Texas	1,017,299	1,411,411	1,570,574	1,193,234	1,110,445	888,387	7,191,350
Simonds-Shields-Theis Grain Co.	1,009,476	1,132,636	1,140,456	1,342,767	1,204,029	1,116,632	6,945,996
Equity Union Grain Co.	1,001,701	940,505	917,107	1,226,627	1,050,622	782,336	5,918,898
Wagner Mills, Inc.	982,433	1,055,480	1,086,657	537,827	1,096,913		4,759,310
International Milling Co.	916,330	910,118	1,638,625	2,059,948	1,544,132	1,698,514	8,767,667
Fremont Elevator Co.	876,968	774,349	984,421	968,567			3,604,305
Addington Grain Co., Inc.	832,798	824,768					1,657,566
Dannen Mills, Inc.[b]	831,172	1,605,453	2,166,612	2,605,322	2,477,522	1,761,138	11,447,219
Sierra Petroleum Co., Inc.	747,362						747,362
Bolin Warehouses	732,053	743,445	785,915	555,801	592,225		3,409,439
Sherley Anderson Grain Co.	725,909	778,477	1,022,823	828,290	634,601	1,256,320	5,246,420
Stockton Elevators	722,314	874,114	867,834	1,020,528	1,120,336	1,179,720	5,784,846
Collingwood Grain, Inc.	708,928						708,928
Coffield Warehouse Co.	706,008	966,376	1,206,455	788,188	592,112		4,259,139
Neuces County Navigation District No. 1	703,582					526,893	1,230,475
Norris Grain Co.	700,252	1,309,583	2,187,953	2,807,640	2,889,238	2,587,198	12,481,864
J. C. Crouch Grain Co.	696,222	1,105,801	1,075,281	1,244,581	1,638,035	1,237,579	6,997,499
Sherley Grain Co.	642,639	655,138	657,997	590,215	719,539		3,265,528
Burrus Mills, Inc.	632,895	802,503	979,529	2,575,778	2,787,837	2,176,166	9,954,708
Sullivan, Inc.	628,733						628,733
Topeka Mill & Elevator Co.	617,963	691,558	650,072				1,959,593
Garden City Coop. Equity Exchange	604,597						604,597
Board of Trustees of Galveston Wharves	594,991	512,642				1,192,274	2,299,907
Pfeffer & Son	590,318		659,825	529,646	1,069,791	1,220,709	4,070,289

	1963	1962	1961	1960	1959	1958	Total
Dodge City Coop. Exchange	$ 582,152						$ 582,152
Ralston Purina Co.	561,452	$ 656,519	$ 788,097				2,006,068
Gulf Terminal Grain Co.	557,599						557,599
Plainsmen Elevators, Inc.	553,679	690,536	737,455		$ 601,987		2,583,657
Port of Stockton	542,800			$ 542,833			1,085,633
Attebury Elevators	523,118	595,297	672,738	517,693	578,334		2,887,180
United Elevators		3,486,335	3,491,713	2,422,372	776,675		10,177,095
Wilson Grain Co.		819,021	512,265				1,331,286
Lawrence Warehouse Corp.		791,900	1,910,421	1,922,400	2,211,720		6,836,441
Harmon-Toles Grain Co.		757,911	677,456	647,257			2,082,624
Palo Duro Grain Co.		746,410	987,503				1,733,913
Business Counselor's, Inc.		731,196					731,196
G. F. Elevator Co.		730,320					730,320
Lindsey Bonded Warehouse Co.		570,575	827,881	775,597	670,004		2,844,057
Great Lakes Storage and Contracting Co.		567,039					567,039
Colorado Milling & Elevator Co.		545,873	852,616	1,021,049	1,217,058	$ 800,843	4,437,439
Sooner Terminal Elevator		525,542	769,573				1,295,115
Dimmitt Wheat Growers, Inc.		512,783			569,329		1,082,112
Texas Grain Storage Co.		511,102					511,102
C. D. Jennings Grain Co.		506,558	529,052	628,334			1,663,944
Farmers Union Jobbing Assn.			2,649,092	2,469,409	1,843,314	718,025	7,679,840
Kerr Grain Corp.			1,312,791	1,677,456	1,639,331		4,629,578
Interstate Grain Corp.			935,487		596,982	533,922	2,066,391
The Andersons			933,790				933,790
Central Soya Co., Inc.			799,964	896,776	1,194,312	613,679	3,504,731
Grain, Inc.			780,076				780,076
Indianapolis Grain Warehouse			719,552				719,552
Apex Terminal Warehouse			711,319	575,200	508,821		1,795,340
Crawford Austin Co.			701,433	778,283	816,012	609,867	2,905,595
Johnston Terminal Elevator			593,580	656,982	824,820		2,075,382
Federal North Iowa Grain Co.			578,972				578,972
Farmers Cooperative Assn.			558,701				558,701
Ponca Grain Corp.			550,932				550,932
S. E. Cone Grain & Seed Co.			550,466		579,067	566,278	1,695,811
The Quaker Oats Co.			538,979	702,646	705,018		1,946,643
Salina Terminal Elevator Co.			529,580	510,551	736,693	528,725	2,305,549
Nebraska-Kansas-Colorado Grain Co.				1,568,222	1,540,705		3,108,927
North Pacific Grain Growers Co.				679,106	745,064	603,736	2,027,906
Heard Elevator Co.				662,871	1,272,328	1,099,263	3,034,462
Dumas Corporation				589,683			589,683
Early and Daniel Co.					741,074	727,873	1,468,947
Pitman Grain Co.					657,363	611,022	1,268,385
Odessa Union Warehouse Corp.					642,522		642,522
Friona Wheat Growers					641,939	630,467	1,272,406
Kansas Milling Co.					562,482		562,482
Montana Milling Co.					535,881		535,881
Patterson Grain Co.					513,751		513,751
Salyer Grain & Milling Co.					510,655		510,655
South Dakota Wheat Growers Assn.					500,582		500,582
Wichita Terminal Elevator						1,269,346	1,269,346
Houston Public Elevators						896,418	896,418
Rice Growers Assn. of California						871,637	871,637
Arkansas Rice Growers						835,195	835,195
The McCabe Company[c]						524,626	524,626
Hunter Milling Co.						520,105	520,105
Total	$110,503,492	$120,421,891	$148,159,535	$150,861,501	$158,149,077	$119,368,024	$807,463,520

[a] Punta Alegre Commission Corp. and C-G-F became separate entities by agreement dated September 1, 1961.

[b] Purchased by Farmers Cooperative Commission Company in 1963.

[c] Purchased by Farmers Union Grain Terminal Association in 1959.

SOURCE: USDA, Commodity Credit Corporation, *Storage and Handling Payments in Excess of $500,000 Made in Calendar Years 1958–1963 to Companies Operating Under Uniform Grain Storage Agreements.*

APPENDIX EXHIBIT VII-1

Cargill Contract of Purchase (Soybeans)

THIS CONTRACT entered into this _____ day of
_____, 1963, between _____ of
_____.

A. Cargill has established a marketing arrangement under
   which growers may enter into contracts to sell soybeans to Cargill. Cargill has made arrangements with
   various elevator owners to receive soybeans from
   growers participating in such marketing arrangement.
   Cargill is willing to make such marketing arrangement
   available to Growers in accordance with the terms
   and conditions set forth below.
B. Grower is willing to enter into this Contract and participate in such marketing arrangement.
   1. The term of this Contract shall be from Septem-
      ber 1, 1963, to August 31, 1964.
   2. It is the intent of this Contract to establish terms
      and conditions governing said marketing arrange-
      ment in respect of all soybeans delivered by Grower
      to the _____ elevator under this Con-
      tract. As and when Grower delivers soybeans to the
      elevator, title to the soybeans shall pass from
      Grower to Cargill. The price payable to Grower by
      Cargill for such soybeans shall not be fixed as of
      that date but shall be retained and paid as follows.
      Payment shall be made in the following manner:
      (a) An initial advance of $_____ payable
          not later than _____ days after soy-
          beans are unloaded at the elevator.
      (b) Periodic advances at dates fixed by Cargill
          during the period thereafter; and
      (c) Final settlement to be made within ten (10)
          days after final settlement made by Arkansas
          Grain Corporation under its pool marketing
          agreement described below.
      The total of these payments is guaranteed to exceed

the *cash* price paid by the Arkansas Grain Corporation under its pool marketing agreement for soybeans grown in the 1963–1964 crop year. Such
pool marketing agreement is the plan made available by the Arkansas Grain Corporation to all soybean growers and under which it acquires substantially all of the soybeans purchased by it in the
1963–1964 crop year. In determining the price
paid by Arkansas Grain Corporation under its pool
marketing agreement, it shall be based only on
cash payments for soybeans and exclude payments
in respect of rice or any other products.
   3. As each load of soybeans is delivered to the eleva-
      tor, Grower and the elevator shall sign a Delivery
      Receipt in the form attached to this Contract on
      which shall be set forth the weight, grade factors
      and adjustments for grade factors. Soybeans de-
      livered under the Delivery Receipt shall be gov-
      erned by the terms of this Contract and only such
      soybeans covered by a Delivery Receipt shall be
      entitled to the advantages of this Contract.
   4. Grower anticipates that he will sell _____
      bushels under this agreement, and Cargill hereby
      agrees that it will purchase up to this amount under
      this Contract, provided that Grower delivers, or
      makes definite commitments with Cargill, by No-
      vember 10, 1963, to deliver at a later date. This
      date may be extended and the amount deliverable
      increased at Cargill's option.

IN WITNESS WHEREOF, the parties hereto have
hereunto set their hands and seals the day first above
written.

ELEVATOR

_____

GROWER

BY _____   CARGILL, INCORPORATED

BY _____

APPENDIX EXHIBIT VII-2

Cargill Elevator Handling Agreement (Soybeans)

THIS AGREEMENT entered into this _____ day of
_____, 1963, between CARGILL, INCORPO-
RATED (hereinafter "Cargill") and _____
(hereinafter "Elevator") :

RECITALS:

A. Cargill plans to enter into contracts, in the form attached as Cargill-Grower contract with soybean growers to purchase soybeans.
B. Cargill wishes to engage the elevator in receiving,
handling and shipping to the Cargill Elevator in Memphis, Tennessee, all soybeans delivered to it by
growers under the Cargill-Grower contract.
C. Elevator agrees to perform the services set forth below:
1. The term of this Agreement shall be from September 1, 1963, through August 31, 1964; and
shall terminate unless renewed by mutual written
agreement.
2. Elevator agrees to receive all soybeans delivered
by growers which have been sold to Cargill under
the terms of the Cargill-Grower contract up to
_____ bushels. This limit is subject to review
and to modification by mutual written agreement
of the parties during the term of this agreement.
3. Elevator shall weigh and grade all soybeans as
received in a manner prescribed by Cargill and
subject to review by Cargill.
4. Elevator shall maintain records relating to this
Handling Agreement and the Cargill-Grower contract as required by Cargill and allow Cargill to
review these records at any reasonable time during business hours.
5. Elevator shall provide for movement of the soybeans purchased under the Cargill-Grower contract, from the elevator to Cargill's Memphis elevator when and as directed by Cargill. Rates for
truck transportation are to be mutually agreed
upon in advance and all of such transportation
shall be in compliance with State and Federal
transportation laws. Rail shipments will be freight
collect.
6. Weights — Elevator shall be responsible for delivering to Cargill's Memphis elevator the net
weight of soybeans as delivered to Elevator by
growers under the Cargill-Grower contracts. In
determining net weight, foreign material in excess of 1% is deducted from total weight. Cargill's Memphis unload weights to govern.
(a) If net weight of soybeans delivered by Elevator to Cargill is more or less than that delivered to elevator by growers, settlement for
such differences shall be made basis the Memphis cash market price the day Elevator ad-
vises Cargill it has made final delivery of all

soybeans to be delivered under this agreement.
7. Grades — Elevator shall be responsible for delivering to Cargill's Memphis elevator soybeans of
quality equal to soybeans delivered to Elevator
by growers under the Cargill-Grower contracts.
Quality is determined by the following grade factors — testweight, moisture, damage and splits.
Memphis grades to govern. If quality delivered by
Elevator to Cargill differs from that delivered to
Elevator by growers settlement for such differences will be basis the settlement schedule applying to Cargill-Grower contracts. Price determination for such settlement to be basis Memphis
cash market the day of final delivery under this
agreement.
8. Cargill shall pay _____ cents per bushel to Elevator for all soybeans received from growers under Cargill-Grower contract and handled pursuant to this Agreement. Immediately upon delivery
of such soybeans to Cargill's Memphis elevator,
an initial payment of _____ cents per bushel will
be made to Elevator with final payment, after
adjustments, within thirty (30) days thereafter.
9. In performing the services hereunder, Elevator
shall not be deemed to be the agent, servant, or
employee of Cargill but shall act as an independent contractor.
10. This shall not be an exclusive agreement nor shall
it be in respect of any defined area. Elevator
agrees, however, to accept all soybeans delivered
by growers having Cargil-Grower contracts with
Cargill.
11. Elevator agrees to use its best efforts to promote
the plan set forth in the Cargill-Grower contract.
12. Upon Elevator's receipt of soybeans sold to Cargill pursuant to the Cargill-Grower contract title
to such soybeans shall pass to Cargill. However,
all risk of loss to or destruction of such soybeans
as well as the risks set forth in paragraphs 6 and
7 above shall be with Elevator until delivered to
Cargill's Memphis elevator.
13. Elevator has, or will promptly procure, insurance
on the soybeans to be delivered to it insuring
against risks of fire, windstorm, and similar risks
in the amount of at least $_____ and will fur-
nish to Cargill evidence of such insurance.

Elevator has or will procure a bond from a surety
company satisfactory to Cargill to cover its satisfactory
performance hereunder the amount of $_____, with
expenses of such bond to be borne by _____.

IN WITNESS WHEREOF, the parties hereto have
hereunto set their hands and seals the day first above
written.

ELEVATOR   CARGILL, INCORPORATED

BY _____   BY _____

APPENDIX EXHIBIT IX-1

Sample of Uniform Marketing Contract
between a Cooperative and Its Members,
and a Pooling Price Arrangement

THIS AGREEMENT, made and executed in duplicate as of the ___ day of _____ 19___, by and between a corporate cooperative marketing association under the laws of Florida, with principal office at party of the first part, hereinafter called "Association," and _____ _____ of _____, party of the second part, hereinafter called "Member," WITNESSETH THAT:

WHEREAS, Association is a nonprofit cooperative marketing association, with capital stock, under the laws of the State of Florida, engaged in furnishing or arranging for the furnishing of services and facilities upon a cooperative basis for the handling, processing, warehousing, financing and marketing of citrus fruit and products thereof belonging to its member-stockholders and others, and Association has, by suitable contract with Corporation, a Florida corporation, which owns and operates citrus fruit processing and concentrate plants, equipment and facilities at different places in Florida, arranged for the handling, processing, distribution and sale of all oranges and products thereof which Association purchases from and handles for the account of its member-stockholders, and others, and

WHEREAS, Member is a member-stockholder of Association and is familiar with and agreeable to all the terms and provisions of said contract between Association and said Corporation, and, in order to effectuate the same for the mutual benefit and advantage of all member-stockholders of Association executing contracts similar to this one, Member desires to assure and guarantee the sale and delivery to Association of the specified number of boxes of oranges hereinafter mentioned for handling by Association under the terms and conditions hereof as well as under the uniform rules, regulations and orders of Association;

NOW, THEREFORE, in consideration of the premises and the mutual undertakings hereinafter provided for and set forth, as well as for other valuable considerations accruing to each of the parties hereto, it is mutually agreed as follows:

1. (a) That during each citrus fruit processing season during the continuance hereof, Member shall sell and deliver to Association and Association shall purchase from Member not less than _____ boxes of oranges. As used herein a box of oranges means ninety (90) pounds net weight of oranges. Members shall also sell and deliver to Association and Association shall purchase from Member such additional quantity of oranges, as well as any quantity of other varieties of citrus fruit, as the parties may from time to time mutually agree. The term "oranges" shall not include satsumas, temples, tangerines, tangelos, or Hamlin or Parson Brown varieties grown on lemon root stock.

(b) Member shall deliver or arrange for the delivery of said oranges, at its or his expense, to such processing plant or plants of said Corporation, and at such time or times during each processing season as Association directs. As used in this contract "processing season" means the period commencing on November 1 of each year and ending on October 31 of the succeeding year.

(c) All fruit delivered hereunder shall be sound and merchantable and shall comply with all Federal and State laws and rules, regulations and orders relating to fruit to be used for the purpose or purposes designated for such fruit by Association and said Corporation. Oranges delivered hereunder shall meet all applicable requirements of the laws of the State of Florida and the regulations of the Florida Citrus Commission relating to quality or otherwise for oranges to be used for the production of concentrate; have a minimum total Brix of ten degrees (10°); and have a minimum Brix-acid ratio of not less than 12 to 1; subject, however, to such averaging of a given load of oranges with other loads within a specified period as may be permitted by Association and said Corporation.

(d) Absolute title to all fruit delivered to and accepted by Association hereunder shall pass to Association at the time when said Corporation takes physical possession thereof, and Association shall have the irrevocable right to immediately pass to and vest in said Corporation such absolute title to all such fruit so delivered and accepted. Said Corporation shall thereafter have no responsibility or liability to Association or Member except to pay over to Association the purchase price for said fruit as determined in accordance with the provisions of said agreement between Association and said Corporation. Member warrants title to all fruit delivered and accepted hereunder and warrants that all such fruit shall be free and clear of any claims, liens or demands whatsoever.

2. The Association agrees to make such advances to Member on account of oranges delivered and accepted hereunder as the Board of Directors of Association in its discretion feels may be justified by marketing conditions. All actual costs incurred by reason of any such advances, including interest paid out by Association on borrowings for Member's account, shall be charged to Member. In all events, however, Association shall not be obligated to make any final settlement on account of all deliveries of fruit hereunder until said Corporation has made final settlement with Association under and in accordance with the said agreement between them.

3. The Association agrees to sell the fruit delivered and accepted hereunder and the products thereof (hereinafter sometimes referred to as "products"), pooled with the products delivered by other patrons of Association, under and in strict accordance with its said agreement with said Corporation and to pay over ratably as the agreed purchase price due Member hereunder the net

amount received from Corporation as final settlement in full to Member, less Association's assessment of not to exceed three (3) cents per box of ninety (90) pounds net weight of citrus fruit, to defray Association's expenses and cost of operations.

4. In the event Member should fail to deliver to Association during any processing season this contract is in effect the entire number of boxes of oranges as specified in paragraph 1 hereof, Member shall immediately pay to Association the sum of twenty-five (25¢) for each and every box of oranges which Member fails to deliver in accordance with the provisions of this contract as liquidated damages, it being impractical and extremely difficult to fix the actual damages suffered by Association. In default of such payment Association may withhold such liquidated damages from any payments due Member hereunder or, at its option, the Association may recover such liquidated damages by action in any court having jurisdiction in the name of Association as plaintiff and in any such action Member shall pay all costs, premiums for bonds, expenses, and reasonable attorney's fee to be fixed by the court.

5. This contract shall be and continue in effect for a period of ten years from the date thereof, subject, however, to the right of either party to terminate the same as of November 1 of any year hereafter by giving the other party written notice of termination during the month of July immediately preceding such November 1.

6. Neither party to this contract, shall be liable for damages for failure to perform hereunder to the extent that performance by either of them or said Corporation is made impossible or delayed by Act of God, war, fire, equipment breakdown, strike, embargo, lockout, quarantine order, governmental order, rule or regulation, in-ability to obtain materials, supplies or transportation or any other causes beyond the control of either of said parties.

7. The by-laws of Association now in existence and as hereafter amended, all rules, regulations and orders promulgated by Association from time to time and any contract or contracts between Association and any other agency which it may employ and utilize to aid it in carrying out the terms of this contract and other similar contracts, including particularly said agreement between Association and said Corporation, shall be parts of this contract and binding upon the parties hereto.

8. The parties agree that there are no oral or other conditions, promises, covenants, representations or inducements in addition to or at variance with any of the terms hereof, and that this contract represents the voluntary and clear understanding of both parties fully and completely.

WITNESS the due execution hereof under the seals of each of the parties hereto as of the day and year first above written.

By _____

Attest:

_____   _____ (SEAL)

_____ (SEAL)

Attest: By

Name of Grove   Location   Acreage   Varieties

Boxes   Delivery Period

Production Contract _____ Limit Contract _____
Do (Do Not) Deduct for Mutual _____

POOLING PRICE ARRANGEMENT

December 5, 1960

To Members of

In accordance with the Charter and By-Laws and instructions from the membership at the annual meeting held March 2, 1960, notice is hereby given of the following:

A. Pooling Method for the season beginning November 1, 1960:

For fruit meeting quality standards required for production of frozen orange concentrate, two pools are provided. The first pool starts on November 1 and runs until such time as deliveries to   become predominantly late varieties. The closing date for the first pool and the starting date for the second pool will be conclusively determined by the Board of Directors from data furnished by   The second pool will end when it discontinues processing of frozen orange concentrate in the 1960–1961 processing season.   will notify   approximately fifteen (15) days prior to the time when it intends to discontinue processing for the 1960–1961 season.

The total pool proceeds will be determined and distributed on a per-pound solids basis to members in the respective pools. The first distribution of returns between the pools is based on the Florida Canners' Association average price per pound solids for each pool period. Upon determination of the total pool credit the pool returns in excess or less than the returns based on the F.C.A. averages are distributed between the pools on the basis of the pound solids in each pool. This tends to equalize the payments while still maintaining a differential in proportion to the index with relationship to Early and Midseason and Valencia varieties of oranges. A theoretical example is as follows:

Pool period	Lb. solids in pool	FCA average price per pound/solids	Pool proceeds based on FCA average	Total pool proceeds	Excess distribution payment	Actual return per pound/solids
To March 15	35,000,000	$.40	$14,000,000	$16,163,636	$.0618	$.4618
After March 15	20,000,000	.45	9,000,000	10,236,364	.0618	.5118
Totals	55,000,000		$23,000,000	$26,400,000	$.0618	$.4800

In this example, members would receive $.4618 for each pound of solids delivered to the first pool and $.5118 for each pound of solids delivered to the second pool.

All concentrate and nonconcentrate fruit for the 1960–1961 season will be pooled in accordance with the amendment to the pooling method as approved by the Board of Directors at its meeting held November 22, 1960, and explained in the letter of December 5, 1960, attached hereto. The fruit will still be divided into two pools as outlined above–that is, Early and Midseason pool and Valencia pool.

B. Guarantee:

              is in receipt of a letter from   in which the following guarantee is made:

"Specifically,   agrees to adjust its processing and marketing fee during the 1960–1961 season to the extent necessary to return to an average price per pound of early and midseason solids used for frozen orange concentrate at least equal to the season average price per pound of early and midseason solids for frozen orange concentrate as published by the Florida Canners' Association, and to return to   an average price per pound of Valencia solids used for frozen orange concentrate at least equal to the season average price per pound of Valencia solids for frozen orange as determined from figures published by the Florida Canners' Association.

" *** the foregoing commitment applies only to orange solids used for the production of frozen orange concentrate during the 1960–1961 season. Also, the season for earlies and mids shall be the period commencing November 1 and ending when deliveries by   to   become predominately late varieties, and the season for Valencias shall be the period commencing when deliveries by   to   become predominately late varieties and ending when   discontinues the processing of frozen orange concentrate in the 1960–1961 processing season as determined under the pooling arrangement adopted by   for the 1960–1961 season. In addition, it is understood and agreed that, notwithstanding the foregoing,   shall be entitled to deduct from its returns to   all advances and all charges and expenditures incurred in connection with the processing and marketing of the oranges delivered by   as provided in Article 3B of the August 1, 1957 agreements."

APPENDIX EXHIBIT IX-2

Sample of Agreement for Orange Concentrate between Processor and Food Retailer

THIS AGREEMENT, made and entered into this the 22nd day of December, 1961, by and between _____ _____, hereinafter referred to as the seller, and _____ hereinafter referred to as the buyer.

In consideration of the promises and undertakings of each of the parties hereto, it is hereby mutually agreed by and between the parties as follows:

1. *QUANTITY*

(A) The seller agrees to pack for and sell to the buyer and the buyer hereby buys _____ gallons of U.S. Grade A Frozen Concentrated Orange Juice.

2. *PACK*

(A) This merchandise is to be packed in 48/6-ounce cans and 24/12-ounce cans as specified by the buyer.

(B) Lithographed cans and cartons to be used in the production of this merchandise shall be furnished by the seller.

(C) The buyer shall notify the seller specifications as to size and label in sufficient time to meet the required packing schedule of the seller.

(D) The buyer agrees to accept a 1/10 of 1% or 150 cases, whichever is the greater, overrun or underrun of the quantity of each item and/or size of merchandise to be supplied under this Agreement.

3. *STORAGE*

(A) Seller agrees to store all concentrate packed and *uninvoiced* under this Agreement in its warehouse without charge to the buyer until January 15, 1963.

(B) Storage will be charged at the rate of 10¢ per ton per day on any merchandise remaining in seller's warehouse after January 15, 1963.

(C) Storage will be charged at the rate of 10¢ per ton per day on any *invoiced* merchandise remaining in storage in seller's warehouse commencing on the 15th day after the date of the invoice, except that merchandise *invoiced* on December 1 will be stored without charge to the buyer until January 15, 1963.

(D) The seller assumes full responsibility and risk of loss of and/or damage to the concentrate and the cans and cartons in which said concentrate is packed while in possession of the seller and until the time the merchandise is loaded for shipment at seller's plant.

4. *WITHDRAWALS*

(A) Between the date on which supplies packed under the terms of this contract become available for shipment and December 1, 1962, the merchandise purchased hereunder shall be withdrawn by the buyer in approximately equal monthly quantities.

(B) Between this date and December 1, 1962, all such withdrawals shall be invoiced by the seller at the price for merchandise of like grade and quality as shown on the seller's published price list in effect on the date of withdrawal.

(C) Any merchandise remaining on December 1, 1962 is hereby purchased by the buyer and sold by the seller on December 1, 1962 and shall be invoiced by the seller at the price in effect on that date as shown by SNIVELY's published weekly price list for merchandise of like grade and quality.

(D) The seller agrees to arrange shipments of the merchandise covered hereunder in accordance with the shipping instructions supplied by the buyer.

5. *INVOICING*

(A) All merchandise invoiced under this contract shall be invoiced in duplicate and shall carry terms "Net Cash Upon Receipt of Invoice."

(B) Should the buyer wrongfully fail to pay any invoice rendered under this contract, the seller, in that event, shall have the right to sell the merchandise covered by such invoice to whomever may desire to purchase it at any reasonable price and no liability shall accrue against the seller for selling such merchandise even though under the buyer's label, brand, trademark or copyright. At least 15 days' notice shall be given the buyer by the seller prior to exercising the rights granted the seller under the terms of this paragraph.

(C) Should the seller exercise the rights under Paragraph 5 (B) above, the buyer shall remain liable for any loss between the price received by the seller for such merchandise sold on the open market and the price as originally invoiced to the buyer. In addition, the buyer shall indemnify and pay the seller for all handling, storage, transportation and any other costs incurred by the seller directly related to and necessary in the resale of this merchandise.

6. *QUALITY & INSPECTION*

(A) The seller agrees to provide continuous U.S.D.A. inspection.

(B) The concentrate to be packed hereunder shall be U.S. Grade A Frozen Concentrated Orange Juice and shall be packed in accordance with the specifications attached hereto and made a part hereof.

(C) The seller, upon request, agrees to furnish the buyer with copies of reports which pertain directly to the merchandise purchased hereunder. The seller further agrees that whatever other records pertaining to processing equipment, freezing or storage temperatures, raw produce grades, etc., that apply to the processing during the times this merchandise is packed shall be made available to buyer's representative upon request.

(D) Buyer's representative shall be permitted to enter the plant of the seller during production or regular business hours to inspect the pack as it is being produced and, thereafter, to inspect the manner in which the concentrate is being stored.

7. *SAMPLES*

(A) The seller agrees to withdraw samples representative of the finished product from the packing line during the times the items under this Agreement are being processed at the rate of not less than one per hour per processing line. Each sample can shall be coded as to the time, date or lot of the pack from which it is drawn. It shall be frozen in the same manner as the lot from which it is drawn and shall be held for later inspection by buyer's representative until 45 days after that lot is shipped.

8. *COMMODITY WARRANTY*

(A) The seller guarantees that as of the date of shipment by seller the concentrate supplied hereunder will not be adulterated within the meaning of the Federal Food, Drug & Cosmetic Act and will not be an article which, under Section 404 or 505 or said Act, may not be introduced into Interstate Commerce.

(B) The seller agrees to carry Product Liability Insurance on merchandise covered by this Agreement and to include the buyer as a named insured thereunder.

9. *FAILURE OF PRODUCT TO MEET SPECIFICATIONS*

(A) Should any of the concentrate packed hereunder fail to meet U.S. Grade A specifications before shipment, buyer shall have the right to reject said concentrate. Likewise, if any of said concentrate should deteriorate in quality after shipment so that it fails to meet U.S.D.A. Grade A specifications and such failure should be shown by buyer to have arisen from defective processing or improper storage or refrigeration prior to shipment by the seller or failure to ship in accordance with buyer's shipping instructions, the buyer shall have the right to return said concentrate to seller at seller's expense and to receive full credit for any amount buyer may have paid seller therefor. Seller shall not sell or otherwise dispose of such rejected or returned concentrate under buyer's label unless permission to do so has been previously obtained by the seller.

10. *GENERAL*

(A) Should the seller be prevented from or interrupted or delayed in "processing" the merchandise under this or any or all other firm contracts or commitments of the seller with others by reason of any causes over which it has no control then and in such event or events, the seller shall be relieved from carrying out its obligations hereunder and shall not be liable for failure to perform under this contract, but shall have the right to complete the contract if and when conditions permit within the then current citrus packing season or to reduce the remaining unprocessed products under this and all other said firm contracts or commitments of the seller proportionately to seller's capacity to process after the cessation of the conditions or the effects thereof that brought about the prevention of processing by the seller, even to the extent of cancelling all remaining unprocessed requirements of said contracts and commitments. Should a reduction as mentioned above be necessary, the seller hereby agrees that such reduction will be applied proportionately to this and all other firm contracts or commitments of the seller with others.

(B) Should either the buyer or the seller be prevented from or interrupted or delayed in complying with the terms and conditions of this Agreement, except "processing," by any cause beyond its control, then and in that event or those events, such party shall be relieved of carrying out its obligations hereunder during the continuance thereof and shall not be liable for failure to perform under this contract during the period of such prevention. These causes shall include, but are not limited to, fire, freeze, storm, flood, earthquake, explosion, accident, cause of public enemy, war, rebellion, insurrections, sabotage, epidemic, quarantine restrictions, labor disputes, labor shortages, strikes or other labor disturbances, transportation embargoes or failure or delays in transportation, inability to secure raw materials, including cans of the type and size for processing frozen concentrate, or machinery for the manufacture of products, acts of God, acts of the Federal Government or any agency thereof and acts of any state or local government or agency thereof, or the operation of statutes, laws, rules or regulations, shortage of fuel or other supplies, failure of parties with whom either the seller or the buyer has contracted for materials to make deliveries or late deliveries thereof, or other causes of like or different kind beyond the control of the seller or the buyer.

11. *NOTICES*

(A) Whenever either party desired or is required to give or make any notice or demand, such notice or demand shall be given or made in writing and shall be deemed to have been given or made when deposited in the United States Mail, certified and addressed to the seller at _____, and to the buyer at _____.

APPENDIX EXHIBIT IX-3
Uniform Marketing Contract Between [grower] and Florida Citrus Mutual

Mail to:
FLORIDA CITRUS MUTUAL,
Box 499,
LAKELAND, FLORIDA

WHEREAS, Florida Citrus Mutual is a cooperative association composed of growers of citrus fruit in Florida, and is incorporated under Chapter 618, Florida Statutes, and has for its objectives, among other things, to provide collective action with respect to the orderly marketing and distribution of Florida citrus fruit, and

WHEREAS, the undersigned (hereinafter referred to as GROWER) is a grower of Florida citrus fruit on lands owned or leased by GROWER, and is in accord with the purposes, objectives and methods of operation of said Florida Citrus Mutual, and desires to join with the other members of said Florida Citrus Mutual (hereinafter referred to as ASSOCIATION) to accomplish its purposes and objectives,

NOW, THEREFORE, in consideration of the mutual promises, covenants and agreements herein contained, ASSOCIATION and GROWER do hereby mutually agree with each other as follows:

1. GROWER hereby applies for membership in ASSOCIATION and agrees to be bound by its charter, by-laws, rules, regulations and orders.

2. In order to provide for carrying out the purposes and objectives of ASSOCIATION, GROWER agrees:

(a) That all the citrus fruit and products thereof produced, acquired or controlled by GROWER will be marketed on an agency or sale basis only through handlers that have entered into contracts with the ASSOCIATION in the form prescribed by it for furthering said purposes and objectives; or, in the event that GROWER desires to personally market his citrus fruit, or any part thereof, then GROWER will enter into contract with ASSOCIATION like that executed by handlers; and GROWER agrees to be bound by such rules, regulations, instructions, and orders with respect to the picking, handling, selling, packing, grading and marketing of citrus fruit that may be issued from time to time by the ASSOCIATION, or the general manager thereof, under authority conferred by the Board of Directors or the Executive Committee of ASSOCIATION.

(b) That ASSOCIATION shall make and collect through handlers for each type of citrus fruit and products thereof, for each marketing season, a uniform charge or assessment per box, the amount in each case to be determined by the Board of Directors of ASSOCIATION for each such type before the beginning of any marketing period, for the purpose of providing the ASSOCIATION with funds for its maintenance, conduct and operation, including a deduction of $.......... each year as the subscription price of any publication that may be published or provided for by the ASSOCIATION covering the Florida citrus industry.

(c) That GROWER will submit, on forms furnished by the ASSOCIATION, such reports and statistical data as may be requested by it from time to time covering the production of each type of citrus fruit, the condition thereof, and the probable amount, by sizes, that will be available at a given time or during a given period for marketing, and the quality thereof.

(d) That GROWER will pay a membership fee of $5.00 at the time of signing this agreement, which may be used for furthering the ASSOCIATION and the objects for which it is formed; provided, however, this provision shall not apply if ASSOCIATION has at any time heretofore received such membership fee from GROWER and same has not been refunded.

(e) That GROWER will promptly notify the ASSOCIATION of the name and address of each handler that is to market or in any way acquire and handle any part of GROWER'S citrus fruit, and the approximate amount thereof that will be marketed and/or handled by any such handler.

3. In consideration of the foregoing, ASSOCIATION agrees:

(a) That it will notify GROWER on request, and at reasonable intervals by mail or through newspapers published in the citrus area of Florida, of the names of handlers that have entered into contracts with ASSOCIATION to enable them to market and handle fruit for members of ASSOCIATION.

(b) That it will offer to enter into such contracts with all handlers of Florida citrus fruit and products thereof who are deemed reliable and responsible and who are duly licensed and qualified as citrus fruit dealers under the laws of Florida, and who express a desire to enter into such contracts with ASSOCIATION.

(c) That it shall regulate the marketing of citrus fruit and products thereof of its members, among the various markets and over the marketing period, and also, in its discretion, provide for the doing of such other things, authorized by its charter and by-laws and consistent herewith, as may be deemed conducive to the best interests of its members.

4. It is mutually understood and agreed:

(a) That if GROWER should market any part of the citrus fruit or products thereof covered hereby, other than through a handler that has entered into a contract with the ASSOCIATION, GROWER shall pay the ASSOCIATION, as liquidated damages, at the rate of Twenty-five Cents (25¢) per box of one and three-fifth bushels, or its equivalent in volume, for all citrus fruit or products thereof so marketed or disposed of by GROWER, together with all costs, premiums for bonds, expenses and fees arising out of, or caused by, litigation, and reasonable attorney's fees expended or incurred, and all such costs and expenses shall be included in any judgement obtained in any such action.

(b) That this agreement shall not cover Florida citrus fruit used for home consumption or other non-commercial uses.

(c) That this agreement shall be considered as having been entered into on, and effective from, the .. day of ...., 19.., and that it shall continue and be in full force and effect from year to year thereafter, subject to the right of the GROWER to cancel the same in June of any year hereafter by giving written notice by Registered Mail in that month; but the cancellation of this agreement, or the failure of GROWER to comply therewith, shall not affect other similar agreements.

IN WITNESS WHEREOF the parties hereto have executed this agreement as of the date aforestated.

PRINT GROWER'S NAME AND ADDRESS BELOW:

_____

_____

$5.00 Membership Fee
Paid by CHECK——☐
       CASH——☐

_____
Solicitor's Name

_____
Solicitor's Address

FLORIDA CITRUS MUTUAL

By _____
      President

_____ (SEAL)
    Grower

NOTE: Please sign both copies

APPENDIX EXHIBIT X-1

Inventory Pool Plan for Frozen Orange Concentrate: Summary of Plan to Handle Concentrate Inventory Pools

June 1966

1. *PURPOSE* — To acquire, store if necessary, and sell volumes of bulk concentrate which may be in excess of what the industry feels it can market in an orderly manner in a given year.

   Thereby, reduce adverse effects of excessive or insufficient (below normal) end of season inventories. . . . Thus tending to prevent excessive price fluctuations.

   As well, to establish rotating stock reserves to be available in periods of production disasters.

2. *STRUCTURE OF ORGANIZATION* — This is to be a cooperative organization of growers and grower cooperatives who grow, process or supply fruit, with stock issue available to members only. . . . It will be run by Board of Directors, Executive Committee, and Manager and other employees as members desire. Membership will be as wide as possible and will include all eligible processors or their associated cooperatives.

3. *FINANCING* — Initial operational financing through stock issue. . . . Advances to patrons on purchases (products delivered) would be in accordance with the cooperative's ability to finance through commodity loans.

4. *METHOD OF OPERATION* — The suggested method of operation is based on ideas advanced by leaders in the industry over a period of years.

   The cooperative would deal in units of 42° Brix bulk concentrate, packed in drums, (at 42° Brix actual or higher), to a standard industry specification, (i.e., as to liners, etc.).

   The concentrate would have to meet retail grade standards as to color, flavor, etc., and would have to be accompanied by a USDA Grade Certificate. Ratio would have to be with a specified range. It may be desirable to establish a standard differential between Valencia and early and midseason concentrate; but the grade definitions may be such as to make this unnecessary.

5. *POLICIES OF OPERATION* — The cooperative would establish policies of operation, but in general it would be this:

   The Board of Directors or Executive Committee would establish daily or weekly prices at which it would buy and sell for the account of its patrons. Proceeds of sale would be pooled.

   Purchases or sales, would on first offering, be prorated among the members according to their established capacity. Subsequent offerings of any unsubscribed amounts would continue to be prorated according to the capacities of the then various subscribers or applicants.

   Purchases and sales would be evidenced by proper documents (non-negotiable). Sales to the cooperative would be for delivery within a single normal processing season at a specified time. If a delivery date in the future was set, the seller could either deliver the concentrate (of acceptable quality) on the date or effect the delivery by a purchase document for the equivalent volume.

   Purchases would be handled in a similar manner.

   The cooperative would operate in a manner so as to stabilize the market, buying bulk when surplus is available and selling when the market was able to absorb it. The cooperative would store the concentrate in packers' warehouses where produced to the extent storage space was available. Storage costs would be paid by the cooperative and included in their computations of buying and selling prices.

   It is anticipated that the cooperative would not carry over stocks produced in one season beyond the end of a succeeding season. This type of policy would avoid the difficulty created by building up excessive inventories over several years and then attempting to put this on the market over a short period of time.

APPENDIX EXHIBIT X-2

Letter to President Johnson about Imports of Frozen Orange Concentrate from the Virgin Islands

AN OPEN LETTER TO —

March 15, 1964

PRESIDENT LYNDON B. JOHNSON
THE WHITE HOUSE
WASHINGTON, D.C.

Dear Mr. President:

The rightful anger and financial fears of 12,500 citrus growers in Florida prompts this letter from the organization which represents them.

Their anger and their fears center on the proposed lease deal between the Virgin Islands Corporation and National Bulk Carriers, Inc., of New York City whose owner is Mr. Daniel K. Ludwig.

A resolution carried unanimously on Friday, March 13, 1964 which was addressed to you (and a copy of which is attached) covers the pertinent details. But to these details, we respectfully recommend these observations for your consideration:

As well meaning as may have been the original intentions of the Virgin Islands Corporation, this plan for the economic uplifting of the Islanders has degenerated into a blatant plot to bring the cheaply produced citrus of Panama into our market free of taxes, free of tariff and aided by extra subsidies,

There is no benefit to the Islanders by replacing sugar cane with a little citrus growth, nor are there great employment opportunities in an automated concentrate plant.

There is only one beneficiary — Mr. Daniel K. Ludwig.

Conversely, the Florida grower will lose, if this plan reaches maturity, $20,000,000 per year in on-tree crop value. The losses in California and Texas will also be appreciable.

We do not mean to imply that we believe the economic security of mainland Americans is more important than that of the Virgin Islanders. The fact is, very simply, that the Islander does not gain and the mainlander loses.

Nor do we, incidentally, ask any restraint on free and fair competition from citrus grown in the Virgin Islands.

But, as we point out in our resolution, this scheme calls for a frozen orange concentrate consisting of 10% Virgin Islands oranges and 90% Panama oranges, from the isthmus groves under the control of Mr. Ludwig. Prejudiced though we may be, Mr. President, we fail to see the moral justice or the economic justification for this proposed deal.

We bring to your attention the fact that this plan was supposed to be signed into fact last Friday the thirteenth of March. The new deadline is Tuesday, March 17.

It is apparent that only your prompt intervention can guarantee that the severe loss to our growers will not be turned into one man's profits with the proposed beneficiaries going unaided.

We respectfully ask for your consideration, your understanding and your intervention.

Very truly yours,

Robert W. Rutledge (signed)
Executive Vice President,
Florida Citrus Mutual

SOURCE: *Special Triangle Issue,* March 15, 1964.

APPENDIX TABLE X-1. Average per Case Costs of Frozen Orange Concentrate: 1958 Season through 1962 Season
(In 48/6-ounce cases)

Particulars	1962	1961	1960	1959	1958
Production cost:					
Materials:					
Cans	$ .9879627	$ .9837556	$1.0669710	$1.1053935	$1.0935361
Cartons	.0639240	.0670562	.0691799	.0717528	.0594038
Total materials	$1.0518867	$1.0508118	$1.1361509	$1.1771463	$1.1529399
Labor:					
Salaries and wages	.2640801	.1626109	.1793771	.1825223	.1666999
Payroll taxes	.0158647	.0093650	.0098742	.0100138	.0086922
Workmen's compensation insurance	.0067523	.0035439	.0036825	.0039475	.0037158
Total labor	.2866971	.1755198	.1929338	.1964836	.1791079
Other production cost:					
Advertising taxes and inspection fees	.2421795	.1002787	.1010445	.1002574	.0946416
Depreciation and rental of facilities	.1535968	.0707848	.0874565	.1001355	.0891608
Extractor royalties	.1052720	.0726026	.0796036	.0834893	.0779465
Steam and electrical power	.0942968	.0743025	.0821283	.0837279	.0740320
Repair and maintenance materials	.0679413	.0465301	.0555782	.0463797	.0394346
Miscellaneous expense	.1101139	.0583826	.0561267	.0540903	.0567438
Total other production cost	.7734003	.4228813	.4619378	.4680801	.4319593
Total production cost	2.1119841	1.6492129	1.7910225	1.8417100	1.7640071
Warehousing and shipping expense	.1874080	.1329084	.1267379	.1238668	.0989541
Selling expense	.1616309	.1739300	.1369774	.1287147	.2319319
General and administrative expense	.1439188	.0820025	.1059877	.0986103	.0950335
Other deductions and other revenue—net	.0791372	.0432918	.0480864	.0445096	.0143906
Total	$2.6840790	$2.0813456	$2.2088119	$2.2374114	$2.2043172

SOURCE: W. O. Daley & Company, Certified Public Accountants, Orlando, Florida, February 5, 1964.

APPENDIX XI-1

General Information on Cooperatives

One out of every five persons in the world is a member of one or more cooperatives. In the United States over 80% of all farmers are members of one or more cooperatives.[1] In total, approximately 20% of all purchases of the $20 billion of cash farm inputs is purchased through cooperatives and approximately 30% of the farmer's cash receipts of $37 billion is sold through farm cooperatives. The cooperative percentages have been increasing over the past several decades at varying rates depending upon the input purchased and the commodity sold. Grain cooperatives have almost doubled their share of sales since 1938 when the old Farm Board's Farmers National Grain Cooperatives broke up and new regional grain cooperatives were organized. The cooperative regional grain storage capacity has grown from 19.5 million bushels in 1938 to 310 million bushels in 1964. Not only have cooperatives expanded in the purchase of inputs and sales of their commodities, they have also integrated backward into (1) fertilizer manufacturing and the production of the basic raw materials for fertilizers, (2) farm chemicals, (3) feed manufacturing, and (4) petroleum products and oil wells, and have integrated forward into the processing and distribution of food including the ownership of a retail food chain in the northeast. Their total investments in 1965 totaled over $5 billion. The accompanying chart indicates the growth of farm supply and farm marketing cooperatives in the 1950s.

As in all forms of business, there are successful and unsuccessful cooperatives when measured in profit terms. Cooperative supply operations in 1965 had net margins on handling farm production supplies of $150 million which represented a 6% return on $2.6 billion sales and approximately a 10% return on net worth. Similarly successes in cooperative marketing have occurred but in many cases the cooperative may pay its supplier-members more for the commodity at the time of sale rather than build up patronage dividends. Tangible net margins on balance sheets are estimated at 3% of sales of $10 billion or $300 million a year. Many of the larger cooperatives with $200 to $300 million of sales are both farm supplying and farmer-marketing cooperatives. One cooperative, Consumers Cooperative Association of Kansas City, is estimating $1 billion of sales revenue in 1980. In 1964–1965 Consumers Cooperative Association had savings (earnings) of over $21 million with sales of around $275 million.

The improved position of farmer cooperatives in the nation's agribusiness structure has resulted from the individual entrepreneurship of the management of coopera-

[1] In many cases producers and other individuals belong to more than one cooperative. These figures were obtained from the Farmer Cooperative Service of the U.S. Department of Agriculture which has attempted to eliminate the problem of duplicate memberships.

COOPERATIVE BUSINESS VOLUME FOR 1961–1962

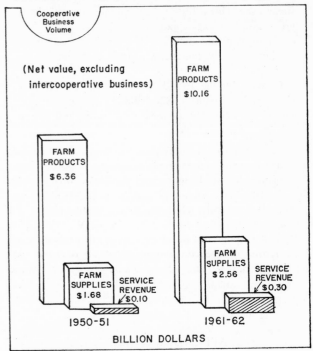

tives. In addition cooperatives have had much public policy and public service support of the Federal Government.

The most recent policy statement on cooperatives by the Department of Agriculture was issued July 9, 1963, and once again reaffirms the nonpartisan policy of encouraging the growth of cooperatives as stated below:

USDA POLICY STATEMENT ON COOPERATIVES

The Department of Agriculture, by the Act which created it in 1862, is directed to acquire and diffuse useful information on matters pertaining to agriculture, in the most general and comprehensive sense of that term.

By numerous subsequent acts, the Department is also specifically directed to carry on research, educational and service work respecting agricultural cooperatives, and to cooperate with local and State agencies to that end, provide credit to rural electric and telephone cooperatives, utilize the cooperative pattern in carrying out a number of its action programs, and accord "recognition and encouragement" to agricultural cooperatives.

It is the policy of the USDA to carry out the full intent of these legislative mandates effectively in terms of today's conditions and needs and in the light of the economic problems confronting American agriculture today.

The trend toward greater concentration of economic power in the nonagricultural segments of our economy — and, particularly, in recent years, in those segments that sell an increasing number of necessities to farmers as well as those that buy from the farmer and process and market his products — makes it more essential than ever that the farmer's bargaining power be strengthened.

The factors that, in decades past, resulted in repeated action by the Congress and the State legislatures to encourage farmers to strengthen their position through cooperatives become more impelling and urgent as the concentration of nonfarm economic power increases.

Cooperatives help farmers to improve their bargaining position. As farmers cooperate with each other to gain mutual advantage and protection through self-help, they strengthen the American family farm system, and enhance the benefits that it provides to the general public.

The USDA will therefore accept fully its responsibility to encourage the growth of cooperatives and through its various agencies provide research, educational and advisory services that will help to strengthen cooperatives in all appropriate activities in the interest of their members and the general welfare.

To that end each of the agencies of the Department will give proper recognition to the basic nature of cooperative enterprise, and will exercise its functions and perform its activities in full accord with the concepts and responsibilities stated above.

The head of each agency in the USDA is expected to insure that full support to the policy herein stated is given through his agency. The Assistant Secretary for Rural Development and Conservation shall serve as liaison to insure coordination within the Department and shall be responsible for working with the National Advisory Committee on Cooperatives.

From Secretary's Memorandum
No. 1540, July 9, 1963, as
reproduced in the September   Signed by:
1963 issue of *The News for*
Farmer Cooperatives.   Orville Freeman

Reprint 270 from News for Farmer Cooperatives

The cooperative as an institution in the United States has had a long history of public support. In the early 1900s laws were passed to provide research and educational help to rural cooperatives. By 1916 a law was passed to enable farmers to sell Farm Credit Bonds and Debentures (with initial capital from the Government) to public investors thus providing funds for farm borrowers. This was the beginning of the Farm Credit Administration. As of 1965 farmers now lend themselves and their marketing, farm supply, and business service cooperatives some $6 billion a year, most of it from funds they borrow from city investors without any formal or legal government guarantee. This $6 billion is used to provide 20% of the total U.S. farm credit, 13% of the farm operating credit, and 60% of the credit used by coopera-

tives. Farmers and their cooperatives have invested more than $549 million in their cooperative credit system. This nationwide system of credit cooperatives comprises (a) 12 Federal Land Banks and their 750 affiliated local Land Bank Associations which provide long-term mortgage credit to farmers, (b) 12 Federal Intermediate Credit Banks and their 483 local Production Credit Associations (PCAs) which provide short-term credit to farmers, and (c) 13 Banks for Cooperatives (12 district and 1 central) which make all types of loans to farmer marketing, purchasing, and business service cooperatives.

Other Federal laws exempt farm cooperatives from antitrust legislation in the formation of their cooperative (once a cooperative is formed, its actions are subject to the same antitrust laws as other corporations). The real justification for special provisions for cooperatives is that of protecting them from prosecution on more technical grounds. For example a marketing cooperative is a combination of producers who previously have been competitors. A practical consideration is the difficulty of a farmers' cooperative to maintain by itself any continuing monopoly control as production decisions remain with the individual members. Of the top seven cooperative firms in terms of "market power," five are centralized associations and six *restrict* membership.[2]

Additional cooperative aids include the Rural Electrification Act which enabled farm cooperatives to set up electric cooperatives in the rural areas to provide electric service that private utilities were unable to furnish. The self-help USDA Federal Crop Insurance programs are another cooperative service. In 1965 over 455,000 crops on approximately 16 million acres were insured against *production* cost lossed from natural hazards. The $580 million of protection was the highest in crop insurance history. These crop insurance policies are also used as collateral for lending agencies of approximately $40 million.

The Agricultural Stabilization and Conservation Service of the Department of Agriculture also works closely with cooperatives in carrying out price support, direct payment, and storage payment programs. More than one-fourth of all dollar disbursements of the price support programs reaches farmers through their cooperatives. Some commodity cooperatives may receive loans for price support in the same way as individual producers through the use of Form G. Nonrecourse loans are supposedly made to growers, but the cooperative is regarded as the grower acting through his agent. This is true of cotton, soybeans, rice, dry edible beans, and tung oil. Because the cash price of soybeans has been above price supports in most years (see Section III of this study), this cooperative arrangement for loan activities has not been too

[2] Youde and Helmberger, "Marketing Cooperatives in the U.S.," *Journal of Farm Economics,* August 1966, page 28. The seven cooperatives are Ocean Spray Cranberries, National Grape Co-op., Sunkist Growers, Diamond Walnut Growers, Sun-Maid Raisins, Sunsweet Growers, and Golden Guernsey Dairy.

meaningful for this crop. However, for a crop such as cotton, the cooperative price support advantage has helped to more than double the volume of cotton and cotton products handled by the cooperative — from $320 million in 1950 to $700 million in 1962. What the cooperative has been able to do is offer their members more money for their cotton at harvest time, store it as agent for the farmer, and collect his price support and storage payment. If the cooperative paid "too much" for cotton, then the government storage payments would offset a portion of the loss. The net effect was an increase in the amount of cotton sold or stored by the cooperative and subsidized by reduced storage payments.

To combat this economic advantage of cooperative-ASCS relations, firms such as Anderson-Clayton formed "cooperatives" of their own — 50% owned by the company and 50% owned by the farmer. This is but one of many examples where a change in the commodity system by a governmental program leads to an adjustment by the businessman in his business organization in order to accommodate his firm to the new structure and in his small way also change the commodity system; e.g., Anderson-Clayton "cooperatives."

There are other ASCS-cooperative relationships: (1) cooperatives may sell farm commodities to the Commodity Credit Corporation for price support activities, (2) ASCS utilizes farmer-owned cooperatives for storage and processing of price-supported commodities, (3) cooperatives handling tobacco, peanuts, and naval stores administer and advance price support to producers from loans made by the CCC. These joint activities are mutually beneficial to the government and the cooperatives—they reduce the cost or program operations, improve farmer-member understanding of the programs, make program operations more convenient for members, improve bargaining power of cooperatives, and stimulate farmers to develop cooperative enterprises.

Not only has the United States domestic policy been one of encouragement to cooperatives, but so has our foreign policy. The Humphrey Amendment to the Foreign Assistance Act of 1961 declares it "to be the policy of the U.S. . . . to encourage the development and use of cooperatives, credit unions and savings and loan association." Such encouragement existed before 1961, but with the announcement of official policy and the establishment of an International Cooperative Development staff to provide technical and program assistance to AID, more overseas cooperative firms have been established but not necessarily having any close ties with domestic farm cooperatives.

One additional major economic encouragement to the growth of cooperatives has been the tax treatment of them. There are two types of farmer cooperatives: tax-exempt and nonexempt. In order to qualify for tax-exemption status (of which about 50% qualify) they must meet the following tests: (1) market over 50% of the business volume from farmer members, (2) purchase over 85% of their supplies for their own farmer members,

(3) be farmer associations, and (4) do not pay more than 8% per annum on capital stock invested. The out and out exemption to those farmer cooperatives that meet the above tests is that which frees such farmer cooperatives from paying income taxes on amounts which they distribute as dividends on capital stock. The argument that such distribution should be viewed as interest on capital would be more convincing if corporations generally were allowed to escape tax on a specified share of their dividends on the same grounds. The remaining 50% of farmer cooperatives and all other cooperatives are nonexempt but have certain features which allow capital formation or distribution to take place for the cooperative acting as an agent of the owner-patron. The 1962 revenue act states that practically all cooperatives[3] must include all gross income in determining taxable income. However, they have the right to avoid paying taxes on this income as a cooperative (exempt or nonexempt) if this income is distributed to their owner-patrons in certain prescribed forms. These forms are as follows:

(1) in cash,
(2) in property, or
(3) in allocations of which at least 20% is paid in cash and provided the member of the cooperative approves the allocation by written consent, by by-laws of the cooperative, or by accepting the 20% cash payment.

The retention of the "book allocated" patronage refunds is an essential element in the growth of farm cooperatives. As noted in Section V of this study, the retention of allocated patronage dividends by the cooperative association puts the burden of income tax payments on the individual owner-patron and not on the cooperative association. Thus a cooperative association that is able to retain 80% of its "earnings" by proper "book allocations" has a source of cash flow build-up advantage over a corporation that has to pay a 48% corporate tax on its earnings.

This cash flow aspect has enabled cooperatives to be the high price bidder for other firms because of the merged operations' cash flows. Such mergers have changed the market structure of the agribusiness commodity systems in this study.

By the retention of patronage refunds 62.2% of the equity capital of regional farm supply cooperatives was accumulated. Of the 19.2% of equity capital obtained by "selling equity" a majority of it would have to be really counted as retention of patronage dividends. This combination method was reported by associations that required members to buy one or more shares of equity capital when they joined the cooperative and to increase their number of shares over the years by *reinvesting patronage refunds in the equities of the association*. In essence, almost 80% of the equity of these regional farm

[3] Those cooperatives exempt from the 1962 act include irrigation, rural electric, telephone, mutual savings banks, and building and loan associations.

supply cooperatives was acquired by retention of patronage refunds, by allocation certificates, or by equity capital notes paid for by patronage retentions.

Cooperative leaders defend the right to exclude allocated patronage dividends from taxation at the cooperative level because they maintain that the cooperative is the agent of the farm purchaser or marketer and the farmer has the right to have his on-farm and off-farm business operation treated as one entity. As John H. Davis stated:

> Therefore to deny farmers the right to exclude patronage refunds from gross income would, in reality, discriminate against them by denying to them the right granted other forms of business to integrate procurement, production, and selling functions into a unified operation. To attempt to tax patronage refunds owed to patrons pursuant to contract, at the cooperative level, would be to attempt to tax as income that which is not income to the cooperative, assuming the same concept and definition of income is applied to all other forms of corporate business.[4]

An opposing point of view was stated in a November 1965 hearing on cooperatives before the National Commission on Food Marketing by Mortimer M. Caplin, former Commissioner of Internal Revenue, testifying on behalf of the National Tax Equality Association. He stated:

> The ability to accumulate untaxed earnings for reinvestment was not critical when cooperatives were small and tax rates were low. But, for the large integrated cooperative of today, the ability to escape the 48% corporate tax rate is, indeed, a formidable advantage. Our tax laws and our economy have reached a stage where this advantage should be carefully reexamined. Under our current tax policy, it is difficult to justify a tax distinction between two large competing corporate enterprises merely because one is privately owned and the other is cooperatively owned. The ultimate goal in taxation should be to have competing businesses pay the same tax on similar dollars of income, regardless of type of business organization or type of ownership.[5]

In addition to all the other incentives to expand the use of cooperatives, the Department of Agriculture through the Farm Extension Service, the Farmer Cooperative Service, and other branches of the USDA have supplied all types of economic consulting services, accounting services, and research services to individual and groups of cooperatives which have improved the operations of this form of business enterprise.

The expansion of farm cooperatives and other forms of cooperative activity have been noted in the wheat,

soybean, and Florida orange sections of this study as well as in Section V. The strategies employed by farmer cooperative members in these industries indicate a responsiveness to governmental aids which have improved the operation of cooperatives and spurred their growth.

New forms of cooperative and corporate conglomerate firms have been set up to coordinate the required inputs in the vertical food structure from producer-supplier to retailer. For example: one such typical entity is Agway, Incorporated, the largest farm cooperative in the world, which is involved in many aspects of the agribusiness system — as supplier and producer of the basic farm use chemicals and commercially manufactured feed; as farm producer; as poultry, crop, and fruit processor; and finally as owner and operator of a retail food chain.

The Ohio Farm Bureau Federation and other groups have urged farm cooperative organization to put themselves in a stronger "bargaining position" in their respective commodity systems. One strategy suggests that farm cooperatives integrate more toward the ultimate consumer by owning and operating major food chains such as A&P.

The argument for such a policy is as follows:

(1) Standardization of quality and quantity of products calls for: (a) specification buying and specification selling through farmer cooperative bargaining associations and market orders, (b) additional processing by the cooperative, and (c) ownership of a major retail outlet as an example of *direct* marketing, innovating, and control of shelf space.

(2) This approach will provide farmers with direct communication as to what product improvements are required.

(3) Farmers have over $200 billion of assets committed to agriculture vs. $27 billion committed to food marketing, processing, and retailing and have financial resources available through allocated patronage refunds cash flow — and could "over time" raise $400 million required to gain control of one of the large chains.

(4) Farmer cooperatives have developed integrated management structures that are capable of managing such an operation.

In spite of the growth of farm supply and farm marketing cooperatives there are several internal policy issues that are not resolved by farm cooperatives. The future of commercial agriculture appears to be in the hands of large-scale family enterprises, yet in a cooperative where each member has one vote, there is a reluctance on the part of the small farmer to want to give price or cost concessions to the big volume operator. To the extent that the larger producer is not given special price concessions, noncooperative farm supply firms or marketing firms will obtain this business which is economical for both parties, leaving the cooperative with a more costly customer-member and one declining in economic im-

[4] Davis, *An Economic Analysis of the Tax Status of Farmer Cooperatives,* p. 106.

[5] National Tax Equality Association *Bulletin,* December 1965.

portance. Some cooperatives have changed their organizational policies, and voting is now on the basis of the amount of business transactions with the cooperative rather than on a one man-one vote principle.

Another cooperative problem is service versus "profits" for their owner-members. Although cooperatives are non-profit enterprises in the sense that they are organized for the economic benefit of members as users of the cooperatives' services and not to make profits for the cooperatives as legal entities or for their members as investors, cooperative management wants to show large patronage dividends at the end of the fiscal year to prove their value to the cooperative and to provide funds for improving and expanding the production, processing, or marketing facilities of the members of the cooperative. However, some members may feel that there are *service* functions that are producing *negative* patronage refunds that are necessary for their survival (e.g., a poultry processing plant). Yet others in the cooperative, not using the facility, may feel that they are subsidizing inefficient members of the cooperative. Others may object to the geographic location of facilities as showing favoritism of one group of producers over another. Another group may want all patronage refunds allocated in cash and prefer to invest in AT&T rather than "their" cooperative. There are farmer cooperatives in existence in which the dominant philosophy of each of these not necessarily com-

patible goals is evident. Although such policy differences are not necessarily peculiar to cooperatives, they become accentuated because the customer and the owner of the cooperative is the same person.

As today's farmer enlarges his farming operations, he may undertake many of his former farmer cooperative services as an individual-integrated producer rather than through his cooperative association (e.g., integrated broiler producer with his own feed mill). Thus, the cooperative has not only to constantly prove its competitive place in the commodity system, but also its more economical use for the producer than unilateral action by the producer.

Although cooperatives seem to be a dominant factor in the food economy, they are not tied to one another in any formal structure, and personal and organizational differences have stirred tremendous competition among them. In spite of this competition, today's leaders recognize that regional cooperative supply and market firms must be tied together if they are to carry out their functions and responsibilities efficiently in the global context of their commodity systems.

Finally, the cooperative and corporate form of enterprises both have advantageous uses as coordinating devices in agribusiness industries. Undoubtedly there will be greater use of both forms in the same business organization.

APPENDIX XI-2

Ferguson Committee Letters re De Angelis Affair and Effects on Futures Markets

Exhibit 1

BOARD OF TRADE
OF THE CITY OF CHICAGO

February 20, 1965

To Board of Directors
of the Board of Trade
of the City of Chicago

Gentlemen:

A Committee was appointed to investigate the financial difficulties caused by Allied Crude Vegetable Oil Refining Corp. and to make recommendations to the Board of Directors of the Exchange that will strengthen commodity futures trading.

Although the Committee was not limited to any specific area of inquiry, it was asked to devote a considerable portion of its activity to such fields as (1) Margins, (2) Capital Requirements, (3) Warehouse Procedures, (4) Exchange Jurisdiction, and (5) Government Cooperation.

The Committee has met with members of Congress, officials of the United States Department of Agriculture and the Harding Committee of the New York Stock Exchange to outline its appointment and objectives. Inasmuch as certain Government agencies as well as some rather influential leaders in Congress are anxiously awaiting the Committee's recommendations, it has decided to report those recommendations it has agreed upon so far. They are:

1. *Margins.*

(a) The Board has strengthened margin practices by requiring maintenance margins for hedgers. The Committee approves of this action. In addition, The Committee recommends an amendment to the Rules requiring floor traders to margin and maintain overnight positions at Clearing House requirements. The Committee feels this will be an important and constructive step in helping to keep control of margins within the jurisdiction of the Exchange.

(b) Some of the difficulties encountered by the three members of the Chicago Board of Trade who carried positions for Allied Crude Vegetable Oil Refining Corp. were brought about by the practice of factoring warehouse receipts in lieu of obtaining margin from the customer. The Committee recommends a rule that prohibits the procedure of a member borrowing money from a bank and depositing warehouse receipts owned by a customer as collateral for the loan other than warehouse receipts eligible for delivery at a regulated futures market. This restriction would not apply to member commercial banks.

2. *Capital Requirements.*

(a) The Committee has no specific recommendation for changing capital requirements, per se, inasmuch as it feels the adoption of all the recommendations made in this report, coupled with the meticulous enforcement of Rules and Regulations of the Exchange, obviate the necessity of such a recommendation. Although capital requirements in effect during the crisis brought about by the collapse of Allied proved to be adequate, the Committee recommends the Business Conduct Committee and the Governors of the Clearing Corporation examine present capital requirements for member firms, making such changes as may be necessary.

(b) There is no provision within the Bylaws of the Clearing Corporation covering a situation brought about by the capital and reserves of the Corporation being insufficient to meet its obligations. Liability of the clearing members is limited to the value of their stock in the Clearing Corporation, which is currently $3,700 a share. The Committee recommends the Bylaws of the Clearing Corporation be amended to provide that the stock in the Clearing House, in addition, be assessable for an amount not to exceed double the minimum subscription value per share, which is declared in the Bylaws to be $2,500 a share, so the assessment would be limited to $5,000 a share. The Committee also recommends the present maximum of 12 shares per member firm be increased to 20 shares per member firm, thereby allowing a more equitable allocation of stock in relation to volume.

3. *Warehouse Procedures.*

(a) The Committee is of the opinion that Federal supervision of crude soybean oil and cottonseed oil warehouses would help to strengthen the futures contract. The Committee has been informed that (i) neither crude soybean oil nor cottonseed oil is eligible under present regulations for supervision under the United States Warehouse Act, and (ii) the Act seems broad enough to permit their supervision if the Exchange petitioned the Secretary of Agriculture for inclusion and the Secretary concurred. The Committee recommends such a petition be made for inclusion.

(b) The Committee recommends the Chicago Board of Trade obtain a fidelity bond to cover residual liabilities of all warehousemen regular for delivery on futures contracts traded at the Exchange. The Committee is attempting to negotiate a bond for $50 million that will protect receipt holders against infidelity, fraud and forgery. The Committee will continue negotiations.

4. *Exchange Jurisdiction.*

(a) Mr. De Angelis joined the Exchange in 1950 but never registered his membership for Allied Crude Vegetable Oil Refining Corp. Consequently,

The Chicago Board of Trade had no jurisdiction over this non-member corporation and no authority to require it to submit financial information. This situation created a vacuum within our Rules. The Committee recommends an amendment to the Rules that will require a member of the Exchange to register a membership for a firm which has a place of business devoted to the commodity or securities business within which he is a partner, officer, director or substantial stockholder unless a membership has been registered for the firm.

(b) The Committee has learned some customers of one of the member firms suspended by the Exchange were unable to arrange for the transfer of trades to another member firm through the lack of cooperation of the firm that had been suspended. When financial difficulties arise that make it impossible for a firm to carry on business, such firm should be required to immediately arrange for a transfer of open positions to another firm designated by each customer. The Committee recommends such a requirement.

5. *Government Cooperation.*

(a) The Committee recommends the creation of a so-called "Positions Surveillance Committee" that will be charged with the sole responsibility for continuously watching positions in order to guard against attempted manipulation and corners. The committee should be composed of the President of the Exchange, the Manager of the Clearing Corporation and the Administrator of the Office of Investigations and Audits. Secretary to the committee should be a staff member from the Office of Investigations and Audits. The committee should have power to issue cease and desist orders which may be appealed by a member to a group consisting of those officers of the Exchange who are elected by the membership. In the event a member or member firm refuses to comply with an order issued by the committee composed of officers of the Exchange, that member or member firm should be suspended or expelled by the Board of Directors. The duties of this committee will be limited to problems suggested above, and all other duties, responsibilities and powers granted to the Business Conduct Committee by the Rules and Regulations of the Exchange shall remain with that committee.

It is necessary the Committee have the reaction of the Board to each of these recommendations in order for it to pursue the drafting of appropriate rules or regulations. Furthermore, the Secretary of Agriculture is awaiting a report from the Committee on recommendations it will make to the Board of Directors to help strengthen our Rules, Regulations and operating procedures.

We are also submitting a suggested draft of regulation to cover speculative trading limits for crude soybean oil, soybean meal, and cottonseed oil along with an opinion from the attorneys for the Exchange.

Respectfully submitted,

s/ Ford M. Ferguson

Ford M. Ferguson
Chairman, Special Committee

encls.

Exhibit 2

BOARD OF TRADE
OF THE CITY OF CHICAGO

April 6, 1964

Board of Directors
of the Board of Trade
of the City of Chicago

Gentlemen:

The Board of Directors at a Special Meeting held on Friday, February 28, 1964, approved sections of a report from this Committee and sent two sections of the report back to the Committee for reconsideration.

One section had to do with margins and the other section had to do with capital requirements. We shall treat each of these sections separately for the purpose of this report.

This is the section on margins suggested by the Committee in its report:

"1. *Margins.*

(a) The Board has strengthened margin practices by requiring maintenance margins for hedgers. The Committee approves of this action. In addition, the Committee recommends an amendment to the Rules requiring floor traders to margin and maintain overnight positions at Clearing House requirements. The Committee feels this will be an important and constructive step in helping to keep control of margins within the jurisdiction of the Exchange."

The Board voted to refer this section back to the Committee along with a copy of a proposed amendment to Rule 210. The amendment had been recommended by a special committee appointed under Rule 156, which brought charges against James McGrath.

The Board wished the Committee to consider whether its recommendation would destroy liquidity in the market and if the amendment to Rule 210 would not accomplish the objective of the Committee. The Committee will comment separately on each of these points.

Liquidity is vitally necessary for sound and proper operation of a futures market. Although the Committee readily concedes its recommendation on margins would have some effect on the liquidity of the futures market, it is more concerned about the effect of liquidity for the market in the event margin control is given to the Commodity Exchange Authority. The Committee still feels its recommendation is a sound one but wishes to modify the original report by recommending an amendment to the Rules requiring floor traders to margin and maintain overnight positions at requirements *set by the Board*. This would be more in line with authority granted to the Board by Rule 210 which states, "The Board, by regulation, shall fix minimum margin requirements." In the Committee's previous report it had recommended margins be required and maintained in accordance with Clearing House requirements.

The Committee unanimously agrees that this is the absolute minimum that should be done at this time inasmuch as the spotlight of the Securities Exchange Commission as well as the Commodity Exchange Authority is on the financial world.

In the event this amendment is not approved by the Board and adopted by the membership, the Committee feels the Exchange can no longer justify selling memberships to individuals who are unable to deposit margins or to allow floor traders to trade who would be unable to meet margin requirements.

The Committee is of the opinion the amendment to Rule 210 would be in the best interests of the Association and strongly recommends its adoption as well as enforcement.

This was the other recommendation made by the Committee:

"2. *Capital Requirements.*

(b) There is no provision within the Bylaws of the Clearing Corporation covering a situation brought about by the capital and reserves of the Corporation being insufficient to meet its obligations. Liability of the clearing members is limited to the value of their stock in the Clearing Corporation, which is currently $3,700 a share. The Committee recommends the Bylaws of the Clearing Corporation be amended to provide that the stock in the Clearing House, in addition, be assessable for an amount not to exceed double the minimum subscription value per share, which is declared in the Bylaws to be $2,500 a share, so the assessment would be limited to $5,000 a share. The Committee also recommends the present maximum of 12 shares per member firm be increased to 20 shares per member firm, thereby allowing a more equitable allocation of stock in relation to volume."

The Board asked the Committee to give consideration to having the Clearing Corporation require margins on the greater side of a clearing member's position in place of the suggestion of the Committee.

The Committee is of the opinion that any requirement which results in clearing members having to margin the greater side of a position has these disadvantages:

1. It very definitely opens up the possibility for further regulation by Federal agencies.
2. It does not necessarily protect the Clearing Corporation from a situation brought about by the capital and reserves of the Corporation being insufficient to meet its obligations.
3. It would result in additional position information circulating through more individuals.
4. It would result in increased expenses to member firms coupled with increased cost to the Clearing House. Gross positions are not furnished the Clearing House, and such information apparently would not have prevented the Ira Haupt collapse.

The Committee unanimously endorses its previous recommendation.

The Committee still feels the present maximum of 12 shares per member firm should be increased to 20 shares per member firm in order to allow for a more equitable allocation of stock in relation to volume. The maximum increase to a few member firms would be $3,700 per share times 8 shares. The Committee does not feel this is an extraordinary tie-up of capital for any member firm. In addition, the stock can be used for house margins. However, the Committee will drop the recommendation if it clouds the possibility of favorable reaction on the other recommendation.

Respectfully submitted,

Ford M. Ferguson
Chairman
Special Committee

APPENDIX XI-3

USDA Charges Against Cargill on Cornering Wheat on the Chicago Board of Trade

FARM AGENCY DETAILS CHARGES THAT CARGILL CORNERED WHEAT MARKET, FORCED UP PRICES

By a WALL STREET JOURNAL *Staff Reporter*

WASHINGTON — The Agriculture Department detailed its charges filed over the weekend against Cargill, Inc., of Minneapolis.

The Government charged in effect that the company temporarily cornered the wheat market on May 21, 1963, at the Chicago Board of Trade and withheld wheat from the market until prices were forced to "artificial" heights. Such alleged price manipulation, the Government said, violates the Commodity Exchange Act, which regulates trading in 22 commodities on 17 exchanges.

Cargill has denied the charges. Company president Erwin E. Kelm said the facts "don't support" the Government's charges. "The price of Chicago May wheat in 1963 rose in the last days of trading as we and others had anticipated it would — because the supply was limited relative to demands and not because of manipulation by Cargill. . . ."

GOVERNMENT'S CONTENTION

But the Government contends Cargill owned or controlled most of the deliverable wheat in Chicago as the Board of Trade's deadline neared for the end of trading in May 1963 wheat futures, and that the company used its dominant market position to manipulate prices.

The trading deadline was noon, May 21, 1963. A future is a contract for delivery of a commodity at a fixed price at a later date. A May 1963 wheat future called for delivery of a quantity of wheat by the end of the day on May 31, 10 days after trading ceased for that particular contract. Failure to deliver wheat called for in a futures contract makes a trader liable for heavy cash penalties imposed by commodity exchanges.

The Federal complaint against Cargill alleges that even though traders committed on futures contracts to deliver wheat by the end of May couldn't find supplies to cover

their commitments, Cargill failed to offer any large quantity of wheat until 15 minutes before the May 21 noon deadline.

"On May 21, 1963," the Government charged, "the price of the (May) future ranged from $2.15¼ to $2.28⅝ a bushel," and the market closed at the latter price. On the previous day, the May future price ranged from only $2.11 a bushel to $2.19. U.S. officials said Cargill's profit in selling more than 1.6 million bushels of May 1963 wheat futures may have averaged 17 cents a bushel.

Cargill, in rebutting this charge, said: "Cargill's judgment of the requirement for wheat in the Chicago area in May differed from that of others. We believed the price was too low . . . and this judgment subsequently proved to be correct. It was therefore inevitable that an increase occurred to bring the May futures price in line with the Chicago cash wheat price and with the Kansas City futures price as well." The company said wheat prices for May futures last year were lower than at any time in the past 10 years.

HEARING SCHEDULED

But the Government says Cargill also manipulated the cash price, that is, the price for wheat available for immediate rather than future delivery. Cargill accomplished this, the Government contends, by shipping out of the Chicago area more than 1 million bushels of deliverable wheat, thereby reducing available stocks in Chicago to a level far below what Cargill knew were the amounts traders needed to fulfill cash orders. "As of the close of business on May 17, 1963," the Government said, "(Cargill) owned all except 20,000 bushels of the deliverable wheat."

A public hearing on the complaint is scheduled before an Agriculture Department administrator Aug. 19, in Minneapolis. The department could suspend Cargill's trading privileges indefinitely at all commodity exchanges if the company is unable to refute the charges to the Government's satisfaction. The Commodity Exchange Act, however, makes price manipulation a misdemeanor, and the Agriculture Department could take the case to Federal court; if found guilty there, Cargill could be fined up to $10,000 or its officers jailed for as long as one year, or both.

SOURCE: *Wall Street Journal,* June 9, 1964.

Selected Bibliography

Selected Bibliography

Abrahamsen, Martin A. and Claud L. Scroggs (eds.), *Agricultural Cooperation.* Minneapolis: University of Minnesota Press, 1957.

Adelman, M. A., "Bases and Bounds of Integration of Firms and Functions," in *The Frontiers of Marketing Thought and Science,* F. M. Bass (ed.). Chicago: American Marketing Association, 1958.

Aguilar, Francis J., *Scanning The Business Environment: Modes of Seeking, Selecting, and Evaluating Information for Strategic Decisions.* New York: The Macmillan Company, 1966.

Aharoni, Yair, *The Foreign Investment Decision Process.* Boston: Division of Research, Harvard Business School, 1966.

American Association of Advertising Agencies, *The A.A.A.A. Study on Consumer Judgment of Advertising,* May 1965.

American Waterways Operators, Inc., *1963 Inland Water-Borne Commerce Statistics.* Washington, December 1964.

Anderson, Donald E., *Policies and Practices of the Commodity Credit Corporation: Effects on Market Structure, Conduct, and Performance.* North Dakota State University (mimeo), undated.

Anderson, Jerry L. (ed.), *Rural Electric Fact Book.* Washington: National Rural Electric Cooperative Association, 1960.

Applebaum, William and Ray A. Goldberg, *Brand Strategy in United States Food Marketing.* Boston: Division of Research, Harvard Business School, 1967.

"An Approach to Production Response," *Agricultural Economics Research,* Vol. XIV, No. 4, October 1962.

Arizona, University of, Agricultural Experiment Station, Technical Bulletin 150, *Policy for United States Agricultural Export Surplus Disposal,* August 1962.

Arkansas Grain Corporation, Stuttgart, Arkansas, *Annual Reports.*

Arthur, Henry B., "Market Structures and Functions in Agricultural Control Programs" in *Theory in Marketing,* R. Cox, W. Alderson, and S. J. Shapiro (eds.). Homewood, Ill.: Richard D. Irwin, Inc., 1964.

Backman, Jules, *Advertising and Competition.* New York: New York University Press, 1967.

Bain, Joe S., *Industrial Organization.* New York: John Wiley & Sons, Inc., 1959.

Bakken, Henry H., *Basic Concepts, Principles and Practices of Cooperation.* Madison, Wisconsin: Mimir Publishers, Inc., 1963.

———, *Historical Evaluation, Theory and Legal Status of Futures Trading in American Agricultural Commodities.* Madison, Wisconsin: Mimir Publishers, Inc., 1960.

Berg, E. R., *Structure of the Soybean Oil Export Market,* Research Report AERR-30, Agricultural Experiment Station, University of Illinois, January 1960.

———, *Structure of the Soybean Oil Export Market Structure,* Bulletin No. 674, Agricultural Experiment Station, University of Illinois, August 1961.

BIG 4 Cooperation Processing Association, Sheldon, Iowa, *1961 Annual Report.*

Bitting, H. Wayne and Robert O. Rogers, "Utilization of Wheat for Food," *Agricultural Economics Research,* Vol. XV, No. 2, April 1963.

Boulding, Kenneth E., *Economic Analysis.* New York: Harper & Brothers, 1st ed., 1941.

Bounds, Vernon, "Hedge A Growing Crop?" *Doane's Agricultural Report,* Vol. 28, No. 17, June 8, 1965.

———, "Why Not Sell Your Grain and Store Futures?" *Doane's Agricultural Report,* Vol. 27, No. 17, June 8, 1964.

Brand, Simon S., "The Decline in the Cotton Futures Market," *Food Research Institute Studies,* Vol. IV, No. 3, Stanford University, 1964.

Breimyer, Harold F., *Individual Freedom and the Economic Organization of Agriculture.* Urbana: University of Illinois Press, 1965.

Buzzell, Robert D., Walter J. Salmon, and Richard F. Vancil, *Product Profitability Measurement and Merchandising Decisions.* Boston: Division of Research, Harvard Business School, 1965.

Cain, Dan, "How ASCS Divvies Up the Wheat Acreage," *Doane's Agricultural Report,* Vol. 28, No. 5, February 8, 1965.

———, "Urea Spells Danger for Soybean Growers," *Doane's Agricultural Report,* Business Issue, December 8, 1964.

California, University of, Division of Agricultural Sciences, Bulletin 786, *Growth Patterns in the Retail Grocery Business,* by Stephen J. Hiemstra and D. B. DeLoach, June 1962.

Canadian House of Parliament, *Proceedings of the Special Joint Committee of the Senate and House of Commons* on Consumer (Prices), 27th Parliament, 1st Sess., Nos. 25, 26, and 27 (1966).

Caplin, Mortimer M., "Comments on Tax Treatment of Cooperatives," *National Tax Equality Association Bulletin*, December 1965.

Cassady, Ralph, Jr., *Competition and Price Making in Food Retailing*. New York: The Ronald Press Company, 1962.

Chapell, Wayman, "Who is 'Big John' Helping?" *Doane's Agricultural Report*, Vol. 27, No. 23, August 8, 1964.

Chappell, Joe Senter, *An Analytical Model for Selecting Optimal Merchandising and Storage Plans for Multiple Commodities*, unpublished Ph.D. thesis, North Carolina State College, 1963.

Chauvin, Michel and Yves Guyomard, "A travers les Etats-Unis, Deux Ans Apres," *Les Industries de l'Alimentation Animale*, No. 160, May 1965.

Chicago Board of Trade
Annual Reports, 1958, 1959, 1960, 1961, 1962, and 1964.
A Commodity Exchange.
Proceedings of the Hedging Symposium for Country Grain Elevator Operators, December 11–12, 1963.
Soybean Futures.
Soybean Meal Futures.
Soybean Oil Futures.
Steer Carcass Beef Futures.
Wheat Futures.

Clarke, James W., "The Road to Greater Economic Development," *Grain Review*, Vol. 3, No. 1, January 1965.

Clarke, W. M., *The City in the World Economy*. London: The Institute of Economic Affairs, 1965.

Cochrane, Willard W., *The City Man's Guide to the Farm Problem*. Minneapolis: University of Minnesota Press, 1965.

——, *Farm Prices: Myth and Reality*. Minneapolis: University of Minnesota Press, 1958.

"Cocoa Producers Lose Market War," *The New York Times*, Sunday, February 7, 1965.

Commodity Research Bureau, Inc., *Commodity Year Book* (annual).

Cooperative League of the U.S.A., *Cooperatives and Taxes*, Chicago, 1959.

Cornell University, New York State College of Agriculture, *Operating Results of Food Chains in 1963–1964*, by Wendell Earle and John Sheehan.

Darrah, L. B., *Food Marketing*. New York: The Ronald Press Company, 1967.

Davis, John H., *An Economic Analysis of the Tax Status of Farmer Cooperatives*, Washington: American Institute of Cooperatives, 1950.

Davis, John H. and Ray A. Goldberg, *A Concept of Agribusiness*. Boston: Division of Research, Harvard Business School, 1957.

De Blois, Eleanor N., "Increased Dollar Sales Brought Agricultural Exports to Alltime High in 1964," *Foreign Agricultural Trade of the United States*, August–September 1965.

Dixey, Roger N. (ed.), *International Explorations of Agricultural Economics*. Ames, Iowa: The Iowa State University Press, 1964.

Domike, Arthur Louis, Jr., *Procurement Strategies and Market Behavior of the Wheat Milling and Barley Malting Industries in the North Central Grain Markets*, unpublished Ph.D. thesis, University of Michigan, 1961.

Dorfman, Joseph, *Institutional Economics: Veblen, Commons, and Mitchell Reconsidered*. Berkeley: University of California Press, 1963.

Doyle Dane Bernbach, Inc., *Meet the New Pre-sold National Brand: The Private Label*, by E. B. Weiss, 1965.

"EEC Farm Policy," *International Federation of Agricultural Producers News*, Vol. 14, No. 9, September 1965.

Ehrich, Rollo L., "The Impact of Government Programs on Wheat-Futures Markets, 1953–1963," *Food Research Institute Studies*, Vol. VI, No. 3, Stanford University, 1966.

Eicher, Carl and Lawrence Witt (eds.), *Agriculture in Economic Development*. New York: McGraw-Hill Book Company, 1964.

Faris, J. Edwin, "Structural Change and Competitive Relationships Among Buying and Selling Firms," *Journal of Farm Economics*, Vol. 46, No. 5, December 1964.

Farrell, Kenneth R., *Grain Marketing Statistics for the North Central States*. Columbus, Missouri: Missouri Agricultural Experiment Station, June 1958.

First National City Bank of New York, "Net Income of Leading Corporations, 1963–1964," *Monthly Economic Letter*, April 1965.

——, "Who Gets the Subsidy?" *Monthly Economic Letter*, June 1964.

Florida Agricultural Experiment Station, Gainesville, Florida
Mimeo Report EC 66-9, *Costs of Processing, Warehousing and Selling Florida Citrus Products, 1964–65 Season*, by A. H. Spurlock, April 1966.
Mimeo Report EC 66-6, *Futures Trading and the Florida Orange Industry*, by B. A. Dominick, Jr., and F. W. Williams, December 1965.
Supplement to Mimeo Report EC 66-6, *Questions and Answers on Futures Trading and the Florida Orange Industry*, by B. A. Dominick, Jr., and F. W. Williams, December 1965.
Mimeo Report EC 64-4, *Movement of Citrus Trees from Florida Nurseries, July 1, 1928 to June 30, 1963*, by Zach Savage, November 1963.

Florida Citrus Commission, Lakeland, Florida
Report No. FCC 64/1, *An Analysis of January–June 1960 Consumer Purchase Data on Frozen Concentrated Orange Juice*, by W. E. Black and L. Mobley, February 14, 1964.
Consumer Purchase Patterns and Trends for Five

Citrus Products — 1962 Compared with 1957 and 1950, by W. E. Black and L. Mobley, January 1964.

Report No. FCC-ERD 66-7, *Economic Outlook for Florida Citrus for the Next Five Years 1966–1971,* by W. E. Black, May 1966.

Report No. 64-7, *Information Related to the Export of Fresh and Processed Citrus from the United States,* by W. E. Black, February 1964.

Regulations Pursuant to Chapter 601. Florida Statutes, As Amended (Citrus Code), to May 1, 1962.

Florida Citrus Mutual, *The Next Five Years,* June 18, 1963.

Florida Department of Agriculture. *Florida Citrus 1965 Sample Tree Survey,* Gainesville, August 31, 1966.

Florida, University of, Agricultural Economics Mimeo Report EC 64-7, *Florida Citrus Fruit and Tree Losses from the December 1962 Freeze,* by Roy G. Stout, January 1964.

Friedmann, Karen J. and Helen C. Farnsworth, "Grains in German Farming: Past Developments and Prospects for 1970 and 1975," *Food Research Institute Studies,* Vol. VI, No. 1, Stanford University, 1966.

Fulop, Christina, *Competition for Consumers.* London: Andre Deutsch Limited, 1964.

Gaston, J. Frank, *Growth Patterns in Industry: A Reexamination,* Studies in Business Economics No. 75, National Industrial Conference Board, 1961.

Gazelle, Stanley A., "Oilseed Meals: Postwar Trends in Production and Use," *Fats and Oils Situation,* January 1967.

Gold, Gerald, *Modern Commodity Futures Trading.* New York: Commodity Research Bureau, Inc., 1959.

Goldberg, Ray A., "Agribusiness for Developing Countries," *Harvard Business Review,* Vol. 44, No. 5, September–October, 1966.

———, "Marketing Costs and Margins: Current Use in Agribusiness Market-Structure Analysis," *Journal of Farm Economics,* Vol. 47, No. 5, December 1965.

———, *The Soybean Industry.* Minneapolis: University of Minnesota Press, 1952.

Graf, George N., and the Staff of Quality Bakers of America Cooperative, Inc., *A Manual for Management on Wholesale Bakery Distribution,* September 1962.

Grain and Feed Dealers National Association, Official Directory, Fall and Winter 1963–1964, Washington, D.C.

Gray, Roger W., "The Attack Upon Potato Futures Trading in the United States," *Food Research Institute Studies,* Vol. IV, No. 2, Stanford University, 1964.

———, "Futures Markets and the Commodity Trade," unpublished paper, Food Research Institute, Stanford University, undated.

———, "Onions Revisited," *Journal of Farm Economics,* May 1963.

———, "The Seasonal Pattern of Wheat Futures Prices Under the Loan Program," *Food Research Institute Studies,* Vol. III, No. 1, Stanford University, February 1962.

———, "Some Thoughts on the Changing Role of Price," *Journal of Farm Economics,* February 1964.

Gray, Roger W. and Roice Anderson, "Advertised Specials and Local Competition Among Supermarkets," *Food Research Institute Studies,* Vol. III, No. 2, Stanford University, May 1962.

Halperin, Haim, *Agrindus: Integration of Agriculture and Industries.* New York: Frederick A. Praeger, 1963.

Harvard Business School, Division of Research. Bulletin No. 148, *Operating Results of Food Chains in 1955,* by Wilbur B. England.

Hathaway, Dale E., *Government and Agriculture.* New York: The Macmillan Company, 1963.

———, *Problems of Progress in the Agricultural Economy.* Chicago: Scott, Foresman and Company, 1964.

———, "The Grass Roots Division of the Free World," *Grain Review,* Vol. 3, No. 3, July 1965.

Heady, Earl O. and Luther G. Tweeten, *Resource Demand and Structure of the Agricultural Industry.* Ames, Iowa: Iowa State University Press, 1963.

Heid, Walter G., Jr., *Changing Structure and Performance of the Northeastern Markets for Grain,* unpublished Ph.D. thesis, University of Maryland, 1965.

Henderson, Kenneth R., *Demand and Substitution Relationships for Frozen Orange Concentrate,* unpublished Ph.D. thesis, University of Florida, June 1965.

Hieronymus, T. A., *Uses of Grain Futures in the Farm Business,* Bulletin 696, Agricultural Experiment Station, University of Illinois, September 1963.

Hirsch, Hans G., "The Fluctuation of EEC Variable Levies," *Foreign Agricultural Trade of the United States,* August–September 1965.

Hlynka, I., *Wheat, Chemistry and Technology.* St. Paul, Minnesota: American Association of Cereal Chemists, Inc., 1964.

Holdren, Bob R., *The Structure of a Retail Market and the Market Behavior of Retail Units.* Englewood Cliffs, N.J.: Prentice-Hall, Inc., 1960.

Hopkins, James T., *Fifty Years of Citrus, The Florida Citrus Exchange: 1909–1959.* Gainesville, Florida: University of Florida Press, 1960.

Houck, James P., "The Soybean Industry in Perspective," *Business and Government Review,* September–October 1965.

"International Compensation for Fluctuations in Commodity Trade," *World Agriculture,* Vol. XI, No. 1, January 1962.

Iowa State University, Center for Agricultural and Economic Development, *Farmers in the Market Economy: Market Organization and Competitive Behavior in Relation to Farmers' Prices, Costs and Incomes.* Ames, Iowa: Iowa State University Press, 1964.

———, *Food, One Tool in International Economic Development.* Ames, Iowa: Iowa State University Press, 1962.

Jamison, John A., "Marketing Orders, Cartels, and Cling Peaches: A Long-Run View," *Food Research Institute Studies,* Vol. VI, No. 2, Stanford University, 1966.

Jewett, Alyce Lowrie and Edwin C. Voorhies, *Agricultural Cooperatives: Strength in Unity.* Danville, Illinois: The Interstate Printers & Publishers, Inc., 1963.

Johnson, President Lyndon B., *Message to the Congress of the United States,* for release February 4, 1965.

Keyserling, Leon H., *Agriculture and the Public Interest Toward a New Farm Program.* Washington: Conference on Economic Progress, February 1965.

Kidder Peabody & Co., Research Department, *People, Food and Farm Machinery,* January 1967.

Kohls, Richard L., *Marketing of Agricultural Products.* New York: The Macmillan Company, 1955.

Kromer, George W., "Factors Affecting Soybean Oil and Meal Yields," *Fats and Oils Situation,* January 1967.

———, "Implications of Shifting the U.S. Soybean Marketing Year to September 1," *Fats and Oils Situation,* August 1965.

Learned, Edmund P., C. Roland Christensen, Kenneth R. Andrews, and William D. Guth, *Business Policy: Text and Cases.* Homewood, Illinois: Richard D. Irwin, Inc., 1965.

Learned, Edmund P., *The Role of General Management,* unpublished manuscript, Division of Research, Harvard Business School.

Learned, Edmund P. and Audrey T. Sproat, *Organization Theory and Policy: Notes for Analysis.* Homewood, Illinois: Richard D. Irwin, Inc., 1966.

Levitt, Theodore, *Innovation in Marketing.* New York: McGraw-Hill Book Company, 1962.

Linden, Fabian (ed.), *Expenditure Patterns of the American Family.* New York: National Industrial Conference Board, 1965.

Arthur D. Little, Inc., *Distribution: The Challenge of the Sixties,* A report to the American Bakers Association, December 1960.

Malenbaum, Wilfred, *The World Wheat Economy, 1885–1939.* Cambridge: Harvard University Press, 1953.

Maryland, University of, Agricultural Experiment Station, Miscellaneous Publication 545, *Changing Structure and Performance of the Northeast Grain Marketing Industry, 1957–1962,* by Walter G. Heid, Jr., James E. Martin, and Russell F. McDonald, June 1965.

McGregor, George J., *The British Flour Market in 1975,* unpublished student report, Harvard Business School, May 19, 1964.

McKinsey & Company, Inc., *McKinsey-Birds Eye Study: The Economics of Frozen Foods.* New York: General Foods Corporation, March 1964.

Mehren, George L., "The Changing Structure of the Food Market," *Journal of Farm Economics,* Vol. XXXIX, No. 2, May 1957.

Miller, Norman C., *The Great Salad Oil Swindle.* New York: Coward McCann, Inc., 1965.

Miller, Raymond W., *A Conservative Looks at Cooperatives.* Athens, Ohio: Ohio University Press, 1964.

Minneapolis Grain Exchange, *Eighty-First Annual Report,* December 31, 1963.

———, *Grain Rate Book No. 4,* June 1, 1964.

Missouri, University of, College of Agriculture, Research Bulletin 847, *Market Organization of Grain Industries in the North Central Region,* by L. B. Fletcher, January 1964.

Moore, John R. and Richard G. Walsh, *Market Structure of the Agricultural Industries.* Ames, Iowa: Iowa State University Press, 1966.

Mueller, W. F. and L. Garoian, *Changes in the Market Structure of Grocery Retailing.* Madison, Wisconsin: The University of Wisconsin Press, 1961.

Nakamura, Hiroshi, *Structure of the Soybean Processing Industry in the United States: Economic, Institutional, and Technical Factors in Its Development,* unpublished Ph.D. thesis, University of Illinois, 1963.

National Agricultural Advisory Commission, *Farm Policy in the Years Ahead,* November 1964.

———, *Report of the Subcommittee on Food and Fiber Reserves for National Security to the National Agricultural Advisory Commission,* October 7, 1964.

National Commission on Food Marketing, *Food from Farmer to Consumer,* 1966.

Technical Study No. 3, *Organization and Competition in the Dairy Industry,* June 1966.

Technical Study No. 4, *Organization and Competition in the Fruit and Vegetable Industry,* June 1966.

Technical Study No. 5, *Organization and Competition in the Milling and Baking Industries,* 1966.

Technical Study No. 8, *The Structure of Food Manufacturing,* June 1966.

Technical Study No. 10, *Special Studies in Food Marketing,* June 1966.

National Soybean Processors Association, *Year Book and Trading Rules 1965–1966,* Hudson, Iowa, 1966.

North Carolina State College, Research Paper 948 *Impacts of Vertical Integration on Output, Price and Industry Structure* by J. A. Seagraves and C. E. Bishop, December 1958.

North Iowa Soybean Cooperative, *1962 Annual Report,* Mason City, Iowa.

———, *1964 Annual Report,* Mason City, Iowa.

Ohio Farm Bureau Federation, Inc., Advisory Council Guide, *Strengthening Our Market Muscle,* Vol. 22, No. 1, January 1965.

Organization for Economic Co-operation and Development, *The Role of Trade Associations in the Study of Markets.* Report of the conference in Vienna, September 27–29, 1961.

Paarlberg, Don, *American Farm Policy.* New York: John Wiley & Sons, Inc., 1964.

Paul, Allen B., *Some Policy Implications of the Wheat Export Program,* unpublished manuscript, Washington, D.C., undated.

Phillips, Almarin, *Market Structure, Organization and Performance.* Cambridge: Harvard University Press, 1962.

Pincus, John A., "Commodity Agreements: Bonanza or Illusion?" *Columbia Journal of World Business,* Vol. 11, No. 1, January-February, 1967.

Productivity Estimates and Technological Change in Grain Processing Industries. Distributed in conjunction with the Symposium on Structure, Conduct and Performance of the Grain Markets of the United States, Lincoln, Nebraska, June 3, 1965.

Progressive Grocer et al., *Consumer Dynamics in the Super Market,* 1965.

Progressive Grocer: Super Valu Study, 1957.

Progressive Grocer: Annual Report for 1964, April 1965.

Progressive Grocer. Colonial Study, 1963.

Purdue University, Cooperative Extension Service, Extension Circular 530, *Guidelines to Advertising and Promotion of Farm Products,* June 1964.

Riley, William R., *Marketing Structure of the Soybean Industry,* unpublished Ph.D. thesis, Purdue University, 1964.

Rossotti, Charles D., *Two Concepts of Long-Range Planning: An Analysis of Current Practice.* Boston: The Management Consulting Group, Boston Safe Deposit and Trust Co., undated.

Roy, Ewell Paul, *Contract Farming, U.S.A.* Danville, Illinois: The Interstate Printers & Publishers, Inc., 1963.

Schonberg, James S., *The Grain Trade: How It Works.* New York: Exposition Press, 1956.

Shepherd, Geoffrey S., *Marketing Farm Products — Economic Analysis.* Ames, Iowa: Iowa State University Press, 3d ed., 1955.

Shonfield, Andrew, *Modern Capitalism. The Changing Balance of Public and Private Power.* London: Oxford University Press, 1965.

Smidt, Seymour, "A Test of the Serial Independence of Price Changes in Soybean Futures," *Food Research Institute Studies,* Vol. V, No. 2, Stanford University, 1965.

Smith, Mervin G. and Carlton F. Christian, *Adjustments in Agriculture — A National Basebook.* Ames, Iowa: Iowa State University Press, 1961.

Sorenson, Orlo and Donald Anderson, *A Review of Grain Marketing Operations of the Commodity Credit Corporation,* Kansas State University (mimeo), undated.

South Dakota State College, Agricultural Experiment Station, Agricultural Economics Pamphlet 102, *Grain Merchandising at the Country Elevator,* August 1959.

Stam, Jerome M., "The Effects of Public Law 480 on Canadian Wheat Exports," *Journal of Farm Economics,* Vol. 46, No. 4, November 1964.

Stanford University, Food Research Institute, *Marketing Orders: Performance, Potential, and Limitations. The Case of California's Cling Peaches and Asparagus,* by John A. Jamison and Karl Brandt, July 1965.

Steen, Herman, *Flour Milling in America.* Minneapolis: T. S. Denison & Company, Inc., 1963.

Stern, Louis W., *The New World of Private Brands,* unpublished manuscript, Ohio State University, undated.

Swank, C. William, *A Solution to the Farmer's Dilemma* (mimeo), Ohio Farm Bureau, undated.

Szarf, Adam, "Modern Flour Mills in Developing Countries," *Monthly Bulletin of Agricultural Economics and Statistics,* Vol. 15, No. 6, June 1966.

Toledo-Lucas County Port Authority, *A Report on the Inequalities Created by Section 22 of the Interstate Commerce Act,* February 1963.

————, *Section 22 of the Interstate Commerce Act. An Analysis of the Arguments Pro and Con,* September 1963.

Tri-County Cooperative Soybean Association, Dawson, Minnesota, *Annual Reports,* 1961, 1962, and 1964.

"Two Good Growth Years Bring Record Crop," *Citrus and Vegetable Magazine,* Vol. 30, No. 3, November 1966.

United Nations, Food and Agriculture Organization, *Agricultural Commodities — Projections for 1970,* May 1962.

————, *Trade Yearbook,* Vol. 16, 1962.

U.S. Congress, House of Representatives

Committee on Agriculture

Food Costs-Farm Prices, 88th Cong., 2d Sess. (March 1964).

Hearings on H. J. Res. 977, a joint resolution to study the food industry from the farm to the consumer, 88th Cong., 2d Sess. (1964).

Hearings on H. R. 10010: Food and Agriculture Act of 1962, 87th Cong., 2d Sess., February–March 1962.

Subcommittee on Departmental Oversight and Consumer Relations, *Hearing on ARA Loan for Construction of Soybean Processing Plant,* 88th Cong., 1st Sess. (1963).

Subcommittee on Domestic Marketing, *Hearings on H. R. 904, a bill to Prohibit Trading in Irish Potato Futures on Commodity Exchanges,* 88th Cong., 1st Sess. (1963).

Subcommittee on Wheat, *Hearings on Wheat Legislation,* Part I, 88th Cong., 1st Sess. (1963), Part II, 88th Cong., 2d Sess. (1964).

Statement on Behalf of Safeway Stores, Incorporated Regarding Bread Price Increases, by William S. Mitchell, August 11, 1966.

Report No. 1123, *Food and Agriculture Act of 1965, Conference Report,* 89th Cong., 1st Sess. (1965).

Subcommittee of the Committee on Government Operations, *Hearings on Investigation of the Commodity Credit Corporation: Part III — Price Support and Storage Activities,* 86th Cong., 2d Sess. (1961).

U.S. Congress, Joint Economic Committee, *Subsidy and Subsidy-Effect Programs of the U.S. Government* (1965).

U.S. Congress, Senate

Committee on Agriculture, *Statement on the Wheat Certificate Plan on Behalf of the American Bakers*

Association and the Biscuit and Cracker Manufacturers' Association, by Joseph M. Creed, February 10, 1964.

Committee on Commerce, *Hearings on S. J. Res. 71, as amended, A Joint Resolution to Establish a National Commission on Food Marketing to Study the Food Industry from the Farm to the Consumer,* 88th Cong., 2d Sess. (1964).

Committee on the Judiciary, Subcommittee on Antitrust and Monopoly

Concentration Ratios in Manufacturing Industries, 1958.

Report No. 1923, pursuant to S. Res. 238, *Administered Prices of Bread,* 86th Cong., 2d Sess. (1960).

Industry Structure and Price-Cost Margins: A Study of Food Manufacturing, by Norman R. Collins and Lee E. Preston, March 25, 1965.

"Cooperatives and Freedom," extension of remarks of Hon. Quentin N. Burdick of North Dakota in *Congressional Record,* Proceedings and Debates of the 88th Congress, 1st Sess., May 28, 1963.

"Cooperatives and the Future," extension of remarks of Hon. John Sherman Cooper of Kentucky in *Congressional Record,* Proceedings and Debates of the 88th Congress, 1st Sess., Vol. 109, No. 79, May 28, 1963.

U.S. Department of Agriculture

Agricultural Marketing Service

ABC's of Federal Marketing Orders and Agreements for Fruits and Vegetables, by Floyd F. Hedlund, June 1962.

Agriculture Handbook 91, *Measuring the Supply and Utilization of Farm Commodities,* 1955.

Supplement for 1959 to Agriculture Handbook No. 91, *Measuring the Supply and Utilization of Farm Commodities,* September 1960.

Agriculture Handbook No. 243, *Compilation of Agricultural Marketing Agreement Act of 1937, Reenacting, Amending and Supplementing the Agricultural Act as Amended,* January 1, 1963.

Grain Transportation in the North Central Region, July 1961.

Marketing Research Report No. 121, *Size of Soybean Oil Mills and Return to Growers,* November 1956.

Marketing Research Report No. 319, *Potential Effects of St. Lawrence Seaway on Costs of Transporting Grain,* April 1959.

Marketing Research Report No. 375, *Dollar Volume of Agriculture's Transactions with Industry,* December 1959.

Marketing Research Report No. 380, *Promotion of Farm Products by Agricultural Groups,* January 1960.

Marketing Research Report No. 442, *Impact of the St. Lawrence Seaway on the Location of Grain Export Facilities,* December 1960.

Miscellaneous Publications No. 741, *Farm-Retail Spreads for Food Products,* November 1957.

Statistical Bulletin No. 268, *Grain Transportation Statistics for the North Central Region,* August 1960.

Agricultural Stabilization and Conservation Service

The Food and Agriculture Act of 1965, October 13, 1965.

Storage and Handling Costs Incurred by Type of Storage on Commodities Acquired Under the Price Support Program, Fiscal Years 1953 through 1963, October 18, 1963.

Circular No. 397, *Analysis of Open Commitments in Wheat and Corn Futures on the Chicago Board of Trade, September 29, 1934,* by D. B. Bagnell, May 1936.

Commodity Credit Corporation, *Summary of 30 Years' Operations of the Commodity Credit Corporation with Report of the President of the Commodity Credit Corporation, 1964* (1965).

Commodity Exchange Authority

Report of the Administrator of the Commodity Exchange Authority, 1949.

Soybean Futures Market, 1960–61, February 1962.

Soybean Futures Trading, 1959–60, May 1960.

Technical Bulletin No. 1001, *An Analysis of Speculative Trading in Grain Futures,* by Blair Stewart, October 1949.

Economic Research Service

Agricultural Economic Report No. 19, *Vertical Coordination in Agriculture,* by Ronald L. Mighell and Lawrence A. Jones, February 1963.

Agricultural Economic Report No. 38, *An Economic Appraisal of the 1961 Feed Grain Program,* June 1963.

Agricultural Economic Report No. 95, *Agricultural Markets in Change,* July 1966.

Agricultural Economic Report No. 105, *The Farm Food Marketing Bill and its Components,* January 1967.

Agriculture Handbook No. 132, *Agricultural Policies of Foreign Governments, Including Trade Policies Affecting Agriculture,* revised March 1964.

Agriculture Handbook No. 325, *Handbook of Agricultural Charts, 1966,* October 1966.

Agriculture Information Bulletin No. 230, *Farm Costs and Returns,* revised August 1963.

An Analysis of Grain Transportation in the Northwest, December 1964.

"The Bill for Marketing Farm Food Products," *Marketing and Transportation Situation,* August 1965.

Changes in Total Market Structure and Implications of these Changes, "Project 1964," by Robert E. Freeman, February 1, 1965.

Demand and Price Situation, November 1965.

Developments in Marketing Spreads for Agricultural Products in 1962, August 1963.

The Farm Index, October 1965.

Farm Real Estate Market Developments, October 1964.

Farm Retail Spreads for Food Products 1947–64, April 1965.

For-Hire Trucking of Exempt Farm Products Operating Practices and Nature, March 1964.

Foreign Agricultural Economic Report No. 17, *Financial Procedures Under Public Law 480,* May 1964.

Foreign Agricultural Trade of the U.S., March 1962 and March 1967.

Frozen Foods, Margins, Costs, and Returns in Relation to Display Space, July 1965.

"The Impact of the Florida Freeze on Prices of Orange Products," *Marketing and Transportation Situation,* May 1963.

"Income of Farm Operator Families by Value of Sales Class," *Farm Income Situation,* November 1964.

Marketing Research Report No. 503, *Returns From Marketing Cottonseed and Soybean Oils in Margarine,* October 1961.

Marketing Research Report No. 609, *Comparative Costs to Consumers of Convenience Foods and Home Prepared Foods,* by Harry Harp and Denis Dunham, June 1963.

Marketing Research Report No. 621, *Changing Shipping Patterns on the St. Lawrence Seaway With Emphasis on U.S. Grain Exports,* August 1963.

Marketing Research Report No. 659, *Market Potentials for Modified Edible Fats and Oils,* May 1964.

Marketing Research Report No. 785, *Food Retailing by Discount Houses,* February 1967.

Miscellaneous Publication No. 863, *Transportation of Agricultural Commodities in the United States, A Bibliography of Selected References 1949–1959.*

Miscellaneous Publication No. 969, *Spreads in Farm-Retail Prices of White Bread,* September 1964.

National Food Situation, May 1965.

"Off-Farm Commercial Storage Facilities for Grain," *Marketing and Transportation Situation,* August 1965.

Publications Containing Recent Farm Enterprise Input-Output Data, March 1963.

Resource Requirements on Farms for Specified Operator Incomes, revised 1964.

Role of Agricultural Commodity Assistance in International Aid Programs, by Frank D. Barlow, Jr., and Susan A. Libbin, March 1965.

Statistical Bulletin No. 297, *Costs and Returns on Commercial Farms Long-term Study, 1930–1957,* December 1961.

Statistical Bulletin No. 364, *U.S. Food Consumption,* June 1965.

Statistical Bulletin No. 376. *U.S. Fats and Oils Statistics 1909–65 — Oilseeds, Oils and Meals, Animal Fats and Oils, Food Fats, Nonfood Fats,* August 1966.

Farmer Cooperative Service

Agricultural Information Bulletin 275, *Farmer Cooperatives . . . Farm Business Tools,* by Beryle Stanton, January 1964.

Bulletin No. 1, *Farmer Cooperatives in the United States,* rev. ed., 1965.

General Report, *Pendleton Grain Growers . . . An Integrated Cooperative,* by Beryle Stanton, July 1960.

General Report 32, *Methods of Financing Farmer Cooperatives,* by Helim H. Hulbert, Nelda Griffin, and Kelsey B. Gardner, June 1957.

General Report 41, *Revolving Fund Method of Financing Farmer Cooperatives,* by Helim H. Hulbert, Nelda Griffin, and Kelsey B. Gardner, March 1958.

General Report 64, *Cooperative Country Elevators in Montana,* by Francis P. Yager, July 1959.

General Report 67, *Pooling and Other Grower Payment Methods as Used by Local Fruit, Vegetable and Tree Nut Cooperatives,* by Clyde B. Markeson, December 1959.

General Report 97, *Exploring Communication Processes in a Farmer Cooperative,* by James H. Copp and Irwin W. Rust, August 1961.

General Report 100, *Integrated Feed Operations through Farmer Cooperatives, 1959,* by Anne L. Gessner, April 1962.

General Report 105, *How the Revenue Act of 1962 Affects Farmer Cooperatives,* by Raymond J. Mischler and David Volkin, October 1962.

General Report 110, *Trends in Growth of Farmer Cooperatives, 1950–60,* by Kelsey B. Gardner and Anne L. Gessner, March 1963.

General Report 115, *Regional Cooperatives Handling Under $10 Million of Supplies, 1960–61,* by J. Warren Mather and Anne L. Gessner, August 1963.

General Report No. 123, *Cooperative Bargaining by Farmers — A Selected Bibliography,* by Wendell M. McMillan, July 1964.

General Report 124, *Financial Structure of Regional Farm Supply Cooperatives,* by Nelda Griffin.

General Report No. 128, *Statistics of Farmer Cooperatives,* by Bruce L. Swanson, July 1965.

Helping Farmers Build Cooperatives. The Evolution of Farmer Cooperative Service, by Andrew W. McKay and Martin A. Abrahamsen, June 1962.

Marketing Research Report 345, *Analysis of Returns and Practices of Florida Fresh Citrus Sales Organization,* by Fred E. Hulse, August 1959.

Marketing Research Report 492, *Coordinated Marketing for Florida Fresh Citrus Shippers — Views on Its Need and Feasibility,* by Fred F. Hulse, August 1961.

Miscellaneous Report No. 73, *Handbook on Major*

Regional Farm Supply Purchasing Cooperatives, 1942 and 1943, by Joseph Knapp, July 1944.

News for Farmer Cooperatives, Annual Review Issue, January 1962 and January 1963.

Service Report 71, *Cooperative Criteria,* February 1965.

"Size of Cooperative Business Continues to Increase," *The News for Farmer Cooperatives,* April 1964.

Federal Extension Service, *Agriculture and Its Relationship to Other Segments of the Economy,* by Richard G. Ford, undated.

Florida Citrus Industry: Market Organization and Performance, Report of a Study Committee, unpublished manuscript, June 1963.

Foreign Agricultural Service
"The ABC's of the Common Market's Grain Prices," *Foreign Agriculture,* Vol. XI, No. 37, September 14, 1964.

Foreign Agriculture, Including Foreign Crops and Markets, October 11, 1965.

"New Rail Rates for U.S. Spring Wheats," *Foreign Agriculture* Vol. III, No. 26, June 28, 1965.

"Soybeans Again Rank as Top Dollar U.S. Export Crop," *Foreign Agriculture,* Vol. III, No. 25, June 21, 1965.

Marketing: The Yearbook of Agriculture, 1954, 1954.

Miscellaneous Publication No. 905, *Analysis of Grain Export Programs: A Report of the Technical Committee on Grain Exports,* May 1962.

Office of Information, *Fact Book of U.S. Agriculture,* revised March 1963.

Statistical Reporting Service, *Agricultural Situation,* Vol. 45, No. 5, May 1961.

Stock of Grains in All Positions: Grain and Soybean Stocks Smaller, January 25, 1965.

Technical Bulletin No. 747, *Grain Prices and the Futures Market, A 15-Year Survey, 1923–1938,* by G. Wright Hoffman, January 1941.

USDA Announces Further Certificate Provisions on Old Crop Wheat, April 24, 1964.

USDA Reports Grain Price-Support Activity Through December 1963, January 17, 1964.

U.S. Department of Commerce
Bureau of the Census
Long Term Economic Growth, 1860–1965.

1963 Census of Business: Retail Wholesale Services, Retail Trade-Summary Statistics, Part 1, 1966.

U.S. Census of Manufactures, 1958, Vol. 2, Industry Statistics.

U.S. Commodity Exports as Related to Output, 1958.

Office of Business Economics, *Survey of Current Business,* April 1963, and Annual Review Number, January 1964.

U.S. Federal Trade Commission
Economic Inquiry into Food Marketing. Part I, Concentration and Integration in Retailing, January 1960.

Economic Inquiry into Food Marketing. Part II, The Frozen Fruit, Juice and Vegetable Industry, December 1962.

Wholesale Marketing of Food, June 30, 1919.

Voorhis, Jerry, *American Cooperatives.* New York: Harper & Row, Publishers, 1961.

Waldorf, William K., "The Demand for and Supply of Food Marketing Services: An Aggregate View," *Journal of Farm Economics,* Vol. 48, No. 1, February 1966.

Walsh, Richard G. and Bert M. Evans, *Economics of Change in Market Structure, Conduct, and Performance: The Baking Industry, 1947–1958.* University of Nebraska Studies, New Series No. 28, Lincoln: University of Nebraska, December 1963.

Wang, Yi, *The Demand and Price Structure for Various Classes of Wheat,* unpublished Ph.D. thesis, The Ohio State University, 1962.

Warden, Thomas A., "U.S. Agriculture's First Year Under EEC Variable Import Levies," *Foreign Agricultural Trade of the United States,* July 1965.

Washington State University, Division of Industrial Research, *Abstracts for the Advancement of Industrial Utilization of Wheat,* Vol. 3, No. 5, April 1965.

Wheeler, Leslie A., "International Commodity Arrangements and the 'Kennedy Round' in GATT," *World Agriculture,* Vol. XIII, No. 3, July 1964.

Wilcox, Walter W., *Farm Programs and Dynamic Forces in Agriculture,* transmitted to the Committee on Agriculture and Forestry, U.S. Senate, February 4, 1965.

Williams, Charles M. "Enterprise on the Prairies," *Harvard Business Review,* Vol. 31, No. 2, March–April, 1953.

Williams, Willard F. and Thomas T. Stout, *Economics of the Livestock-Meat Industry.* New York: The Macmillan Company, 1964.

Wolf, Jurgen, "The Citrus Economy and the Feasibility of International Market Arrangements," *Monthly Bulletin of Agricultural Economics and Statistics,* Vol. 14, No. 9, September 1965.

Working, Holbrook, "Futures Markets under Renewed Attack," *Food Research Institute Studies,* Vol. IV, No. 1, Stanford University, 1963.

The World Food Problem, A Report of the President's Science Advisory Committee, Vols. I and II, The White House, May 1967.

Wright, Carlton E., *Food Buying.* New York: The Macmillan Company, 1962.

Wyoming Agricultural Experiment Station, *Wheat Programs, Their Effects on Income,* March 1961.

Youde, James G. and Peter G. Helmberger, "Marketing Cooperatives in the U.S.: Membership Policies, Market Power, and Antitrust Policy," *Journal of Farm Economics,* Vol. 48, No. 3, Part II, August 1966.

Speeches

Andrews, Kenneth R., *Toward a Theory of Management; The Firm and Its Future.* Third International Investment Symposium, Harvard Business School, July 10–15, 1966.

Arthur, Henry B., *Economic Risk, Uncertainty and the Futures Market.* Futures Trading Seminar, Chicago Board of Trade, April 28–30, 1965.

Bakken, Henry H., *Futures Trading — Origin, Development and Present Economic Status.* Futures Trading Seminar, Chicago Board of Trade, April 28–30, 1965.

Barlow, Frank D., Jr., and Susan A. Libbin, *World Grain Trade and Pricing Policies and Their Effects Upon International Trade.* Symposium on the Structure, Conduct and Performance of the Grain Markets of the United States, North Central Regional Research Committee on Grain Marketing, Lincoln, Nebraska, June 1–3, 1965.

Breimyer, Harold F., *Markets, Market Structure and the Institutional Organization of Agriculture.* Four lectures delivered before Graduate Seminar of the Department of Agricultural Economics and Sociology, Texas A & M College, March 11–13, 1963.

————, *Future Organization and Control of United States Agricultural Production and Marketing.* American Farm Economic Association, Purdue University, August 17, 1964.

Brown, Lester R., *The Changing World Market for Grain,* U.S. Department of Agriculture, Advisory Committee on Feed Grains and Wheat, November 1964.

————, *Looking Ahead at World Population Growth and Food Needs.* Agricultural Science Lecture Series, Rutgers University, February 3, 1964.

————, *The World Food Problem: A Hard Look Ahead.* Annual Conference of the American Dairy Science Association, University of Kentucky, June 22, 1965.

————, *Implications of Changing Trade Programs to U.S. Agriculture.* National Agricultural Policy Conference, Allerton Park, Illinois, September 15, 1965.

Butz, Dale E., *Research Challenges and Opportunities in Grain Marketing.* Grain Marketing Symposium, Lincoln, Nebraska, June 1, 1965.

Buzzell, Robert D., *Competitive Behavior and Product Life Cycles.* American Marketing Association Conference, June 15, 1966.

Carey, Bernard P., *Regulation and Supervision of Futures Trading.* Futures Trading Seminar, Chicago Board of Trade, April 28–30, 1965.

Cochrane, Willard W., *Some Observations of an Ex-Economic Advisor; or What I Learned in Washington.* American Farm Economic Association, Chicago, December 29, 1964.

Cragg, Henry, *How Shall We Preserve the Florida Citrus Industry?* Annual Membership Meeting of Florida Orange Marketers, Kissimmee, Florida, March 29, 1967.

————, *The Positive "Triple-A" Program — Let's Eliminate the Negative and Accentuate the Positive.* Citrus Seminar, American Institute of Real Estate Appraisers, Orlando, Florida, April 13, 1967.

Daly, R. F., *Agriculture in the Years Ahead.* Southern

Agricultural Workers Conference, Atlanta, Georgia, February 3, 1964.

Freeman, Orville L., Secretary of Agriculture, at Governor's Conference on Agriculture, Louisville, Kentucky, February 3, 1965.

————, before Rice Millers Association, Houston, Texas, January 31, 1964.

Goldberg, Ray A., *The Future of U.S. Commercial Agricultural Exports.* Public hearing of the National Advisory Commission on Food and Fiber, New York City, July 13, 1966.

Goldberg, Ray A. and others, *The Dynamics of Brand Competition,* a discussion. Mid-Year Meeting of Grocery Manufacturers of America, Inc., June 14–16, 1965.

Goodman, Richard J., *Discussion of Paper of Frank D. Barlow, Jr.: "World Grain Trade and Pricing Policies and Their Effects Upon International Trade."* Symposium on Structure, Conduct and Performance of the Grain Markets of the United States, North Central Regional Research Committee on Grain Marketing, Lincoln, Nebraska, June 1–3, 1965.

Gray, Roger W., *Fundamental Price Behavior Characteristics in Commodity Futures.* Futures Trading Seminar, Chicago Board of Trade, April 28–30, 1965.

————, *Why Does Futures Trading Succeed or Fail: An Analysis of Selected Commodities.* Futures Trading Seminar, Chicago Board of Trade, April 28–30, 1965.

Greutzmacher, Alfred H., *The Philosophy of the Market Place as Seen From a Pit Speculator's Viewpoint.* Futures Trading Seminar, Chicago Board of Trade, April 28–30, 1965.

Heckman, J. H., *AID Cooperative Programs and Policy,* at Taipei, Taiwan, November 23, 1962.

Heid, Walter G. Jr., *Grain Marketing — A General Description.* Symposium on the Structure, Conduct and Performance of the Grain Markets of the United States, North Central Regional Research Committee on Grain Marketing, Lincoln, Nebraska, June 1–3, 1965.

Heifner, Richard G., *The Function and Structure of Country Elevators in the United States.* Symposium on Grain Marketing, Lincoln, Nebraska, June 1, 1965.

Hieronymous, T. A. and Glenn S. Fox, *Discussion of "Pricing Institutions and Procedures."* Symposium on Grain Markets, Nebraska Center for Continuing Education, Lincoln, June 1, 1965.

Holdren, Bob R., *Competition in Food Retailing.* American Farm Economics Association meeting, Stillwater, Oklahoma, August 24, 1965.

Hoofnagle, William S., *The Role of and Limitation to Advertising and Promotion in the Solution of Agricultural Problems.* Workshop on Agricultural Market Development and Promotion, University of California, Berkeley, June 21, 1965.

Johnson, Loren, at Farm Forum, Spokane, Washington, February 10, 1964.

Knapp, Joseph G., *Will You Be in Business Tomorrow?*

62nd Annual Convention of Farmers. Grain Dealers Association of Illinois and Illinois Grain Corporation, Peoria, Illinois, February 10, 1965.

Kramer, George W., *Outlook for Fats, Oils, and Oilseeds in 1966–67.* 44th Annual Agricultural Outlook Conference, U.S. Department of Agriculture, November 17, 1966.

Mehren, George L., *Farm Policy for the Future.* Ninth Federal District Farm Forum, Minneapolis Chamber of Commerce, March 8, 1965.

———, *Government and the Food Industry.* Annual meeting of National American Wholesale Grocers Association, Mexico City, September 17, 1965.

———, *Marketing Challenges in the American Economy.* Symposium on on the Structure, Conduct and Performance of the Grain Markets in the U.S., North Central Regional Research Committee on Grain Marketing, Lincoln, Nebraska, June 2, 1965.

Miller, Clarence J. and David C. Nelson, *Relationships Between the Grain Processing Industries and the Federal Antitrust Laws.* Symposium on the Structure, Conduct and Performance of the Grain Markets of the United States, North Central Regional Research Committee on Grain Marketing, Lincoln, Nebraska, June 1–3, 1965.

Ogren, Kenneth E., *The Food Marketing Outlook and the Consumer.* Forty-first Outlook Conference, U.S. Department of Agriculture, Washington, D.C., November 16, 1963.

———, *Marketing Research: A Tool for Decision Making, A Look Ahead at the Food Service Industry.* Spring meeting of Society for the Advancement of Food Service Research, Washington, D.C., April 18, 1966.

Parrott, Robert P., *Use of Futures Markets.* Midyear Conference of The National Independent Meat Packers Association, Scottsdale, Arizona, January 19, 1967.

Paul, Allen B., *Examining Selected Features of Commodity Markets Through Balance Sheets.* Annual meeting of the Western Farm Economics Association, San Luis Obispo, California, July 15–17, 1964.

———, *Futures Trading: An Industry Decision.* 36th Annual Conference of the Southern Economic Association (with the Southern Marketing Association), Atlanta, Georgia, November 10, 1966.

Peckham, J. O., *Manufacturers' Advertised Brands — The Consumer's Choice.* 57th annual meeting of Grocery Manufacturers of America, Inc., New York City, November 9, 1965.

Powers, Donald J., *Price Reporting and Dissemination; the Placement and Execution of Orders.* Futures Trading Seminar, Chicago Board of Trade, April 28–30, 1965.

Raclin, Robert L., *Exporting Oilseeds from the State of Illinois.* Export Advisory Committee, Illinois Department of Agriculture, September 14, 1964.

———, *The Role of Futures Markets in Determining the Flow of Commodities in Domestic and International Trade.* Futures Trading Seminar, Chicago Board of Trade, April 28–30, 1965.

Schertz, Lyle P., *Foreign Development and Trade Division, Trends in Grain and Soybean Exports.* Ninth Agricultural Industries Forum Grain Marketing Program, University of Illinois, February 1, 1967.

Schnittker, John A., Undersecretary of Agriculture, at 15th Annual Convention of the National Association of Wheat Growers, Portland, Oregon, January 6, 1965.

———, at the Annual Meeting of the National Soybean Processors Association, St. Charles, Illinois, August 9, 1965.

Schruben, Leonard W., *Developments and Prospects in Grain Marketing.* Symposium on Structure, Conduct, and Performance of the Grain Markets of the United States, North Central Regional Research Committee on Grain Marketing, Lincoln, Nebraska, June 1–3, 1965.

Seaborg, Glen, at the Women's National Democratic Club, Washington, D.C., February 6, 1967.

Stanfield, D. R., *What's the Big Idea?* Meeting of Ohio Farm Bureau Federation, Inc., Columbus, Ohio, November 9, 1964.

Thuroczy, Nicholas M., *Is Distribution the Major Problem in the Wholesale Baking Industry?* Columbia University, Harriman Campus, Harriman, New York, November 18, 1963.

Williams, F. W., *Futures Trading: An Industry Decision.* 36th Annual Conference of the Southern Economic Association (with the Southern Marketing Association), Atlanta, Georgia, November 10, 1966.

Wilson, Raleigh B., *Merchandising and Inventory Management of Commodities: Carrying Charges and Basis.* Futures Trading Seminar, Chicago Board of Trade, April 28–30, 1965.

Wright, Bruce H., *Tranportation and the Grain Industries.* Symposium on the Structure, Conduct and Performance of the Grain Markets of the United States, North Central Regional Research Committee on Grain Marketing, Lincoln, Nebraska, June 1–3, 1965.

Index

DATE DUE

MR 7 '73			
OC 12 73			
DC 74			
DEC 0 7 2002			
			PRINTED IN U.S.A.